PRIZE CONTEST PLAYS
for
YOUNG PEOPLE

Prize Contest Plays

for

Young People

A collection of royalty-free, one-act plays
for drama contests and festivals

Edited by

A. S. BURACK

Publishers   PLAYS, INC.   *Boston*

CONTENTS

PRIZE CONTEST PLAYS
for
YOUNG PEOPLE

Orchids for Margaret

BY PEARL AND THATCHER ALLRED

Characters

PROFESSOR ADAMS, *Uncle Will*
JULIA, *his sister*
MARGARET, *his niece*
JACKIE, *a co-ed*
KOCH, *a student*

SETTING: PROFESSOR ADAMS' *home on Faculty Row.*
TIME: *Early evening.*
AT RISE: JULIA, *a woman in her middle forties who still retains traces of a girlish prettiness, comes into the room. Her hair, which is just beginning to gray, is a little rumpled. She wears an apron over her dark dress. She has been working on a pale lavender evening frock with an overskirt of white tulle dotted with silver sequins or something silvery. The effect should fit the line in the play: "grapes frosted with silver." A tape measure hangs about her neck. She goes to the window, parts the curtains and looks out intently for a moment. She turns and calls toward study door.*

JULIA: Will! (*Pause, then louder.*) Will! It's finished. Come on out. I want you to see it before Margaret gets home. (*She spreads the dress over a chair, fluffs out the skirt, and surveys it critically.*) Will! (*Insistently this time.* PROFESSOR ADAMS *enters reluctantly, a sheaf of papers in one hand, his pipe in the other. He is ten years older than Julia. His hair is gray and his shoulders are a little stooped. He is a scholar preoccupied with distant things; but he is in no sense the absent-minded professor. He has a gentle kindness, a certain whimsicality and a wise humor that shows in his voice, eyes and gestures.*)

PROFESSOR: Now, Julia, I'm busy. I told you I wasn't under any circumstances to be disturbed.

JULIA (*Interrupting him as she frowns intently at the dress*): Look, Will. Do you like this new neckline better than the way it was before? Or do you like the bodice sort of built up?

PROFESSOR (*Coming closer and adjusting his glasses*): We-e-ll now, Julia, since you ask me, I think I like it built up—just the way it is now.

JULIA (*Patiently*): But it isn't built up now. I've changed it!

PROFESSOR: You said yesterday you'd changed it.

JULIA: That was the skirt, dear brother. You remember how the gathers bunched a little at the side?

PROFESSOR: Remember? How could I forget? I hope you tell Margaret that her feeble old uncle designed and practically made this dress. Tuesday we deliberated about the tucks; Wednesday, as I recall it, we pondered the waistline; Thursday, I advised you about the hem. My last chapter on the literature of the Renaissance is going to sound as if it had been run up on the sewing machine! (*He turns as if to leave.*)

JULIA: Wait a minute, Will. I want to talk with you. You've been working in that musty old room ever since your last lecture. Sit down a minute while I finish— I've only a few more stitches. (*Sits down and begins to sew on dress*) I've been so worried.

PROFESSOR (*Seating himself*): Worried?

JULIA: About Margaret.

PROFESSOR: Now, Julia, don't start that again. You'd think, from all the fuss you've been making over that child the last week, you were getting her ready for the altar instead of a Junior Prom.

JULIA: Maybe there's more relation between the two than you think. Plenty of romances begin with nothing more important than a school dance, Will. If Margaret would only see that and come out of herself a little . . .

PROFESSOR: Leave the child alone. She's all right just as she is, and if any presumptuous young idiot . . .

JULIA: You don't see what I mean.

PROFESSOR: I may be obtuse, but I admit I don't see any reason for your getting into a state simply because your daughter gets a date for a dance. First you worry because she hasn't one, and then you worry because she has. That's a woman for you!

JULIA (*Biting off thread*): Why can't you understand, Will? You've been like a father to Margaret ever since she lost her own. She's not like other girls—having dates, going to parties. Not getting a bid from a sorority when the girls she grew up with got theirs—well, it's put a kind of blight on her.

PROFESSOR (*With sudden severity*): You're not to say such things, Julia. What if she isn't like the others? It's you and the thousands of mothers like you who have brought about this foolish worship of conformity. Conformity! (*He gets up and paces, gesturing with his pipe.*) All you ask from your daughter is that she be like the others—dress like them, speak like them, think the same thoughts, have the same kind of shoddy little mind! (*Pausing in front of her*) Shame on you, Julie! Because Margaret is different from the herd, you are stricken. Teach her to wear her difference with pride instead of self-consciousness. That's your job. (*More gently*) Your privilege, my dear.

JULIA: You make it sound very simple, but you don't impress me a bit. All the high thinking in the world isn't going to help a young girl when she begins to feel left out of things.

PROFESSOR (*Shaking his finger at her*): You're going to laugh at yourself some day, Julie. Some day, when Margaret is happy and settles down.

JULIA: But that's just it. Margaret's been at Westlake College for three years, and I could count on one hand the dates she's had. (*Touching her hair*) I'd had three proposals when I was Margaret's age.

PROFESSOR (*Wearily turning away from her*): How many times must I remind you that Margaret is supposed to be preparing to graduate from a university—not from a matrimonial bureau!

JULIA (*Tossing her head*): It's all about the same thing as far as a woman's concerned.

PROFESSOR: Not Margaret. That girl has brains.

JULIA (*Sighing*): Yes, heaven help her!

PROFESSOR: Not that they'll be much use to her with a chap like Shep Warren.

JULIA (*Sharply*): Now, Will, don't you dare start discouraging the first eligible young man who presents himself this season simply because he doesn't happen to have a taste for the classics.

PROFESSOR: Eligible, Julie? (*He places a light chair before her and sits facing her.*) What makes him eligible? (*Leaning forward*) The young man in question does, I believe, play football and drive a sports car. It would be extremely bad taste, I take it, to inquire into this young man's morals, or to look too closely into his intellectual achievements. (*He leans back wearily.*)

JULIA: You needn't be so emphatic. (*A bit defensively*) Margaret's a lucky girl to be going with Shep Warren, and I'm not going to analyze his faults through a microscope. (*Smoothing the dress lying across her lap*) I ought to know what's best for my own daughter, and I'll do anything I can to get it for her!

PROFESSOR (*Rising*): Aren't you being a little dramatic, Julie? (*He picks up chair and puts it back where he got it from.*) Margaret seems happy enough to me. She has friends—everybody respects and admires her. (*He goes to some trouble to move chair carefully and place it against the wall.*)

JULIA: There's no pulse beat in admiration. And the only kind of flower that thrives on respect is a wallflower. (*He moves chair several inches away from the wall.*) A pretty fatal variety for any girl to be.

PROFESSOR (*More disturbed than he pretends to be*): Wallflowers and poppycock! (*Facing her*) Margaret's got sense, I tell you. Sororities! Good heavens! What's a sorority but a bunch of silly girls making a fetish of some snobbish little class system! I tell you, Margaret's better off without 'em. (*Puts his hands in his pockets and goes to the window*)

JULIA (*Rather fiercely*): Try to make her believe that when she lies awake with a lump in her throat listening to the fraternity men serenading along sorority row— knowing that not one scrap of their singing is intended for her.

PROFESSOR (*Not looking at her*): I still say it's a pack of nonsense. (*Uncomfortably*) And even if it isn't, I still don't see what you're going to do about it.

JULIA: I'm going to do something right now. (*Holding dress at arm's length and admiring it critically*) And I've a kind of feeling that tonight will change things—a silly feminine hunch, perhaps, but—I'm counting on tonight, Will. (*There is a minor explosion from off-stage, followed by a series of smaller ones. JULIA jumps to her feet. The PROFESSOR keeps staring out of the window.*)

JULIA: Good heavens! What's that? Koch again?

PROFESSOR (*Gently*): That, I take it, is our young friend in the basement. He seems to have miscalculated a little on one of his experiments again. You ought to be used to Koch by now, Julie.

JULIA: I'll never get used to him. It's just like you, to take in a European refugee. But I wish you had chosen a quieter one.

PROFESSOR: He's all right, Julie, and his staying here has proved a good arrangement all around. The furnace may have been a little erratic in his hands at times, but the grounds look fine.

JULIA: I can't say he's lazy, but I do wish he were just a little less . . . uh . . . peculiar.

PROFESSOR: He's all right. He'll be a fine scientist some day.

JULIA (*Going to window to stand next to PROFESSOR*): You

have one great fault, Will. You're just too good to everyone.

PROFESSOR: Oh, come now, Julie.

JULIA: I mean it. (*He puts his hand on her arm for an instant.* JULIA *parts the curtains and looks out.*) Isn't that . . . yes, I believe it is. Margaret's coming now along the row. Yes. Oh, dear, her posture. (*Fretting*) Why won't she take a little interest in her figure!

PROFESSOR: Now, Julie . . .

JULIA: Do you think she'll like the dress, Will? I wanted it for a surprise and now maybe it won't be right. (*Holds up dress critically*) It needs something. . . .

PROFESSOR (*Turning away from window*): Stop worrying. It looks fine.

JULIA (*With sudden inspiration*): A corsage would do it! If she only had a corsage!

PROFESSOR (*Taking out watch*): Good heavens, I'll be late for the printer's. (*Goes into study for his hat and coat, calling to Julia.*) Don't bother about food for me, Julie. (*Comes back putting on his coat*) I'll be gone for a while; I'll get a snack at the Inn if I want it. (*He buttons up his coat. He has his portfolio under one arm and his hat in the other hand.* JULIA *is gathering up her sewing materials and the dress, as* KOCH *appears in the kitchen doorway.* KOCH *is a wild-looking young man with unruly hair and eyeglasses. His eyes, behind the glasses are startlingly dark and intense. He is drying his hands on a paper towel which he later stuffs into his pocket. He has a slight accent.*)

KOCH: You are not, I hope, frightened by my little explosion. (*He shrugs and gestures his dismissal of trivial matter. He turns to the* PROFESSOR.) One failure and another failure and after that perhaps another. But eventually—you shall see—success! Another time . . .

PROFESSOR (*At the door, filling his pipe preparatory to leaving*): If you're not careful, my boy, you'll be blowing yourself up. And then there won't be another time. (KOCH *shrugs.*) But I suppose you want to use the books. I haven't time to get them out for you; but you'll find the whole set in my study, top shelf on the right. Help yourself. (*As he leaves.*) I shan't be late, Julie. (*He leaves, lighting his pipe.* KOCH *goes into the study.* JULIA, *starting upstairs with the dress and sewing materials, calls to* KOCH.)

JULIA: Koch, I think you'd better work at this table out here. It'll be much safer. (*A slight note of criticism*) Dr. Adams doesn't want his papers touched, you know. I haven't even dared dust his room for two weeks.

KOCH (*Coming from study with several heavy volumes*): The professor's wish I always respect. I disturb nothing. (JULIA *goes upstairs.* KOCH *settles himself at the table and loses himself in the books, murmuring something aloud at times and running his fingers through his disheveled hair.* MARGARET *comes in from the street. She is a slender girl with serious, intelligent eyes, not pretty in the accepted sense of the word and not vivid enough to suit the taste of the average young person. But older eyes, used to seeking for the more lasting qualities, would see in her a certain rare and touching loveliness—something of spirit rather than form. Her hair is brushed back neatly, but obviously it has not been arranged to attract. She is wearing glasses and carrying an armful of books.*)

MARGARET (*Setting down books*): Hello. Where is everybody? (*She notices* KOCH.) Oh, hello, Koch. Maybe you could give me those last notes on Walter Pater. Do you mind? I didn't quite get . . .

KOCH (*Interrupting. He snorts his contempt*): Walter Pater! He is not worthy for me to take notes. I ignore him! I forget Walter Pater. Sooner, Margaret, would I take notes on Little Bo-Peep. Drivel! I memorize a little, yes, I say two, three, four lines, maybe—after that I use a mouthwash, quick! Walter Pater! Bah! What the . . . (*Contemptuously*) "students" here so charmingly call "tripe."

MARGARET (*Quietly*): All right, all right, Koch. You don't like Walter Pater. I do. To me he seems delicate and subtle. (*Thoughtfully*) You read his prose aloud, and it makes a kind of pattern and sound like music, or falling water.

KOCH: You are right. He gives much sound and little sense. Walter Pater. He is . . . yes, tripe! (*His voice trails off into a mutter. He buries himself in his book as* JULIA *appears on the stair landing.*)

MARGARET: Hello, Mother.

JULIA (*Hurrying downstairs*): Margaret darling, tonight of all nights! Why couldn't you have come home a little early? Your hair—whatever are we going to do with it? (*She regards her daughter critically.*) Take off your glasses, dear. Don't you remember Dr. Ferrin said you needn't wear them except for reading? I do think, dear . . .

MARGARET: Sorry, Mother, I forgot. I had my lab book to finish up. (*Takes off glasses.*) What's that couplet some-one wrote—you remember—"Men seldom make passes at girls who wear glasses." (*Puts glasses away*) Is that better, darling? (*She kisses her mother lightly.*) I suppose

I'd better go and press the little old chiffon and see if I can look more like Mother's daughter. (*She starts upstairs.*)

JULIA (*A little too eagerly*): It's on your bed, dear. Try to make it presentable. (MARGARET *runs upstairs.* JULIA *looks after her for a while, then, feeling that someone must share her excitement, she turns eagerly to* KOCH.) Now let's see what she does, Koch. I've put the new dress on her bed where she expects to find the old one. Oh, I do want her to like it. Now watch, Koch! Watch.

KOCH (*Uncomfortably*): Please, no. My opinion is no good on this subject. Clothes, they are not important. I ignore them.

MARGARET (*Appears on the landing holding the dress. She pauses, then runs down the stairs. She places dress carefully on a chair and embraces her mother excitedly*): Mother! How did you do it? When did you do it? It's too lovely! I'll never be able to live up to it.

JULIA (*Pleased*): It's just your style, and I want you to put it on and be very gay. (*A little too insistently*) You're going to be as lovely as any girl at the Prom.

MARGARET (*Enchanted by the dress*): It's like something out of a book—out of a seventeenth-century portrait. It's like grapes—grapes frosted with silver. If it had a name it would be "Dawn." "Dawn in Lyonesse"! That's the title of a book, but it does fit, doesn't it?

JULIA (*Moved, kisses her*): I'm glad you like it, dear. (*Businesslike*) Now you must have something to eat. You look tired.

MARGARET (*Still obsessed with the dress*): Oh, I'm not tired, nor hungry, really, Mother. (*The doorbell rings.*)

JULIA (*Running upstairs*): You answer it, dear. I have to change my dress. Belle's having the bridge club tonight and . . . (*She is upstairs.* MARGARET *admits* JACKIE. JACKIE *is as delectable a feather-brain as one would find on the campus. She starts talking the moment the door is opened. Most of her conversation is in italics. She carries a sheaf of crumpled papers which she thrusts at* MARGARET.)

JACKIE: Margaret, darling, I'm so glad you're home. I'm in the most frightful trouble. (KOCH *looks up and snorts, then resumes reading.*) It's this report for Comparative Lit., and it's all such a hectic scramble. I mean it's positively weird, the things they expect you to know.

MARGARET: Come on in, Jackie.

JACKIE (*Coming into the room*): Oh, you're such a comfort, darling. I mean there isn't a girl at the Delta House I can turn to the way I can you. All they do around there is gripe, gripe, gripe! They're down on you if you don't hold up the sorority average—but nobody wants to help you with anything. And here I am with a report I have to get in, or else! The only time I really mind being dumb is at the end of the quarter. My brain simply can't hold up under any more of those grotesque examinations. (MARGARET *smiles and* KOCH *rolls his eyes in exasperation.*) And the reports they make you write! Margaret darling, you've got to help me.

MARGARET (*A bit wearily*): This is almost the zero hour, Jackie; and I can't perform miracles, you know.

JACKIE (*Sitting down and fumbling through her papers*): Oh, dear! I know I should have come around here before but, darling, I was out with Tom. In his new yellow convertible, and I don't know where the time went. I really don't. I mean the hours simply *melted* away.

MARGARET: I see. What's the matter with the report?

JACKIE (*Innocently*): That's just what I don't understand.

I mean, it sounds good to me, especially the part I copied out of the encyclopedia. After Professor Nichols read it, he said the only thing a man could do after wading through a mess like that was to go home and take a good cold shower. (MARGARET *laughs*.) Those were his very words! I've got till Saturday to work it over. So I thought you might help me with it the way you do. (KOCH *bangs his book shut*.) You always know what to do with my ideas, darling. It's funny—I have ideas, but I never know what to do with them.

KOCH (*Acidly, as he gets to his feet*): No? Then I tell you. Miss Jackie, I suggest for *your* ideas the garbage can!

JACKIE (*Startled*): Well! Of all the rude . . .

MARGARET (*Interrupts laughingly*): Oh, don't mind Koch. We'll talk a little lower. He's reading up for his orals, and he's just an old bear.

JACKIE (*Still outraged*): I don't care what he's doing, but I know how he looks—like the Missing Link, or the Forgotten Man, or something. (KOCH *glares at her for a second, then sits down and resumes his reading. The girls speak in lower tones*.)

MARGARET (*Sitting down*): This report, now . . .

JACKIE: Well, you see, there's the formal tonight and all, and I haven't even had my nails done. (*Displays her faultlessly manicured fingertips*.) I mean, I thought maybe you'd work my paper over—just the finishing touches, dear, changing the organization and correcting the spelling and maybe typing it so I could get it in.

MARGARET: Well, I'd be glad to help you, Jackie, only you see . . .

JACKIE (*Alarmed*): You haven't a report of your own to do, have you? You're always weeks ahead of time.

MARGARET: No. Not that, but—well, Jackie, I'm going to the Prom, myself.

JACKIE (*Sitting bolt upright*): Not really! I didn't dream you'd . . . well, I mean, how . . . well, darling, how clever of you!

MARGARET (*Smiling at her*): I don't blame you for being surprised, Jackie. You might as well say right out what you think. "Margaret Arnold Dates for Junior Prom!" Campus headlines!

JACKIE (*Contritely*): I'm a little beast, bringing my paper over for you to slave on while I play around. I see it now, really I do, and I'm glad you're going, dear. (*Pause*) I hope it's someone half nice enough to rate a girl like you. (*Eagerly*) Who is it?

MARGARET (*Trying to be casual*): It's Shep Warren.

JACKIE: *No!* Not Shep! Not *Shep Warren!* Oh, oh! Wait till Kit Madsen hears about this. (*She gets up on her knees on chair in excitement.*) I mean, it's priceless! Simply priceless! (*With concern*) Dear me, she'll chew off all her nail polish again. I tell you she *will*.

MARGARET: Calm down, Jackie. What about Kit?

JACKIE (*Thrilled*): Come close and let Jackie tell all. (*Pulls* MARGARET *down beside her*) Now don't breathe it or the darn Delts will slap some more demerits on my not-so-spotless record. (*In the excitement, she forgets to keep her voice lowered.* KOCH *groans and claps his hands over his ears.*) Listen! (*She grabs* MARGARET's *arm.*) For the first time in history, Kit Madsen's without a date!

MARGARET: No!

JACKIE: And she's practically clawing down the yellow wallpaper. I mean she's absolutely *poisonous!* Walt Bradford, the senator's son—you know, well, he was going to take her till he threw out a knee today, in track.

So now she's left flat. (*Clapping her hands*) **Goody, goody! Am I sorry!**

MARGARET: What has Shep got to do with it?

JACKIE: You don't know Kit. When Kit breaks a man's heart, she expects it to stay broken. Shep's been on her doormat for so long she's not going to like it that he's no longer underfoot. She's been so sure he'd come crawling back after he learned about Walt's accident, but he hasn't! And you're the reason, you darling! (*She hugs* MARGARET.)

MARGARET (*Thoughtfully*): Should I be sorry? In a way I am. I shouldn't like to think I'm responsible, even indirectly, for poor Kit's frenzy.

JACKIE: Margaret lamb, you're too good for this world. Sorry, my eye! Every little Delta is going to God bless you. I mean we've had about enough of Kit's fatal fascination for men. It burns us up. (*Giggles*) And she was all set to wipe the rest of us right off the map tonight— a new flame-colored dress with practically nothing above the waist and . . . (KOCH *can stand no more. With a swipe of his arm, he pushes his books aside and stands up, knocking over his chair in his fury.*)

KOCH: Of what use is it I should study when all around is nothing but babble, babble, babble! Some things I ignore but not dresses with nothing to here. (*Vaguely indicates his waistline. Then he strides to door.*) I come back to my books when there is not so much what you call—this sex appeal. (*He goes out through the kitchen slamming the door after him.*)

MARGARET (*Amused, but not unkindly*): Poor Koch!

JACKIE: I don't know why your uncle puts up with him— unless he's a count or something in disguise.

MARGARET (*Laughing*): Oh, no. Koch is brilliant, though,

in a kind of fanatical way, and Uncle Will understands him—even likes him. And the only things Koch doesn't hate in this world are Uncle Will and Einstein.

JACKIE (*Innocently enough*): Who's Einstein? One of the profs?

MARGARET (*Gently*): No, dear, nor one of the fraternity men, or you'd know him.

JULIA (*Coming down the stairs*): Hello, Jackie. I heard your voice.

JACKIE (*Rising*): Hello, Mrs. Arnold.

JULIA: You girls ought to have a bite of food before the party. Margaret, there's a tray of sandwiches in the kitchen.

MARGARET (*As she runs out to kitchen*): Oh, thanks, Mother.

JACKIE: How awfully nice of you, Mrs. Arnold.

JULIA: I'll simply have to force Margaret to eat. She's too skinny as it is. (*The doorbell rings.* JULIA *opens door, steps outside.* MARGARET *re-enters with tray of food, which she holds before* JACKIE.)

JULIA (*Off*): Thank you.

JACKIE (*Takes sandwich, lifts top*): Umm! I adore tomato sandwiches. (*Replaces top and eats.* MARGARET *takes a sandwich.*)

JULIA (*Re-entering carrying a florist's box*): Margaret, look, dear, from the florist's—for you! (*She's pleasantly excited. The girls forget their sandwiches.*)

JACKIE (*Excited*): Open it up, quick!

MARGARET (*Taking box incredulously*): For me? (*She undoes the string with shaking fingers, opens box and looks in. Gently, she lifts out an exquisite corsage of orchids. Speechlessly, she looks from* JACKIE *to her mother.*)

JULIA: How lovely! It's all your dress needed, darling—

just the thing to finish it off.

JACKIE (*Reverently*): Orchids! Shep Warren's no cheap-skate. I'll say that for him. Read the card, Margaret. What does it say?

MARGARET (*In a low voice*): It says . . . It says . . . Oh, here, Jackie, read it yourself if you must know.

JACKIE (*Snatches and reads card*): Can you beat that? Listen! Can you believe it? Spoken like a gentleman of the old school. (*Reads*) "To the lovely Margaret."

MARGARET: Oh!

JACKIE: Such sweet simplicity. I mean, what's come over Shep? I'll bet he's been reading "When Knighthood Was in Flower" since you crossed his trail. (JULIA *seems much affected. During* JACKIE's *speech, she pats* MAR-GARET's *shoulder. Surreptitiously, she wipes her eyes, picks up tray, stands undecided for a moment, places tray on small table near kitchen door and goes out into the kitchen.* MARGARET *stands as if in a dream.*)

JACKIE: Say something. Orchids deserve a few ladylike "wahoos," don't they? (MARGARET *bites her lower lip and raises her hand to brush tears from her eyes.* JACKIE, *suddenly conscious of her friend's emotion, pounces on her.*) Margaret, for cryin'-out-loud, what's the matter, honey? Did you want a diamond bracelet or something?

MARGARET (*Her usual reserve abandoned*): Jackie—I'd hate to have anyone but you know this—but this is the first—the very first corsage I've ever had. And now that I have it—well, I . . . I . . . (*Near tears again*) Oh, don't tell on me, Jackie. I couldn't bear it! Don't tell!

JACKIE (*Genuinely*): Listen, my sweet darling fool. I'd bawl, too, if anybody ever liked me enough to send me orchids. Gardenias are the best I rate and I'm plenty thankful for them. Orchids! This is going to absolutely lay Kit Madsen out!

MARGARET (*Simply*): Jackie, I've got to tell you. I'm panicky about tonight. It sounds silly, but outside of class I'm scared of people my own age. I'd like to be gay and free and easy with them—but somehow I can't.

JACKIE: It's just that you're different.

MARGARET (*Bitterly*): Yes, I'm different.

JACKIE: Don't say it as if you had some kind of disease. There's nothing the matter with you. I mean, all you need is a little more window dressing. Put on a little more ga-ga and act dumber. You have nice eyes and a good figure, but you know too many big words.

MARGARET: Yes, I guess my technique is bad.

JACKIE: Bad? Darling, it's *fatal!* (*Pointedly and sincerely*) I mean, when a woman has too many brains, it takes a man's mind off her legs.

MARGARET (*Laughing in spite of herself*): What a philosopher you are, Jackie.

JACKIE: Yes, little Ann Landers—that's me. (*Looks at her watch*) Oh, oh, I've got to run. If I don't hurry up, I won't have time to watch Kit Madsen turn a rich dark green when she hears about Shep and the orchids. (*Gathers up her papers*) As I see it, Professor Nichols will have to take another shower.

MARGARET: Leave the papers here, Jackie. We'll see that they get in before the deadline.

JACKIE (*Not able to refuse*): You angel! You angel out of heaven! (*Embraces* MARGARET.) Remember, darling, try not to look too innocent tonight. (*Turns in doorway*) And don't use any eight-cylinder words.

MARGARET: I'll try to remember. (*As* JACKIE *leaves*) Goodbye, Jackie. (*She collects* JACKIE'S *papers, looks at them with a smile and lays them neatly on table.*)

JULIA (*Entering from kitchen*): I thought Jackie'd never go. You'll have to hurry, dear. It's so important that you look your best tonight. (*Picking up orchids*) Here, I'll put the flowers in the refrigerator.

MARGARET: Thanks, Mother.

JULIA: Now get ready. And oh, Margaret, let your hair go a bit looser. It has such a nice wave when you encourage it. Young men don't want their girls to look too prim.

MARGARET: Not too aloof and holy, Mother? Is that what you mean? You and Jackie seem of one mind. I'm afraid I'm just not the sophisticated type, and a change of hair-do won't help much.

JULIA (*Defensively*): You know very well what I mean. I wouldn't change you in any of the ways that matter, but I want you to be happy and have fun like other girls.

MARGARET (*Affectionately*): I know, Mother, and I'll try not to look strong-minded—if you think that will help.

JULIA (*At kitchen door*): All right, dear, don't stand talking. I want to see you dressed before I leave. Belle's having our Friday night bridge club, and I promised to be early. I'm almost sorry I'm going.

MARGARET: I wouldn't have you miss it for anything. There's no reason for you to stay. (JULIA *goes out to the kitchen with the flowers as the* PROFESSOR *comes in from the street.*) Hello, Uncle Will.

PROFESSOR (*Removing his hat and coat*): Well, well, how's my favorite niece this evening?

MARGARET: A little end-of-the-quarterish, sir, she said. And how's my super-favorite uncle?

PROFESSOR: Jealous, my dear—just a bit jealous. (*Kisses*

her gently on the cheek) I hear you're leaving me to-night.

JULIA (*Calling sharply from the kitchen*): Will, send that child upstairs. She'll never be ready. (PROFESSOR *smiles at* MARGARET *and goes into his study to put his hat, coat and portfolio away.*)

MARGARET (*Picking up the dress*): But, Mother, how does one use up the time? I never can think of things to do to myself—anything that helps. (*Starts up the stairs cheerfully humming a popular tune. The* PROFESSOR *comes from his study.* MARGARET *pauses on the stairway.*)

PROFESSOR (*Looking up at her*): Getting ready in your mother's day was a long and mysterious ritual, my dear. Of course they wore more clothes, then.

JULIA (*Entering from the kitchen*): A little mystery never hurt any woman. (*Calling to* MARGARET, *who is now upstairs*) If you need any help, dear . . .

MARGARET (*From upstairs*): If I do, I'll call. Stop worrying over me.

JULIA (*Straightening things about the room*): I think the dress will be perfect for her after all. (PROFESSOR *is standing at window, engaged in filling his pipe.*) But, goodness, she's so unpredictable—you never know what she'll like. (*Pause, then triumphantly.*) Well, she got her corsage—orchids—from her young man, Will. (PROFESSOR *turns slowly from window.*) And I'm sure it made all the difference. (*She sighs. He looks at her, then lights his pipe.*) There's something about getting flowers from a man that just does things to you, and I'm not so old I don't remember.

PROFESSOR (*Sincerely*): No, you're not, Julie. Sometimes I think you're younger than Margaret herself. (*He sits in easy chair.*)

JULIA (*Changing position of vase of flowers*): Don't be silly. If Margaret acts old for her age, it's because she's never learned to have fun.

KOCH (*Coming from kitchen*): I should like, please, if I can go on with the books, Doctor. I have discovered just what I need. But the first time I am here I find also too much competition when I try to read.

JULIA (*Quickly*): I'm sorry, Koch, but I'm afraid you'll have to wait. Margaret's going out tonight, and we'll need the living room for a while. I hope you won't mind?

KOCH: Mind? Why should Franz Koch mind? He is used to making way for others—for the fraternity men. They are important, yes. Big automobiles and dances. These are also important. But some time Franz Koch—he, too, is important. Now, it is all right. He can wait.

JULIA: Now, Koch, don't get delusions of persecution just because I make a simple request. You may work here in a very little while, but after all . . .

PROFESSOR (*Quietly*): Hadn't you better see if your daughter needs you?

JULIA: Perhaps I should—and get my things on. (*During next speeches, she goes to kitchen for corsage, re-enters, and goes upstairs.*)

PROFESSOR (*His hand on* KOCH's *shoulder*): Women, my boy, have no sense of proportion. Our research is far more important than these feminine trivia, isn't it? But what can we do? (KOCH *shrugs.*) Come back up later. There won't be a petticoat in the house and you can spread out all you like for a whole evening of study.

KOCH (*With a slight bow*): Doctor Adams is very kind. Yes, I go now, Doctor. (*Worshipfully*) Sometime, perhaps, when I have studied long, I have also the name of "Doctor"—Doctor Franz Koch. And I remember then that you have been very kind.

PROFESSOR (*Modestly*): Yes . . . I'm glad to be of help. How is everything coming along? Dissertation plans all complete, I understand.

KOCH: The plans for the dissertation are approved, yes. But the dissertation is too slow. But I shall study, I shall manage. Yes. (*With intensity*) Some time, after my name, Franz Koch, there will be for everyone to see the letters that testify that I am a scholar. Yes, some time, we shall see. And all that I will be, I will give to the service of this good America, whose people have been so kind to me.

PROFESSOR (*Picking up a book*): Yes, Koch, we shall see. I have great faith in you. (*He looks up and sees* JULIA *coming down the stairs. She has her hat on and carries her coat over her arm.*) Come back later to use the books, Koch. (KOCH *goes back to his cellar.*)

JULIA (*Eagerly, as she goes to* PROFESSOR): She's nearly ready and the dress is beautiful. It does things to her. I'm almost sorry that I'm going out.

PROFESSOR (*Who has risen at her approach and now helps her into her coat*): Nonsense. You run along and win the bridge prize. Margaret will be better off without you.

JULIA: That's a fine thing to say to her own mother. (*Kisses him lightly on the forehead. He pats her arm.*)

PROFESSOR: Goodbye, Julie. I'll behave like a perfect gentleman to this young . . . young man of Margaret's. (JULIA *leaves.* PROFESSOR *leans back comfortably, examines his pipe, then lights it. He picks up a book and leafs through it.* MARGARET *appears on the stairs. She is wearing the new dress and corsage. She is transformed.*

For a moment, she pauses on the landing, and then with swift young grace comes down the stairs. In tribute, the PROFESSOR *rises to his feet. She stands before her uncle.*)

MARGARET (*After a pause*): Uncle Will, is it . . . am I all right? Will I do?

PROFESSOR: Wait a minute. Stand right there. (*He is startled and moved by her loveliness. He takes his glasses off, polishes them slowly and meticulously and replaces them carefully.*) Well! (*With playful and loving charm.*) My niece, if I'm not mistaken. But come closer. I want to make sure you're real. (*She goes to him, puts her arms about him and presses her cheek to his coat.*)

MARGARET (*Thrilled and hardly daring to be*): I'm not sure I'm real, either. I'm not the everyday Margaret, am I? *She's* probably off in a corner somewhere grubbing over her irregular French verbs. (*Does a little dance step*) Poor dear, she has a kind heart, you know.

PROFESSOR (*Loyally*): And a sweet face.

MARGARET: The face of a girl who wins essay contests. (*She grimaces, then laughs.*) But let's not think about her. Let's think about me—the lovely Margaret.

PROFESSOR (*Sitting down*): I'm agreed to anything. (*Delighted with her*) You've put me in my mellow mood. It comes on just after twilight. But now, for this new Margaret. (*Looking at her with fond admiration.*) "She walks in beauty like the night . . ."

MARGARET (*Echoing him as if in a dream*): "Of cloudless climes and starry skies."

PROFESSOR (*Holding the spell*): "And all that's best of dark and bright . . ."

MARGARET: "Meet in her aspect and her eyes." (*She is lost in a strange enchanted reverie. Then she sits on a stool at his feet.*) I feel as if I've swallowed a butterfly.

PROFESSOR (*Puts his arm around her and speaks gently*): Is it this young man you're going with tonight who inspires this unusual excitement, my dear?

MARGARET (*After considering*): N-o-o-o. That's the odd part of it. (*Laughingly*) I'm certainly not falling in love. I have the silly feeling somehow that I ought to be going to a court ball. (*Smiles nervously and shyly*) With an eighteenth-century cavalier to dance the minuet.

PROFESSOR: You look it, too, Margaret. But you'd better remember it's only Shep Warren you're going with—a young fellow who can't get Shakespeare through his somewhat dense head.

MARGARET: Darling, literal old professor! I'm not going off the deep end simply because I've got a new dress and feel just like the Lady Vere de Vere. It's just . . . oh, how can I say it?

PROFESSOR: Your heart's had a spring thaw?

MARGARET: That's just it! Goodness, I've even stopped seeming dull and uninteresting to myself. And all because a not-too-intelligent young man has sought my company and sent me flowers, Uncle Will. Orchids! (*She touches her corsage.*) You know . . . at first . . . just at first when Shep asked me, I thought he was doing it so that, well . . . to win *your* favor . . . so you'd be easier on him in class. He needs the credit, you know, for spring track, and you *have* been a little hard on him, darling.

PROFESSOR: He'd better not try . . .

MARGARET (*Laying a finger on his lips*): Sh! I'm only telling you what I *thought*. He told me he was fed up with glamour girls and wanted somebody—well, somebody like me. I thought he had some other motive for asking me. But it was only my own uncertainty—my own awful sense of being a wallflower.

PROFESSOR: Now, Margaret . . .

MARGARET: There! The horrid word is out. It made me think that someone like him couldn't possibly find me interesting. (*Brightly*) But when the flowers came, I knew I was wrong! That's when the spring thaw started and I realized that I'd been a very stupid person—never giving fellows like Shep Warren credit for being half as decent and fine as they really are.

PROFESSOR (*Disturbed, takes her hands gently*): The message on the card must have been eloquent.

MARGARET: They were new and beautiful words to me. (*Dreamily*) "To the lovely Margaret." Could anyone like Shep Warren think that of me? (*Her voice grows husky as she repeats.*) "To the lovely Margaret."

PROFESSOR: A masterpiece of understatement.

MARGARET: Oh, no! I lack so much. I'm shy and awkward. I'd give my place on the dean's list just to be able to banter a little and laugh and say witty meaningless things. But I can't. Why, Uncle Will? Why?

PROFESSOR: I'll tell you. Remember this, Margaret. (*He is gentle and grave.*) You are like a person holding a piece of gold but moving in a world where everyone else trades in nickels and dimes. Somehow, my dear, you've never learned to deal in their small change.

MARGARET (*Seriously*): I'll remember that, Uncle Will. It's a very lovely thought.

PROFESSOR: You've always been an understanding child, Margaret, and it's made you a little older than most . . . beyond your years, I mean. But I'm counting on it to help you over some of the hard places when they show up.

MARGARET: I've wanted to be older than my years. What's so wonderful about being young, if you're like me? It means going around with an ache inside and pretending that it doesn't matter. I used to wish to be old and past the stage where things can hurt you so much. (*With a quick change of mood, she jumps to her feet*) But that was before tonight. (*She goes to the window. Faint strains of a dance orchestra can be heard from somewhere on the campus. She listens with her head up and her hands clasped. Her voice is deep with ecstasy.*) Tonight I'm glad I'm young. (*The telephone rings piercingly.* MARGARET *looks at her uncle but doesn't move.*)

PROFESSOR (*Going to phone*): For me, very likely. (*Into receiver*) Hello . . . yes, that's right. Doctor Adams speaking. (*Looks at* MARGARET.) Yes, Miss Arnold is here. One moment, please. (*Sets receiver down slowly, speaks carefully*) For you, dear.

MARGARET (*Goes to phone with fear and questioning*): Hello. Yes. (*Pause*) Shep? (*She listens.*) But has something happened? (*Pause*) A mix-up? (PROFESSOR *begins to pace slowly*) How do you mean? (*Her voice trembles.*) Of course. (*Long pause*) Of course . . . of course, Shep. It seems the only thing to do. You have to do the gallant thing. (*Her voice is benumbed and wooden.*) *Noblesse oblige,* Shep. (*Pause*) What? Oh, look it up in the dictionary. . . . Yes, I'm afraid I do . . . I said, I'm afraid I understand perfectly. No. (*Pause*) No. Please don't bother. It's all right. Everything's quite all right . . . all right. (*Her voice trails off as she replaces receiver carefully. Pause. In a dull, lifeless voice.*) He's not coming, Uncle Will.

PROFESSOR (*Angrily*): The young whelp! The ill-mannered baboon. Does he think he can get away with this? I'll show that young . . . (*Goes to her. Tenderly.*) Margaret, my dear . . . Margaret . . .

MARGARET (*Trying for control*): Please, please, Uncle Will. There's nothing we can do. It's just the way things were . . . were supposed to turn out. (*Frantic*) I knew . . . *knew* it couldn't be real.

PROFESSOR (*Going to phone*): There's something I can do. I'm going to tell that irresponsible young ape a thing or two! He'll learn . . .

MARGARET (*Stopping him*): No, no. It can't help. He's not to blame really. Kit Madsen's fatal fascination was just too much for him. From what I can make out, she must have got hold of him and cried on his shoulder. He was upset. He tried to be decent about it. (*Quiveringly*) He seemed quite sweetly apologetic, really. (*Pause*) He offered to send one of his frat brothers over—one who wasn't too particular, I suppose. (*Starts to cry quietly*) No, no, Uncle Will, everything's all right. Everything's just as it was before. I told you it was only a spring thaw.

PROFESSOR (*Goes to her, puts his hands on her shoulders but she turns her face away*): Margaret . . .

MARGARET: Don't feel sorry for me, Uncle Will. I couldn't bear that. (*Touches her corsage, smiles shakily*) I'm afraid I forgot to thank Shep for the orchids. (PROFESSOR *looks at her suddenly.*) It's funny about the flowers . . . (*As she unpins them*) I was so sure they meant something. (*She lays them aside gently.*) And the card! *Especially* the card.

PROFESSOR: Margaret, about the flowers . . .

MARGARET (*Tensely*): Yes?

PROFESSOR: The flowers . . . I meant to tell you. . . .

MARGARET: Uncle Will! What are you trying to say?

PROFESSOR (*Turning away from her. He is miserable*): I intended . . .

MARGARET: Oh! (*Stunned silence*) Oh! I know now. It's all clear. The orchids weren't from Shep after all. (*He turns his face away from her.*) You sent them! Why didn't I guess? (*Her voice breaks on a sob.*) Even the flowers . . .

PROFESSOR (*After clearing his throat*): Margaret, I didn't mean to deceive you about the orchids. I wanted your evening to be flawless and that was my small gesture toward making it so. When I saw you thought the corsage was from your escort . . . (*He makes a helpless gesture.*) I'm sorry, my dear.

MARGARET (*In a flat, level voice*): It's like you to be so thoughtful. I might have known. (*Goes to him. Compassionately.*) Don't worry about me, dear. We needn't tell Mother—not tonight, at least. (*Breaking down*) Oh, please let me sit here alone for a while! Please, *please!*

PROFESSOR (*Kisses her gently*): If that's the way you want it, my dear. (*Presses button. All lights but lamp on table where KOCH worked, go out. PROFESSOR goes into his study. MARGARET looks after him for a second, then sits on the divan. Suddenly she buries her face in her arms and is shaken with long, shuddering sobs. After a while KOCH comes in. He crosses to the worktable. He hears a sound, looks toward divan and sees MARGARET. He stands undecided.*)

KOCH (*Gently*): Excuse me. I did not know you are still here. I go. (*He starts to leave.*)

MARGARET (*Pulling herself together with an effort*): No. We've kept you away from your books long enough, Koch. (*She sits up and, heedless of him, dries her eyes.*)

KOCH (*Uncertain*): You have been crying. So? (*There is understanding and accusation in his tone.*) But you were going out. You were going dancing with the famous Mr. Shep Warren.

MARGARET: Yes. The famous Mr. Warren. (*Preoccupied and sorrowfully, not accusingly*) But he got a little mixed up. He remembered just in time that it was Kit Madsen he wanted to take—and not me. (*Trying to smile*) Lucky he got it all straightened out in time, wasn't it? (*The tears come again.*)

KOCH (*Upset*): No! No, don't! I ask you. Shep Warren! I ignore him. Sometime I, Franz Koch, whom nobody notices now—sometime I . . . (*Passionately*) Margaret, you say the word and I choke Shep Warren with my hands like this. (*He illustrates.*)

MARGARET: That wouldn't solve my problem. I wasn't crying about Shep—just about what he stood for. He was a symbol of all the things that passed me by without so much as a nod. Oh, Koch, why can't I be like Kit or Jackie!

KOCH: So! You are like all the others. A little dancing, a little playing—a toy that jingles . . . Bah! You cry for nothing. I should ignore you . . . (*In an uncertain and gentle voice*) But I don't.

MARGARET (*In a faraway voice*): I'm crying because I'm young, and it happens to be spring. And if you lean out of the window, you can smell lilacs—lilacs under a spring moon. (KOCH *looks toward the window.*) Lilacs in the moonlight.

KOCH (*Softly and with shy kindness*): You are the professor's niece, but you do not know everything. Yes, it is true. I am nothing. (*Poignantly*) But sometimes I have feeling. Yes, I too. I have feeling.

MARGARET (*Gently*): I'm sorry. I've been thinking only of myself. Maybe you just pretend to hate people because you're afraid they won't like you. Maybe you like the things Shep Warren likes—the things I wish I had. (*With understanding*) You can't stop being young any more than I can. (*He turns away, his face full of misery.*) You know loneliness, too, don't you, Koch?

KOCH (*Gently*): You are very kind, and now I say something I feel. You are not like these others, no! And you are, after all, very lovely. This I have always said to myself. You have—how shall I say—the kind of light that glows from within.

MARGARET (*Tremulously*): You don't mean—someone else, do you? You meant to say that to *me*?

KOCH (*Sincerely*): I say this only to you. (*She throws open the window. Orchestra music floats in and the faint sound of laughter. Suddenly, it is more than she can bear. She buries her face in her hands. Slowly,* KOCH *removes his glasses. He sets them on the table. He draws himself up and stands straight. He is quite good-looking. In a new voice*) Margaret! (*Slowly she lowers her hands and looks at him. He bows with old-world grace.*) Margaret, if I may have this dance . . . (*He holds out his arms. She smiles tremulously as she slowly moves toward him. He places an arm about her waist and takes her hand. Slowly, her arm goes around his shoulder. The music swells. They begin to dance in perfect rhythm with each other, as the curtain falls.*)

THE END

ORCHIDS FOR MARGARET

Characters: 2 male, 3 female.

Playing Time: 45 minutes.

Costumes: Professor Adams wears a shabby smoking jacket and baggy trousers. Julia wears an apron over a dark dress. Koch is dressed carelessly in old corduroys and a shirt open at the throat. When first seen Margaret is dressed in a sweater and skirt. She wears glasses. Later in the play Margaret appears in an evening gown of pale lavender, with an overskirt of white tulle and dotted with silver sequins or something silvery. She wears a corsage of orchids. Jackie is dressed in extreme co-ed style—a silk dress, high heels, hair becomingly done, etc., in direct contrast to Margaret. Her fingernails are faultlessly manicured, covered with dark red polish.

Properties: Tape measure, pipe, sheaf of papers, books, thread, needle, tray of sandwiches, milk, cookies, florist's box with orchid corsage, card inscribed, "To the lovely Margaret."

Setting: The living room is unpretentiously pleasant. The furnishings are solid and comfortable, and there are cheerful chintz curtains at the windows. The slip covers on the furniture are also very cheerful and gay. There are books and lamps about, pictures on the wall. Upstage center is a fireplace. To the right of it is the lower part of a staircase, consisting of three steps and a landing, which leads to the upstairs rooms. Left of the fireplace is the door to the professor's study. Two long windows are in the left wall. A door, downstage of windows, leads to outdoors. In the upper part of the right wall is a door leading to the kitchen. This is also the entrance to the cellar. There is a comfortable divan in front of the windows and a small table holding a telephone near the staircase.

Lighting: No special effects.

N for Nuisance

By Helen Louise Miller

Characters

SARALEE GIBSON, *a high school artist*
BILLY, *her younger brother*
MRS. GIBSON
BLAIR KELLEY, *a university junior*
CELIA BAYLOR, *an unprofessional model*
MR. HENDERSON, *an art instructor*

SETTING: *Saralee's studio.*
AT RISE: SARALEE *is working at her easel. Her subject, posed on the model stand, is her brother,* BILLY. BILLY *wears an aluminum stew pot on his head, carries the lid of a tin wash boiler as a shield, and brandishes a long-handled toasting fork. His eyes are fixed on an alarm clock on the table. He is very unhappy.*

BILLY: I'm warning you, sis, every second I stand here from now on is costing you time-and-a-half overtime.
SARALEE: Sh! It will take me only a jiffy. That nose of yours is giving me trouble.

BILLY: If you're working on my nose, why can't I put down this artillery?

SARALEE: Don't talk. When you talk, your nose wriggles like a rabbit's. (BILLY *makes effort to scratch his back with toasting fork.*) Billy, stand still! You're impossible this morning.

BILLY: Can I help it if I have a bite?

SARALEE: Please try to hold your pose just a little longer. It's almost finished.

BILLY (*With a sigh of resignation*): O.K., but remember my rates are going up every minute.

SARALEE: And so is my blood pressure. (*There is a knock at the door and* BLAIR KELLEY *enters, carrying a large, empty picture frame.*)

BLAIR: Sorry to interrupt, but this is strictly business. Here's your frame, Saralee. Do you think it will do for your masterpiece?

SARALEE: Oh, Blair, it looks wonderful. Just put it down wherever you can find room. I'll be finished in a second.

BLAIR (*Looking around*): Say, this is a neat set-up you have here. Pretty ritzy, aren't you, with a studio all to yourself?

SARALEE: I still feel apologetic when I see the family Ford parked outside, while I inhabit the garage.

BILLY: What about Pop and me? We had to move our workshop into the cellar.

BLAIR: (*To* BILLY): Hi, chum. Is she giving you a hard time this morning?

BILLY: Not *chum,* mister. Say *chump* when you speak to me. I'm the original guinea pig in this establishment. Only guinea pigs are lucky. They just have to *die* for their art.

SARALEE: Oh, come now. It's not that bad. There! I've finished. You may come and look.

BILLY: (*Getting off the platform and divesting himself of his kitchen armor*): That's not in my contract. I only pose for your pictures; I don't have to look at 'em.

SARALEE: O.K., if that's the way you feel about it.

BILLY: That's the way I feel. Say, Blair, did you hear the big news?

BLAIR: No, what?

BILLY: I got my "N."

BLAIR: Your "N"?

BILLY (*Pulling letter from pocket*): Sure, my varsity letter. See—got it yesterday in assembly.

BLAIR: Well, congratulations! (*Admiring the award*) Say, that's really sharp! Boy, I'll never forget the day I got mine, but I was a lot older than you. I never managed to get enough points till I was in the ninth grade. You must be a big wheel to get yours in eighth. "N" for Newcastle Junior High.

SARALEE (*Sharply*): "N" for *Nuisance,* if you ask me.

BILLY: Well, nobody asked you, see. The only thing I did ask you was to sew this on my sweater, but you never even did that. All you ever think about is this messy old painting.

SARALEE: Oh, I'm sorry, Billy. I forgot it. Honestly, getting ready for this exhibit is driving me crazy. Peel off your sweater and leave it here. I'll sew it on this morning if it kills me. I promise.

BILLY: O.K. (*Takes off sweater and tosses it on the table with the letter*) I'll be needing it this afternoon.

SARALEE: I'll have it ready for you. Now please get out of here. I have a million things to do.

BILLY: (*At door*): With pleasure.

SARALEE: Oh, wait a minute. I want you to take these canvases down to the gallery. Mr. Henderson will take care of them.

BILLY: Not now, sis. I'm due at the "Y" for a swimming meet.

SARALEE: But, Billy, Mr. Henderson must have them this morning so he can place them.

BILLY: Sorry, no can do! (MRS. GIBSON *enters.*)

MRS. GIBSON: Sorry to interrupt you, dear, but Celia just phoned and says she's on her way over. Oh, hello, Blair.

BLAIR: Good morning, Mrs. Gibson.

MRS. GIBSON: It's wonderful that you're going to be here for Saralee's first showing. We're all so thrilled.

SARALEE: Mother, can't you make Billy take these paintings down to Mr. Henderson? He wants them this morning.

MRS. GIBSON: Billy will take them, won't you, dear?

BILLY: I can't, Mom. We've got this swimming meet down at the "Y" this morning, and I'm in one of the relays.

MRS. GIBSON: But this is important, Billy. It isn't every day your sister gets to show her paintings.

BILLY: And it isn't every day I get in a relay, either.

MRS. GIBSON: Now, look, dear, we can't be selfish, can we? Run along and take the paintings down to Mr. Henderson. Your little friends will wait for you.

BILLY: Little friends? Mom, don't you understand? It's the swimming team!

MRS. GIBSON: Don't argue, Billy. Get along.

SARALEE: And be sure to come right back so you can take the contest entry in before twelve.

BILLY (*Grabbing pictures and stalking out*): This is the last straw!

SARALEE: Honestly, that boy!

MRS. GIBSON: Never mind, dear. He'll get the paintings there on time.

BLAIR: I could have taken them down for you, Saralee.

MRS. GIBSON: Nonsense, Blair. Billy's glad to run errands.

BLAIR: He didn't look glad to me.

MRS. GIBSON: You know how boys are at this age. (*Laughing*) In fact, I can remember you when you were in Junior High. It seems impossible you're a junior at the University. Let me see, what is it you're specializing in?

BLAIR: Psychology, Mrs. Gibson.

MRS. GIBSON: Oh, yes. I understand that's quite a field these days. Well, Saralee, if there's nothing I can do for you, I'll scoot back to the house. Celia should be here any minute now.

BLAIR: Celia? Not Celia Baylor?

SARALEE: Yes, she's done a lot of posing for me this winter. I've used her as the model for the contest entry. . . . "Typical Teen-Ager." (*Picks up picture and places it on easel*) Look, isn't she lovely?

BLAIR: It's a lovely picture, but that's as far as I'll commit myself.

MRS. GIBSON: Show him that one you did of Celia with her hair up in curlers. That's the cutest thing I ever saw, but Celia won't hear of putting it in the exhibition.

SARALEE: I can't say I blame her. Even for art's sake, I wouldn't want to be on display in the town hall with my hair in pin curls. I only wish my technique was as good in this one.

BLAIR (*Looking at picture of* CELIA *on easel*): Is this your prize entry?

SARALEE: Yes, this is the one I'm banking on. If Celia carries off top honors in the competition, I go to art school next year. So wish the lady luck.

BLAIR: I wish *you* luck, Saralee, and lots of it.

SARALEE: Thanks, Blair.

MRS. GIBSON: You always were such an understanding boy, Blair, and that psychology course seems to have made you even more so.

BLAIR: That's what it's supposed to do, Mrs. Gibson.

MRS. GIBSON: Well, dear, I must go press your dress for this afternoon. I want you to look your best for that French painter.

SARALEE (*Laughing*): Monsieur Bourget won't be looking at me, Mother. He'll be looking at the paintings.

MRS. GIBSON: I'm still going to press that dress. I know these Frenchmen. (*Exits*)

BLAIR: I think I'll follow in your mother's footsteps if Celia Baylor is headed this way.

SARALEE: Scared?

BLAIR: Two years of college have not dimmed my memory of that man-trap.

SARALEE: And she still considers you the best catch in Culver County.

BLAIR: Not me, sister. I'm already caught. At least, I think I am.

SARALEE (*Demurely*): And who is the lucky lady?

BLAIR: As if you didn't know. By the way, I've signed you up for the Junior Prom.

SARALEE: Just like that, eh?

BLAIR (*Firmly*): Just like that. And here's the proof. I'm on the printing committee, and here's a sample of the dance program. You'll observe the name Saralee, Saralee, Saralee, written in for every dance. You wouldn't want to make a forger out of me, would you? (*Tosses dance program on table*)

SARALEE: Certainly not.

BLAIR: Then think it over, girl. Think it over.

SARALEE: I'm thinking, boy, and hard, but right now, I've got worries.

BLAIR: Name one.

SARALEE: Celia.

BLAIR: Now look here. You're not the jealous type.

SARALEE: Silly! I mean *this* Celia. (*Pointing to easel*) I'm still not satisfied with that shadow under her right eye. That's why she's dropping in this morning—so I can have another try at it.

BLAIR: And that's why I'm dropping out. So long, Miss Paint-Pot. See you around!

SARALEE: See you this afternoon at the exhibit . . . I hope.

BLAIR: You bet. And by the way, Saralee, if you have any more errands, why not call on me for some of them? Billy's a busy man.

SARALEE: Are you kidding?

BLAIR: No, I'm serious. Life has problems for a kid of his age. He's got more important things to do than play nursemaid to an art exhibit.

SARALEE: Well, if that's the way you feel about this exhibit, Blair Kelley . . . you can just. . . .

BLAIR: Now don't get stuffy! It's not the way I feel about your exhibit. It's the way I feel about Billy. He's a good kid. I hate to see him pushed around.

SARALEE: Pushed around! Well, I like that!

BLAIR: Oh, women! Women! You've always got to take everything personally. I only meant that you ought to go easy on Billy right now. He needs somebody to pay a little attention to him once in a while. You're so much in the limelight, he'll soon feel like the forgotten man!

SARALEE: What is this? A psychology lecture? If it is, save it! I guess I don't need psychology to get along with my own brother!

BLAIR: O.K. Skip it! Sorry I mentioned it! But if and when the worm turns, don't blame me.

SARALEE: Don't worry, I won't.

BLAIR (*Taking her hand*): Oh, come on now, don't be sore.

SARALEE (*Snatching her hand away and knocking over jar of paint*): There! Look what you made me do! Oh, for heaven's sake! All over Billy's sweater and that darned letter! Oh, Blair! I could cry! (*Snatching up sweater and letter and mopping up paint.*) If it's ruined, he'll never forgive me.

BLAIR (*Grabbing sweater*): I'll take it right down to the cleaners'.

SARALEE: It's the letter, his precious "N," that I'm worried about. It's his most cherished possession.

BLAIR: Never mind. I'll stop and see Coach Sanders. Maybe he can supply us with a spare. We'll try to avert tragedy.

SARALEE: Oh, thanks, Blair. And make no mistake about Billy. Most of the time I think he's Pest Number One, but I wouldn't hurt his feelings for the world.

BLAIR: I know you wouldn't. Now don't worry. Here goes Mr. Fix-It to the rescue. (*Exit* BLAIR.)

SARALEE (*Cleaning up paint*): What a mess! Thank goodness none of it got on Celia's picture! That's all I'd need. (CELIA *enters. She is wearing her hair in pin curls.*)

CELIA: Hello, sugar. Are you all set for your big moment?

SARALEE: Anything else but, Celia. Everything's gone wrong.

CELIA: Not with my picture, I hope, I hope, I hope.

SARALEE: Oh, no, thank fortune. That would be the last straw. You're a dear to come over and let me re-work that eye shadow.

CELIA: I thought you wouldn't mind the pin curls if you were just going to work on the eyes. I'm saving my hair-do till the last minute so I'll look my best for the exhibit.

SARALEE (*Adjusting her paints and setting up her picture*): You'll have the judges all confused, if you stand too close to the painting.

CELIA (*Mounting model stand*): I think I could take this pose in my sleep.

SARALEE (*Smiling*): Now you look just the way you did when I did my first portrait of you. You're the only girl I ever saw who could manage to look beautiful in pin curls.

CELIA (*Giggling*): All of you artists are flatterers. You know I look a fright. Remember, you promised to destroy that first picture. I certainly don't want it in circulation.

SARALEE: Don't worry. It will never see the light of day, but I can't bear to part with it. I still think it's the best brush work I ever did.

CELIA: Just the same I don't want my public to see me like this. I'd positively die.

SARALEE: And leave a string of broken hearts all over this part of the state.

CELIA: Speaking of heart-throbs, wasn't that Blair Kelley I saw going down your drive as I came in?

SARALEE: The very same.

CELIA: Want to know a secret about him?

SARALEE: A secret? About Blair?

CELIA: Yes. I'm going to the Junior Prom with him next week.

SARALEE: You're what?

CELIA: Isn't it dreamy? Grif Powers is fixing it up for me. You remember Grif. He and I used to double-date before he went to the University, but now he's got a girl in Lewistown, and she's a cousin of Blair's roommate, so it's all kind of in the family, if you know what I mean.

SARALEE: It sounds sort of international to me.

CELIA: You really ought to take some time out for social life, Saralee. After all, there's more to life than just painting pictures.

SARALEE: Well, right now, that's my first concern. There! (*Wiping brushes*) That's the best I can do. I'm going to call it quits.

CELIA: Is it better now?

SARALEE: I think it gives you a little more sparkle, and that's what I was after. You may get down now.

CELIA: Thanks. I'd like a last look before you pack me up. (*Coming around to look at picture*) Umm! That *is* nice, Saralee. You really do sling a wicked brush. Do I get framed?

SARALEE: Framed? Oh, sure. (*Picks up frame that* BLAIR *brought and fits it around picture.*) There! How do you like yourself?

CELIA: That frame does it! That really gives it class, doesn't it?

SARALEE: Yes, but it's not the frame they'll be judging, Celia. It's the work. That's what will tell the tale.

CELIA: It looks like me, doesn't it? What more can they want?

SARALEE (*Laughing*): I wish it could be that simple. (BILLY *enters. He is in a tearing hurry.*)

BILLY: Say, do you have that old picture ready? I have to take it down right away.

SARALEE: There's no rush, just so it gets there by noon.

BILLY: There *is* a rush . . . a big rush. Mr. Henderson says to tell you that French fellow wants a preview before the exhibit opens; and anyhow he wants to try some sort of fancy frame on it.

SARALEE: But I have a frame.

BILLY: I know, but this is different—some kind of antique job. He says if you want to know anything special, call him right up.

SARALEE: O.K. I will. I'll run right up to the house and call him this minute. You're sure he's at the gallery?

BILLY: He's there all right. (*Exit* SARALEE.)

CELIA: Isn't it a beautiful picture, Billy?

BILLY: I've seen better.

CELIA: Where?

BILLY: In the comic books!

CELIA: Oh, you're just kidding.

BILLY: Am I? (*Searching on table*) Say, did you see anything of a blue sweater around here? I wonder if she sewed that letter on yet.

CELIA: You know something, Billy?

BILLY: Yeah, but I'm not telling.

CELIA: The most wonderful man in the world is going to see that picture this afternoon.

BILLY (*Still hunting for the sweater*): You mean the Frenchman?

CELIA: No, I mean a certain young man from a certain University who's going to take a certain young lady to a certain Junior Prom!

BILLY: If you mean Blair Kelley, he's seen it already.

CELIA: He's seen this picture?

BILLY: I suppose so. He's seen everything else out in this studio—that is, if he can take his eyes off Saralee long enough to look at anything else.

CELIA: You mean he comes out here to see Saralee?

BILLY: Who else? You don't think he hangs around here to see me, do you? Now what on earth is this stuff? And where could she have put that sweater and that letter? (*Picks up Prom program*) Oh, mush! "Saralee, Saralee, Saralee!" That guy should have his head examined!

CELIA (*Snatching it out of his hand*): Let me see that! Why, it's the dance card for the Junior Prom! "Saralee, Saralee, Saralee!" Of all the low-down good-for-nothing dirty tricks, this is the lowest! Why, that abominable two-timing, paint-slinging wretch! She knew all the time he was taking her to the Junior Prom. I'll fix her!

BILLY: Say, what's wrong with you?

CELIA: So she took me for a ride, did she? Sappy Celia! Posing for her silly old picture, while she cops off Blair Kelley. I'll settle her hash. She'll never win any art scholarship on *my* face! (*Starts to take picture out of frame.*)

BILLY (*Alarmed*): Hey! Quit that! What do you think you're doing?

CELIA: I'm taking this picture right straight home where it belongs.

BILLY: But you can't do that. It's not yours.

CELIA: It's a picture of me, isn't it? It's my face, and it's going to hang on my wall, not in any stupid old art gallery.

BILLY: But that's where the exhibit is. It's got to be there to win the prize.   .

CELIA: What prize, sugar? What prize?

BILLY: You know what prize. The scholarship prize, the one she's worked so hard for.

CELIA: She's already got one prize, buddy. She's got Blair Kelley, and that's enough for any girl. (*Starts walking off with picture.*) This baby's going home with mamma.

BILLY: Hey, you come back here! (*Makes a lunge for picture. Grabs it and puts up a struggle in which the picture is ruined.*) There! See what you've done! Saralee will kill you for this.

CELIA: (*In a highly affected voice*): I'm so sorry! So terribly sorry! Please give my regrets to your dear sister. And remember to explain to her about the prize! (*Exits*)

BILLY (*Stands for a moment in a daze looking at ruined picture*): Oh, my gosh! What'll I do? This is terrible! (*Goes back and looks at easel with empty picture frame*) If only I could find another one to fit. (*Rummages through pile of paintings*) Oh, my goodness! These are nothing but bowls of fruit and vases of flowers! Sufferin' cat fish! There's nothing here that looks like a "Typical Teen-Ager"! These are all sunsets! Well, bless Aunt Susie, if here isn't Frizzie Lizzie herself, curl papers and all! Boy, oh boy! If the frame fits, we're on our way! (*Tries picture in frame. It fits.* BILLY *strikes a pose beside it, putting his own head close to the picture*) Which twin has the Toni? (*Snatches picture out of frame, takes frame in other hand and makes a quick exit.* BLAIR *enters from opposite side a moment later.*)

BLAIR: Saralee! Saralee! Where are you? Everything's under control. The cleaner's doing a rush job on the sweater, and Coach Sanders fixed me up. . . . (*Sees ruined picture*) Hello! What's this? (*As he picks up picture,* SARALEE *enters.*)

SARALEE: It's O.K., Billy. Mr. Henderson says to take this frame along, and he'll use his own judgment. Why, Blair, what's wrong? Where's Billy? (*Sees picture*) Oh, my heavens! What's happened? Oh, Blair! Blair! It's ruined! My painting! What could have happened to it?

BLAIR: It looks as if somebody deliberately wrecked it.

SARALEE: But who? Who would have done such a thing? There was nobody here but Billy and . . . Billy! Oh, Blair, you don't suppose! Oh, no, he'd never do such a trick, never!

BLAIR: No, I'm sure he wouldn't . . . not unless . . . (*Suddenly looks down at floor. Stops dead still and stares.*)

SARALEE: Not unless what?

BLAIR: Not unless he was goaded into it. (*Leans over and picks up the dirty, trampled "N"*) You don't suppose he saw this, do you?

SARALEE: Oh, my goodness! His letter! He probably found it!

BLAIR: And had no way of knowing I was getting him another. (*Takes new letter "N" from his pocket.*) Coach Sanders gave me this one, and the cleaner will deliver the sweater as soon as it's finished. But it's too late now. The damage is done.

SARALEE: Look at it, Blair. Look at the picture. It's almost torn to pieces. I don't care how mad Billy was, he'd never do a thing like that! Never! You said yourself he's a good kid!

BLAIR: He was pushed too far this time, Saralee. Look at it from his angle. You're everything, grown up, talented, free to do all the things he'd give an eyetooth to do. You drive a car, you go places, you're important. He's still a kid. Has to go to bed early. He's shoved out of this garage to make room for you. His best efforts bring no applause. Winning this "N" meant nothing to you and your mother. You yourself said "N" is for nuisance. That's all he is in his own mind. He missed out on his swimming meet because of your art exhibit. Now his prize possession is ruined! And by you! Is it any wonder he backfired?

SARALEE: Now you listen to me, Blair Kelley. You can take all your fancy psychology notions right back to the University. I guess I know my own brother! And I say wild horses wouldn't get him to do such a low-down dirty trick! (*Enter* MRS. GIBSON.)

MRS. GIBSON: Saralee, I've been calling and calling. Mr. Henderson phoned, and I've been shouting my head off trying to make you hear. I finally told him you'd call back.

SARALEE (*Dully*): There's no need to call him now. As far as I'm concerned the exhibit's over.

MRS. GIBSON: What on earth do you mean? What's wrong?

BLAIR: There's been an accident, Mrs. Gibson.

MRS. GIBSON: An accident? Is someone hurt? Billy? Well, don't just stand there! Tell me what's wrong.

SARALEE (*Turning the ruined picture toward her*): It's the contest picture, Mother. It's ruined.

MRS. GIBSON: Oh my heavens! Saralee, what's happened

to it? Oh, my poor child! My poor child! All your hard work! (*Starts to cry.*)

SARALEE: Don't cry, Mother. There's nothing anyone can do about it. I'll go phone Mr. Henderson and tell him I've changed my mind about the whole thing.

MRS. GIBSON: But he'll think you're out of your mind. I was just talking to him. He seemed so excited.

SARALEE: I don't care what he thinks. I'm going to phone. (*Exit.*)

MRS. GIBSON: Oh, Blair! Blair! I don't understand it. Her beautiful picture . . . ruined, spoiled! What could have happened to it? Do you suppose someone could have broken in?

BLAIR: Oh, no, Mrs. Gibson. There was someone here all the time.

MRS. GIBSON (*Examining painting*): It looks almost as if it had been done on purpose, and (*Looking around*) where's the frame?

BLAIR (*Also looking around*): That's right! The frame! What could have happened to that? Maybe he busted that up, too!

MRS. GIBSON: He? Then you know who did it. Blair Kelley, tell me this minute who did this awful thing. I'm going to call the police.

BLAIR: Now, now, Mrs. Gibson. Calm yourself. This is no case for the police, believe me.

MRS. GIBSON: But it is, I know it is! I'm going to call City Hall.

BLAIR: Please, Mrs. Gibson. The police can do nothing. If anything, it's a case for a psychologist. (SARALEE *enters.*)

MRS. GIBSON: A psychologist? You mean a lunatic did it?

BLAIR: Heavens, no, Mrs. Gibson.

MRS. GIBSON: Then what *do* you mean?

SARALEE: He means he thinks Billy did it, Mother.

MRS. GIBSON: Billy!

BLAIR: Neither one of you is in any condition to discuss this case. You've both had a terrible shock. Let's go back to the house and talk this over quietly.

SARALEE: There's no need to talk anything over. Give me that picture, and I'll throw it in the trash.

MRS. GIBSON: What did Mr. Henderson say? And what's this about Billy?

SARALEE: I couldn't get him. He had left. As for Billy, there's nothing to discuss, till he gets home. Then if you still think he did it, you can ask him about it yourself.

MRS. GIBSON: How can you be so calm, Saralee? Don't you realize what this means?

BLAIR: Only too well, Mrs. Gibson. She's in a sort of daze.

MRS. GIBSON: But it's horrible to think Billy could have done this . . . Oh, Billy! Billy! (*Enter* BILLY, *bright and smiling.*)

BILLY: Did somebody call me?

ALL: Billy!

BILLY (*Seeing picture*): Well, I see you got the bad news! Gee, I'm sorry, sis. I should never have left it here like this . . . I . . . .

SARALEE: Billy! You didn't! You couldn't!

BILLY: No, I couldn't do anything else. There just wasn't time!

MRS. GIBSON (*Taking* BILLY *by shoulder and shaking him*): Billy Gibson! Answer me this minute! How did this dreadful thing happen?

BILLY: Well, gee whiz, Mom, she was pullin' and I was

pullin', and the first thing you know, it just sort of folded up on us!

BLAIR: Easy, son, easy! One thing at a time! Who else was in on this?

BILLY: Take a good guess! Old Frizzle Top herself! Celia.

SARALEE: Celia! You mean she was here when it happened?

BILLY: Was she here when it happened! Jeepers! How do you think the whole thing started? The minute she picked up that goofy card with "Saralee, Saralee, Saralee" scribbled all over it, she went completely off her rocker! Ranted and raved around here something awful! You'd never get a prize with her face! And a whole lot of baloney about how you had a prize already with Blair here.

BLAIR: Oh, she found the Prom card with your name on it!

SARALEE: And she was working a big deal for you to take her to the dance!

BLAIR: So that's who that screwy roommate of mine was trying to sic on me! A mystery woman, he said. I'll mystery woman him when I get back on the campus.

MRS. GIBSON: And then what happened?

BILLY: Well, I tried to stop her from walking off with the painting, but she had too much muscle and the blamed thing just couldn't hold up under the strain.

SARALEE: Oh, Billy, I'm so glad! (*Starts to cry*)

BILLY: Glad! Gee, I thought you'd be crazy! Crazy mad, that is!

SARALEE (*To* BLAIR): Now you see . . . it wasn't psychology, after all.

BLAIR: Oh, yes it was, and the most deadly kind. *Female*

psychology. But I know what you mean, Saralee, and I apologize.

SARALEE: Apologize to Billy instead. I don't want your apologies.

BILLY: What's all this double-talk about apologizing? What we ought to do is go after Celia Baylor's scalp!

MRS. GIBSON: And I'm in a mood to do it, if it would only help poor Saralee. Just wait till I see Mrs. Baylor.

SARALEE: You might as well forget the whole thing, Mother. The main thing is that Billy didn't do it!

BILLY: Me? Don't tell me you thought I'd do a trick like that?

BLAIR: Not Saralee, Billy. I was the one who got the idea.

BILLY: But why? Why would you ever get such a crackpot idea? Do I look like the kind of guy who'd go around tearing up pictures?

SARALEE: He thought you were sore, Billy, about a lot of things. Mostly about this (*Holds out the ruined "N."*)

BILLY: Wow! What happened to this?

SARALEE: I spilled paint on it, Billy, and I'm sorry. For that matter, I'm sorry about a lot of things.

BLAIR (*Giving him the new "N"*): But we got a replacement, Billy, and as soon as that sweater comes back from the cleaners, you're going to see some first-class sewing. (*Enter* MR. HENDERSON, *carrying a small box.*)

MR. HENDERSON: Excuse me. I knocked, but I couldn't seem to make myself heard.

SARALEE: Mr. Henderson! I just called you!

MR. HENDERSON: Yes, I came right over as soon as I hung the painting. I couldn't wait to find out what made you change your mind.

SARALEE: Oh, then you know?

MR. HENDERSON: Only that you entered the other portrait, and I certainly want to congratulate you on your good judgment.

SARALEE: What other portrait?

MR. HENDERSON (*Smiling*): You couldn't have made a better choice. (*To* MRS. GIBSON) Wait till you see it in the frame, Mrs. Gibson. You'll be delighted! The combination of that saucy little face, those bewitching pin curls and that antique frame is simply irresistible. I might be talking out of turn, but when I left Monsieur Bourget was standing in front of it, simply entranced! For the "Typical Teen-Ager" you couldn't have done better!

SARALEE: Billy, you took Celia's pin-curl picture!

BILLY: It was all I could find except a lot of silly fruit and sunsets!

SARALEE: Oh, Billy! Billy! (*Hugs him*)

BILLY: Cut out the mush-gush! We have company.

MRS. GIBSON: You really think Saralee has a chance, Mr. Henderson?

MR. HENDERSON: I always did *think* she had a chance, Mrs. Gibson; now I *know* she has a chance . . . a very good chance! But I still want to know what made you change your mind, Saralee.

SARALEE: Well, I hardly know, Mr. Henderson. Maybe it was . . . well . . . just psychology.

MR. HENDERSON: If you can combine that kind of psychology with your artistic ability, Saralee, you'll go a long way. Well, I must be off. See you folks this afternoon.

MRS. GIBSON: Thank you, Mr. Henderson. I'll see you to your car.

SARALEE: Thanks a million, Mr. Henderson. Goodbye.

MR. HENDERSON: Oh, by the way, as I came through the yard, a boy from the cleaning establishment asked me to deliver this box. I almost forgot it. (*Gives* BLAIR *the box*)

SARALEE: Thanks again.

MR. HENDERSON: Don't mention it. (*Exit* MR. HENDERSON *and* MRS. GIBSON.)

BLAIR: Talk about quick work! It's the sweater! (*Opens box and tosses it to* BILLY.) Here, Bud, put it on. I want to see this letter firmly fastened where it belongs. (BILLY *struggles into sweater.*)

SARALEE: I've learned a lot about psychology today, Blair. You were right about a lot of things. I think I'll know how to be a better big sister from here on in.

BLAIR: And I've learned a lot about loyalty, Saralee. I wish I had somebody who has as much faith in me as you have in that kid brother of yours.

BILLY: O.K., I'm ready. Where's the letter?

BLAIR: Right here. Now pick your spot.

BILLY (*Pointing to chest*): Right here! Center front.

SARALEE (*Pinning letter in place*): And before I sew this on, Billy, do you know what this "N" really stands for?

BILLY (*Resigned*): Yeah, I know. NUISANCE!

SARALEE: Wrong! "N" stands for NECESSARY, and I want you to know that kid brothers are the most necessary things in the whole wide world! (*Curtain*)

THE END

Production Notes

N FOR NUISANCE

Characters: 3 male; 3 female.

Playing Time: 30 minutes.

Costumes: Modern dress. Celia has her hair in pin curls. Billy has a sweater.

Properties: Aluminum stew pot, lid of a tin wash boiler, long-handled toasting fork, large empty picture frame, two letter "N's," paintings, dance program, box containing Billy's sweater.

Setting: Saralee's studio. The furnishings consist of a small platform or model's stand, an easel, a plain work table loaded with brushes, jars, bottles, an alarm clock and several large paintings in various stages of completion. A few large charcoal sketches displayed on the walls will lend atmosphere.

Lighting: No special effects.

Mind Over Matter

By Jessie Nicholson

Characters

ALF TREADWELL, *narrator*
LUTHER PRINGLE, *storekeeper*
JIM
TIM } *his sons*
SLIM
DR. HORACE POLE, *a famous hypnotist*
GRANDPA STEEVES
GRANDMA STEEVES
SHERIFF PEASE
LEM PARDY, *storekeeper of the play within a play*
EMERALD (EMMY MAE), *his daughter*
LUTIE, *her half sister*
DEWEY POINDEXTER, *the tonic salesman*
ZACHARY PROUDFOOT, *the poor but honest farmhand*
LOBELIA PRATTLE, *who helps run the town*
HORATIO ARMSTRONG
2 MEN CHECKER PLAYERS

SCENE 1

TIME: *A weekday morning.*

SETTING: *The general store in Goose Creek.*

AT RISE: *The stage is bare, except for a few orange crates, between two of which rests a board with some empty pop bottles standing on it.* ALF TREADWELL *strolls on stage, hands in pockets, cap resting on back of head.*

ALF: I want to apologize to you folks out there for this stage setting. (*Waving his hand toward the orange crates*) Doesn't look like much, that's a fact, but the Thespians hope you won't hold it against us. We tried to borrow some props, but we couldn't get a smidgen of cooperation. All we needed was some outfitting from Luther Pringle's country store, right here in Goose Creek, but Luther turned us down cold. (*Sorrowfully*) We found out Luther just isn't a patron of the arts.

LUTHER (*Shouting from rear of hall*): No such thing, Alf Treadwell. We Pringles are very artful folks. But if you'd had your way, you'd have cleaned me out lock, stock and barrel.

ALF: Anyhow, Luther, we've worked out our problem just fine and dandy without you. Dr. Horace Pole, the famous hypnotist, who is visiting in our midst, has kindly consented to join me here on the stage tonight. He'll spellbind you folks into seeing a fancy stage setting, all through the power of mind over matter. He's already tried it out on me and I tell you I was really fooled. (*Calling off-stage*) Draw the curtains, Sammy. (*He comes downstage.*) We're going to start all over again after Doc hypnotizes us. (*Curtain falls.* ALF *now stands in front of curtain.*)

LUTHER (*Shouting again from back of hall*): I demand a refund for me and my three boys. I came to see a play with real, honest-to-goodness scenery, and I'm not going to pay for any mind-over-matter stuff.

JIM: Shucks, Pa, we want to stay and get hypnotized.

TIM: We don't mind a little mind.

SLIM: Sure, what's the matter with mind? All us folks in Goose Creek could use some mind.

LUTHER: I'll teach you what's mind and what's matter, right where you sit down. (*He chases the three boys around the hall and out the door.*)

ALF: Well, now that that ruckus is over, we'll settle down to the business of the evening. Folks, I want you to meet that distinguished gentleman and patron of the arts, Dr. Horace Pole. Right this way, Doctor. (DR. POLE *comes up on stage from the front row of the audience. He is tall and thin, with piercing eyes and beetle brows.*)

DR. POLE (*In a hollow voice*): Greetings, friends. I want you all to relax in your seats and focus your undivided attention upon me. I want the silence to be so complete that I can hear a pin fall. (*He fixes the audience with a penetrating stare and waits with outstretched arms for absolute quiet. There is a loud snore from down near the front of the audience.*)

ALF (*Leaning forward, hand beside mouth*): Pss-t— Pss-t—Grandma Steeves, can't you keep your old man quiet? And you kids out there, stop snickering. (*Turning to* DR. POLE, *who looks annoyed*) 'Scuse me, Doc, for interrupting. I don't think you'll have any more trouble.

DR. POLE: Well, I certainly hope not. Now, let us concentrate deeply—deeply— (*Holding them spellbound*) on

what I am about to make you see. When the curtains
part, you will find yourself looking at the interior of a
country store, much like the one here in the village
with which you are all familiar. Nothing will be lack-
ing, from the cracker barrel to ladies' hats, from the
pot-bellied stove to the friendly game of checkers beside it. Indeed, I am proud to be able to assist in this—
ah—worthy enterprise of your Thespian society. (*He
waves his hand towards curtains and they part to reveal
the promised scene. If desired, for quick change, most
of setting may be depicted on a back drop, including
the pot-bellied stove. The two checker players, pipes
in mouths, are absorbed in their game. There is loud
applause from the rear, where* LUTHER's *three sons have
sneaked back into the hall again.*)

JIM: Now if that isn't cute!

TIM: I'd swear that was a real live mouse just jumped
out of the cracker barrel!

SLIM: Pa would sure believe this if he'd just stayed and
watched.

ALF: Glad you're pleased, fellows—as I am sure you all
are. If anybody isn't satisfied, his twenty-five cents will
be cheerfully refunded by the management.

GRANDPA STEEVES (*From the audience, in a cracked voice*):
I don't see a thing but a few old orange crates and
some empty soda pop bottles. I came to see a show!

GRANDMA STEEVES: Oh, hush up, Pa, and go back to sleep.
You haven't heard a word the man said.

JIM: Better hurry up with the show, Mr. Alf Treadwell.
Pa's gone to hunt the sheriff and have you arrested for
fraud.

SHERIFF PEASE (*From the audience*): Let him go on looking for the sheriff. He isn't going to find me, because

I'm here enjoying myself and I aim to stay put. This is better than seeing a magician pull a rabbit out of a hat.

ALF: And the best is yet to come. We Thespians haven't spared ourselves. Rib-tickling comedy, tear-jerking tragedy, the doings of high society and a happy ending for all. First, I'll introduce the characters to you. We'll start with the storekeeper, Lem Pardy, since he has a big speaking part. (*Leading towards right wing*) Hey, Lem, come on out. The audience is waiting to see you. (*Aside*) Lem wouldn't really make a very good grocer, folks. He'd eat up all his profits. (LEM *enters. He ambles behind the counter, cuts himself a generous hunk of cheese and begins munching on it.*) And next there's Emerald, Lem's daughter. Her real name's Emmy Mae, but she claims Emerald suits her personality better. I'll let you folks judge for yourselves. (*Calling into wings*) On stage, Emmy—I mean Emerald. (*Enter* EMERALD *in a slinky green dress, powdering her nose and fluffing up her hair. She gives the audience a supercilious stare.*) See what I mean? (LEM *points to a carton of cans, then to a high shelf, pantomiming that the cans should be stacked on the shelves.* EMERALD *tosses her head disdainfully and exits.*) Emmy isn't much use to her pa, I'm afraid. She has Hollywood notions. (*With a resigned shrug* LEM *starts opening the carton, climbs heavily up ladder*) No, sir, it's Emmy's half sister, Lutie, who does all the chores. (*Calls into wings*) Come on in, Lutie. (*Enter* LUTIE, *dressed in patched blue jeans, faded shirt, her face dirty, her hair pulled back in a tight knot.*) Sort of a Cinderella character. (LUTIE *is sweeping vigorously*) It's a fact her pa doesn't rightly appreciate her. He expects he's going to have trouble marrying her off. (ALF *gives a terrific sneeze as she sweeps dust in his direction. She exits, left.*) Then there's Dewey Poindexter, the flashy tonic salesman from the deep south. Emerald's always on hand when he shows up. (*As* DEWEY *enters right,* EMERALD *darts in from left and climbs the stepladder nimbly to help her father stack cans on the shelf. She turns and offers* DEWEY *a coy smile as he crosses the stage. He is nattily dressed and has a wicked black mustache, which he twirls between his fingers. He sets his bag down and shakes a reproving finger at* LEM.)

DEWEY (*With southern drawl*): I'm always telling you, Mr. Pardy, you work that poor, sweet girl too hard.

ALF (*In exasperation*): Look here, Dewey, you aren't supposed to say anything yet. I'm just introducing the characters!

DEWEY: It distresses me so, Mr. Treadwell, to see this delicate, flowerlike creature working her lily white fingers to the bone that I simply can't wait to recite my lines.

ALF (*Grumpily*): You'd better go off and drink a bottle of your tonic with Emerald, and simmer down. (EMERALD *promptly descends the ladder.*)

DEWEY (*Reaching into his bag*): What flavor will you have, Emerald?

EMERALD (*Dreamily*): L-i-me, Dewey. (*They exit, left, arm in arm.*)

ALF: And then there's Zachary Proudfoot, the poor but honest farmhand who is hopelessly and silently in love with our Emerald. (*Enter* ZACHARY *from right, as* EMERALD *enters left and picks up a bottle opener, which hangs beside the counter. He regards her with doglike devotion.*)

EMERALD (*Scornfully*): Get lost! (*She exits left.* ZACHARY *exits right, dejectedly.*)

ALF: You'll have to excuse her, folks. You can see she really gets worked up in her part. (LOBELIA PRATTLE *strides in from left. She is lean, sharp-faced, and obviously excited. Her hat is askew and she flourishes a long-handled umbrella.*)

LOBELIA: You know what's going on outside, right under your nose, Lem Pardy?

ALF (*Protesting*): Now, Lobelia—Miss Prattle—we haven't begun the play yet! (*His protest goes unheeded.*)

LOBELIA (*Prodding* LEM *with the umbrella*): Well—do you?

LEM (*Mildly*): If it's outside it isn't exactly under my nose, Miss Prattle. And I'm not psychic.

LOBELIA: The more's the pity. That girl of yours is sitting right out there on the steps, as bold as brass, drinking sarsaparilla soda with the tonic salesman!

LEM: Lime, Miss Prattle, lime.

LOBELIA: Land sakes, what's the difference? One's as bad as the other.

LEM (*Stiffly*): I sell only the best tonic, I'll have you know, Miss Prattle. Super Golden Sunlight brand.

LOBELIA (*In exasperation*): That isn't the point, Lem Pardy. The point is—

ALF (*Exasperatedly, towards right wing*): *Draw* the curtains, Sammy, *draw* the curtains, (*Curtain falls as* LEM *appears to be listening resignedly to* LOBELIA's *harangue.* ALF *steps in front of curtain.*) We'll just have to let them get started, folks. There's no holding them back, even though I haven't introduced you to our hero, Horatio Armstrong. But you'll recognize him all right when he comes in. He's the sheriff's son and is strong and handsome. (ALF *bows and exits. The curtain rises again.* LEM *is behind the counter, munching on an apple,* EMERALD *is trying on hats and preening before the mirror, while* ZACHARY *leans against the wall, a lovesick glimmer in his eye. The* CHECKER PLAYERS *maintain a lively pantomime with their game.* LUTIE, *with brush and pail, is scrubbing the floor vigorously.*)

LEM (*Plaintively*): Lutie, I declare, you're wearing the floor plumb out with your everlasting cleaning!

LUTIE (*Firmly*): I have to do something creative with my life, Pa. I can't be always trying out for beauty contests like Emmy Mae—like Emerald, I mean.

LEM (*Pointedly*): What you need to do is set your cap for some nice, hardworking fellow like Zach there. Hitch your wagon to a—to a—

LUTIE: To a space monkey like him! I'd rather be an old maid, Pa, and tend to you for the rest of your living days. (LEM *groans.* LOBELIA PRATTLE *comes rushing into the store through door at right, waving her umbrella.*)

LOBELIA: Have you heard that there's a criminal loose in our midst, Lem Pardy, a dangerous, gun-toting criminal?

LEM: Now, now, Miss Prattle, calm down. There's no gun-toting criminal loose in my store, I can vouch for that.

LOBELIA (*Agitatedly*): How do you know for sure, Lemuel? He might be hiding out in your storeroom right now. (ZACHARY *looks alarmed.*)

LEM (*Grinning*): Not if he knows you're trailing him, Miss Prattle.

ZACHARY (*Nervously edging towards door*): I just remembered I have to get home and milk Daisy, the cow.

LOBELIA: You stay right here on the premises, Zachary Proudfoot, and protect us helpless womenfolk.

ZACHARY (*Woefully*): But there are three of you to only one of me.

LEM (*In exasperation*): Come on, all of you, out to the storeroom and I'll show you there's no sly dog lurking in my supplies. (*All follow* LEM *through center door up-stage,* CHECKER PLAYERS *holding their game between them and continuing to play.* EMERALD, *who is last, pauses as a loud "Pssst" is heard from behind a barrel labeled "Flour," which is in the corner. A head appears cautiously above it.*)

EMERALD: Land sakes, Dewey Poindexter, you gave me an awful scare. What are you doing there?

DEWEY (*Stepping out*): Sh-h-h! I've just been waiting for a chance to talk to you alone, Emerald, honey. What would you say to marrying up with me right soon?

EMERALD (*Dazedly*): Right soon, Dewey? How soon?

DEWEY (*Looking towards storeroom stealthily*): Strike while the iron is hot, my old Pappy always used to say. How would you like to elope with me tonight, honey, after your pa's gone to bed?

EMERALD (*Weakly*): Oh, Dewey, I declare, you sweep a girl right off her feet. I always did think it was so romantic to elope.

DEWEY: Sure, it's romantic, sugar, but we have to be practical too. Do you know the combination to the safe, so you could get your dowry money without having to trouble your pa for it?

EMERALD: What do you mean—my dowry money?

DEWEY: Sh-h-h—not so loud, my little petunia. Every girl

has the right to her dowry money—it's the law. There probably won't be anywhere near what you're worth in that little old safe, but you can take what there is and we'll make the best of it.

EMERALD (*Doubtfully*): Sounds kind of sneaky to me.

DEWEY: You hurt me, honey, implying I would do anything dishonest. I guess the elopement is all off if you don't trust me. Likely you'll never get another chance at a stylish city fellow—a backwoods country girl like you.

EMERALD (*Hastily*): I didn't mean to hurt your feelings, Dewey. Honest I didn't. What time would you want me to be ready?

DEWEY: Nine o'clock sharp. You can open the door for me and we'll count the money together. Here's a bottle of lime soda to seal our pledge with, sugar.

EMERALD: Oh, Dewey, you're so generous! (*He opens a bottle from his bag, and both drink from it.* DEWEY *exits just as* LEM *and* LOBELIA *return from storeroom.*)

LEM: Were you waiting on a customer, Emmy Mae? Thought I heard voices.

EMERALD (*Airily*): Just someone dating me for tonight, Pa.

LOBELIA (*With hand to ear*): What did you say his name was, Emmy?

EMERALD (*Bitingly*): I didn't say.

LOBELIA: Well, I never—such impudence to your elders. I'd keep an eye on that girl if I were you, Lem Pardy. How do you know she isn't flirting with that gun-toting stranger behind our backs?

LEM (*Patiently*): I told you, Miss Prattle, that gun-toting stranger is just a figment of your imagination. (ZACHARY *pokes his head in, looks around nervously, enters cautiously*)

LOBELIA: I overheard the sheriff on the party wire telling his deputy to bring this criminal in dead or alive. (ZACHARY *starts to retreat hastily.*)

LEM: If by deputy you mean his boy, Horatio, I don't think he's sent him on any killing jobs yet. You must have your wires crossed.

LOBELIA (*Tossing her head*): Seeing my word isn't to be trusted, I'll take my business elsewhere, Lem Pardy. (*Giving her head a jerk, she sweeps out of the store.*)

LEM (*Darkly*): Her business is minding everybody else's business.

ZACHARY (*Nervously*): Just the same, Mr. Pardy, where there's smoke, there's bound to be some fire. I reckon I'd better go home and see if Daisy, my cow, is all right.

EMERALD (*Scathingly*): You don't think anybody's going to shoot her, do you? (LUTIE *enters again, sweeping.*)

ZACHARY: I'm not taking any chances. (*Mournfully*) Daisy's never let me down. Thirty quarts a day, every day. But don't forget, if you should ever need me, Emmy Mae—Emerald, I mean—just whistle and I'll come running. (*He exits hastily.*)

LEM: Now isn't that touching? (*Glances at* LUTIE, *who is sweeping vigorously toward him*) I declare, Lutie, if you could just arouse such sentiments, I'd give you a dowry that would make any poor man's eyes stick most out of his head.

EMERALD (*Eagerly*): Dowry? How much dowry would you allow me, Pa?

LEM (*Pursing up his lips*): You don't need a dowry, my girl. Your looks are your dowry. You catch yourself a rich man, and you'll be all set. Somebody like (*Slyly*)

Horatio Armstrong, the sheriff's son, maybe. He's a lad with expectations. (HORATIO *enters*.)

HORATIO (*Cheerfully*): Did I hear somebody mention my name?

LUTIE (*Snickering*): Pa was just saying a rich feller like you wouldn't have to marry for money, Horatio.

HORATIO: Ha, ha. (*Turning out his empty pockets*) That's how rich I am, Lutie. But if I can just get the reward that's offered for a gentleman wanted by the F.B.I., I won't have to worry about pocket money for a while.

LEM: You mean there's really a criminal loose in Goose Creek, Horatio?

HORATIO: Pa and I have our sights set for him. I came in on purpose to see if any suspicious characters have been in your store today, maybe trying to flirt with Emerald (*Gallantly*)—or—ah—Lutie.

LEM (*Regarding* LUTIE): No such luck! Unless (*Grinning*) you want to count Zachary Proudfoot. He's always hanging around and I'm suspicious of *his* intentions.

HORATIO: Poor Zach! He's too scared of his own shadow to even *have* any intentions. No, our man is a real city slicker with dark hair and mustache. He's a very snappy dresser. Has a southern drawl and a way with the ladies. Seen anybody around here of that description?

LEM (*Musingly*): Well no, not just lately. Sounds like our tonic salesman but he hasn't been here in weeks, has he, Emerald?

EMERALD (*Swallowing hard*): No, Pa. I haven't seen hide nor hair of him.

LUTIE: What's he wanted for, Horatio?

HORATIO: That's something I'm not at liberty to reveal, Lutie.

LUTIE: He isn't a cattle thief, is he?

HORATIO: Good heavens, no!

LUTIE (*Sarcastically*): Zachary Proudfoot will be mighty relieved to hear that.

EMERALD (*Desperately*): I'm going home to wash my hair.

LEM (*Calling after her as she exits*): Good idea. And while you're at it, you can just wash that man right out of your hair that you have a date with for tonight. No daughter of mine is going to go out into danger in times like these.

HORATIO (*Apologetically*): See here, Lem, I'm not aiming to throw a scare into anybody. If Emerald needs an escort—

LEM (*Interrupting eagerly*): If you're asking my permission to take her out, why shucks, son—I mean Horatio—you have it. I know she couldn't be in better hands.

LUTIE (*In exasperation*): Pa!

HORATIO: That wasn't exactly what I had in mind, Mr. Pardy. I just meant I'd keep an eye on the young couple during the evening, so no harm could come to them. A sort of police escort to set your mind at rest. (*Graciously*) Not but what it would be an honor to take Emerald or—or Lutie (*With a glance in her direction*) out for the evening.

LEM (*His jaw dropping*): Lutie!

LUTIE (*In an agonized tone*): Pa!

LEM (*Not heeding her*): Well, now, Horatio, I'm pleased to hear you say that. People don't always appreciate Lutie. What time will you be calling for her this evening? I promise you, she'll be all spruced up so you'd hardly recognize my little girl. Lutie, go pick yourself a hat at the counter there, any hat, the best is none too good. You work hard and you deserve it. (LUTIE *stamps her foot furiously and rushes off.*)

HORATIO (*Uncomfortably*): Doesn't look like she'd care for my company, Mr. Pardy.

LEM: Shucks now, Lutie's just high spirited. Like that lady in the play "The Taming of the Shrew," that Mr. Will Shakespeare wrote about.

HORATIO (*Thoughtfully*): Um—yes.

LEM: Just takes proper handling, that's all. And you're the man for the job, I can see that. (*Laughing jovially*) Yes, sir, I'll see that Lutie's ready for you at nine prompt, right here in the store.

HORATIO: Whatever you say, Mr. Pardy. I'll take her to the square dance at the schoolhouse.

LEM: Fine, Horatio, fine—I'll tell her to wear her dancing shoes. (*Aside, as* HORATIO *exits*) There'll be such a crowd there he'll likely never know who 'tis that's stepping on his feet! (*Curtain*)

*   *   *   *   *

SCENE 2

TIME: *Evening.*

SETTING: *Same as Scene 1. There is only one light on stage.*

AT RISE: ZACHARY PROUDFOOT *climbs through window, right, and limps across stage. He is dressed in his country best.*

ZACHARY: I'm glad that window was unlocked. I had to get some liniment for this leg of mine. Emerald kicked me in the shins when I finally got up my nerve to invite her to go square dancing with me tonight. (*Puts hand on bottle*) I've half a mind to go drown myself, instead of wasting this good liniment.

DR. POLE (*From audience*): Hold it, boy, hold it! (*He rushes up on stage.*) No need for suicide, Zachary. You just have a mental block. Now, with my help you can make friends and influence people.

ZACHARY (*Gawking at him*): Female people?

DR. POLE: That's right, my boy. (ALF TREADWELL *steps out from wings.*)

ALF: Pssst—hey, Doc. You're not supposed to be up here. It isn't in the script.

DR. POLE: As a doctor I have taken my oath to save lives. This boy has threatened to drown himself. I had to interfere.

ALF: Shucks, Doc, there isn't so much as a drop of water backstage.

DR. POLE: There's a watering trough for the horses in the yard, isn't there? I can't take any chances with this young man's life. I am determined to save it at all costs.

ZACHARY: Please, Doc, save me. I'm all fired tired of this mental block.

ALF (*Gloomily*): It's two against one, I guess. I know when I'm licked. (*To audience*) No telling where this may lead, folks. (*He exits.*)

DR. POLE: Now, Zachary, I am going to hypnotize you. Look me straight in the eye. (*He holds his gaze in silence for a moment.*) You are a dashing, self-assured young man. You are not frightened; you are not timid any more. You are—yes—you are even a little handsome and you wear your clothes stylishly. (ZACHARY *straightens up to his full height and turns down the cuffs of his coat sleeves as the doctor speaks, then pulls up his tie neatly and sets his hat at a rakish angle.*)

ZACHARY: How's this, Doc?

DR. POLE: You're catching on. You will now be able to make friends and influence people easily.

ZACHARY: And girls?

DR. POLE: The very first girl you meet, you'll sweep off her feet!

ZACHARY: Doc, I'm raring to go.

DR. POLE: Good luck to you, my boy. (*He returns to audience.* ZACHARY *struts back and forth across the stage, whistling. When he is at left stage in the shadows,* LUTIE *enters door right. She does not observe* ZACHARY. *She is also dressed in her Sunday best, with squeaky shoes and an outlandish hat.*)

LUTIE (*Forlornly*): Pa meant well and I did my best, but it just isn't any use trying to make a cutie out of Lutie. (ZACHARY *strides across the stage and* LUTIE *jumps with surprise.*)

ZACHARY: Evening, Miss Lutie Pardy. (*He tips his hat.* LUTIE *walks all around him, staring at him goggle-eyed.*)

LUTIE: Jumping grasshoppers, I can't believe my eyes!

ZACHARY (*Regarding her admiringly*): I can't either, Lutie. You look mighty pretty tonight—as beautiful and glamorous as a movie queen.

LUTIE: Who—me?

ZACHARY: Sure enough. How about us going square dancing together?

LUTIE (*Taken aback*): Well now, I sort of have another date.

ZACHARY (*Thrusting out his chin*): You can just sort of forget about that one, see. I'm your date for tonight.

LUTIE (*Meekly*): Yes, Zachary. (*They dance step off-stage.* HORATIO *enters and looks all about.*)

HORATIO (*With false heartiness*): Come out, come out, wherever you are. (*He tiptoes around, peering under counters and behind barrels.*) Hm—I guess she's not here yet, or else (*Hopefully*) she's come and gone. Mighty careless of her and her pa to leave the store unlocked and the window wide open. I figure I'd better just have a look around and see that everything is O.K. (*He exits to storeroom upstage center leaving door ajar.* DEWEY POINDEXTER *pokes his head in at the window.*)

DEWEY: Pssst—Emerald—where are you? Drat that girl! She's late for our elopement. (*He climbs inside.*) Wonder if she's fetched her dowry money yet? I declare, I'm as nervous as a cat. (*He tiptoes over to the safe and gives the dial an experimental twirl.* HORATIO *watches through the partially open door.* EMERALD *enters, carrying a suitcase.*)

DEWEY: Where in the name of my grandma have you been, Emerald? If there's anything I can't abide, it's a tardy woman—especially when I'm doing her the honor of taking her to the altar.

EMERALD (*Sulkily*): Couldn't get Pa off to bed.

DEWEY: You mean to say he hasn't gone to sleep *yet?*

EMERALD: He says he aims to wait up for Lutie. She's gone square dancing with Horatio.

DEWEY (*Scratching his head*): Lutie must be two-timing her date, then. I saw her heading towards the hall with Zachary Proudfoot in tow. Looked as though he was enjoying it, too. I declare, that girl must have something more than meets the eye. (*Aside*) Could be I picked the wrong sister.

EMERALD (*Indignantly*): Lutie and Zach! Well, I never. She can't get away with that. He belongs to me. I'll show her! (*She rushes towards the door.*)

DEWEY (*In dismay*)· But Emerald, surely you haven't forgotten we're eloping?

EMERALD (*Stamping her foot*): Not while Lutie is trying to take Zach away from me, we're not! (*She exits.*)

DEWEY: I would have to open my big mouth! Guess I'll be forced to go after that dowry myself. Leastways, I won't have to share it. (*He looks all around nervously, goes back to safe, tries turning the dial again. After several twirls, he succeeds in opening the door, and removes a boxful of money. His back is towards the storeroom door.* HORATIO *comes out and seizes him by the shoulder. There is a brief struggle and then* HORATIO *claps handcuffs on him.*)

HORATIO: I arrest you, Dewey Poindexter, as the kidnapping dowry thief who's been breaking hearts and ransacking safes all over this county.

DEWEY (*Forlornly*): Well, it was fun while it lasted. What do you aim to do with me now?

HORATIO: Lock you up in jail for the night, and then go over to the square dance. That poor little Emerald girl needs a bit of consoling. Losing two men in one day is enough to break any girl's heart, and it's plain to see she has a tender one.

DEWEY (*Shouting towards audience as* HORATIO *drags him to the door*): See what you did, Doctor Pole, with your precious meddling. This is all your fault. (*They exit. Curtain falls. Enter* ALF TREADWELL *from right.*)

ALF: Well, folks, it turned out better than I expected. You got everything I promised you, comedy, tragedy, and doings of high society—Horatio's ma was a Vanderfeller—and of course a happy ending. Hope you all feel you got your money's worth.

LUTHER (*Shouting from halfway back in the hall*): Not

me. I didn't even get to see the show. I only just now found the sheriff. (*To sheriff, sitting in audience*) I demand you arrest Alf Treadwell for putting over a hoax on the public and cheating honest people, Sheriff Pease.

SHERIFF (*Rising from his seat in audience*): Now, look here, Luther. If I'm satisfied, I guess you have to be, and I don't have any complaints.

JIM, TIM, SLIM (*From rear*): Neither have we, Pa.

LUTHER (*Threateningly*): You will have when I get you home. Now, just you listen to me, Alf Treadwell. I dare you to open those curtains, and prove that what meets the eye is really there. That's all I ask.

ALF (*In exasperation, looking towards wings*): *Open* the curtains, Sammy—*open* the curtains. (*When curtains part, the original setting of orange crates and empty soda bottles is all that "meets the eye."*) I really have to apologize for this setting, folks. It wasn't what we'd rightly planned. If one, whose name I won't mention, hadn't been so all-fired stingy, we Thespians would have done you proud. Still, we hope you've enjoyed yourselves anyway. Evening. (*He saunters off-stage as curtain falls.*)

THE END

Production Notes

MIND OVER MATTER

Characters: 14 male; 4 female.

Playing Time: 30 minutes.

Costumes: Doctor Pole wears a suit. Emerald wears a slinky, green dress. Dewey wears flashy sports clothes, and has a mustache. Lem wears overalls, a plaid shirt, and a white apron. Lutie wears patched blue jeans and a faded shirt, but later changes to a dress, squeaky high-heeled shoes, and an outlandish hat. Other characters wear typical country-style clothes.

Properties: Pipes, cheese, powder puff, carton of tin cans, broom, floor brush, pail, bottle opener, umbrella, apple, bag with soda bottles in it, small medicine bottle, box of money, and handcuffs.

Setting: The general store. When the play opens, the stage has only a few orange crates, a board counter, and some empty soda bottles. Then the scene is transformed to depict a real country store. For quick change, this may be partly depicted on a backdrop. In the scene, there should be several chairs, some crates, a cracker barrel, a flour barrel, a pot-bellied stove, a mirror, several ladies' hats, and a carton painted to look like a safe. There are two doors, leading outside and to the storeroom.

Lighting: No special effects.

The Cuckoo

By Marion Murdoch

Characters

Mrs. Constance Hillyer
Frances Hillyer
Roberta Hillyer
Miss Minerva Parminter
Mrs. Nicholas Westmoreland
Iris Westmoreland
Sally Green

Time: *The present. A bright October afternoon.*
Setting: *The living room of the Hillyer home in Glendale, a town within a hundred miles of New York City.*
At Rise: Mrs. Hillyer *hurries in from door, left, carrying a large package, loosely wrapped. She swiftly unwraps package disclosing a new lady's suitcase.* Constance Hillyer *is a slight, very pretty widow of thirty-nine, with a gentle, anxious expression, and a tendency to "flutter." She is very feminine and appealing, but not unusually clever or intellectual. She is*

obviously the gentlewoman, strongly maternal and do-
mestic.
After unwrapping suitcase and setting it at far end of
sofa, she hurries out left, and returns immediately with
a wedding veil which she carefully lays on table. Her
movements show that she is hurried and anxious.
The telephone rings. She utters a small exclamation
of impatience and dismay, frowns, shakes head, crosses
with sigh to take up phone, and sits at desk.

MRS. HILLYER (*In a weary, resigned tone. She has repeated*
this conversation many times.): Yes, this is Constance
Hillyer. . . . Oh, it's you, Helene. . . . Yes, it's true.
Frances is being married next Wednesday. . . . Yes, it is
sudden, but she's been engaged for three months. . . .
He's Lt. Richard Gordon—he's in the Navy. Frances
met him last August when she was visiting my sister
in California. He's just received his orders for transfer,
and she's going out there to be married. . . . No, she
didn't announce her engagement. She thought it was
better to say nothing until the day was set. . . . Oh,
yes! I'll miss her—terribly! . . . (*Her voice loses its*
enthusiasm.) Yes, I'll still have—Roberta. But Roberta
is just at the difficult age—it's like living with The
Charge of the Light Brigade. . . . Yes, I'm fearfully
busy—Frances is leaving by plane tonight—I'm just
fitting her wedding dress. . . . (*Desperately patient*)
Yes, Helene, we're making it ourselves, but I'd rather
you didn't tell anyone. . . . Yes, I know you won't say
a word. . . . Yes, yes, goodbye, dear— (*Lays down*
phone with a sigh as FRANCES *enters from the left, in*
wedding dress. She is a lovely girl of nineteen, with a
fine face full of distinction, charm, and intelligence.

She is intensely alive, deeply imaginative, and sensitive, with a natural gaiety and humor, which cover a deep love of Beauty and Romanticism. Just now she is unnaturally keyed up with a very occasional lapse into "bridal jitters.")

FRANCES (*Smiling ruefully and cynically*): Oh, no, she won't say a word!

MRS. HILLYER (*Crossing to table to get workbasket*): Oh, I'm sure Helene won't—she's one of my best friends.

FRANCES: Yes, but let something like a wedding happen to you, and all your friends turn into broadcasting stations.

MRS. HILLYER (*Taking up workbasket*): But, Frances—

FRANCES: Yes, they do. They put you under a microscope like a tadpole and report on your every wiggle. (MRS. HILLYER *crosses to* FRANCES, *center, and kneels beside her to adjust dress hem, placing basket on floor.*)

FRANCES (*Deeply*): Do you know what I'd like to do? I'd like to draw an enchanted circle around Richard and me and This Moment. (*Stands, center, entranced*)

MRS. HILLYER: But that sounds selfish, and you aren't— (*Frowning at hem*) Oh, I'll have to let out this hem—

FRANCES (*Deeply, ecstatically*): Darling, I'm *in love!* (*Pause*) Do you know what the French call love? "That lovely egotism of two." (*Ardently, appealingly.*) Oh, Mother, do you think I'm asking *too much?*

MRS. HILLYER (*Abstractedly. Intent on hem*): What?

FRANCES: Well, the only thing Life lets us keep is our memories. (*Deeply, passionately—to herself and Deity*) Oh, "Stay with me, Beauty!" (*Slowly, passionately*) If I can just have this moment—perfect, always! Something nothing can take!—not Time nor enemies—

MRS. HILLYER: But you haven't any enemies.

FRANCES: One.

MRS. HILLYER: You mean Iris?

FRANCES: Yes, Iris Westmoreland. As long as she lives she will hate me.

MRS. HILLYER (*Rising and going back of* FRANCES *to adjust neck of dress*): That's because you've been rivals since you were children.

FRANCES (*Thoughtfully*): That made her furious, I suppose—the village doctor's daughter daring to compete with the heiress of the Westmoreland Mills.

MRS. HILLYER (*Proudly, as she crosses behind* FRANCES): You always walked off with all the honors! You were Queen of the Winter Carnival, class orator. . . . Why, when you were both only six, she was jealous of you!

FRANCES: You mean when I won first prize in Sunday School?

MRS. HILLYER (*Going to get veil from table*): Yes, and when they gave her second prize, she threw it at the superintendent. Oh, darling— (*Emotionally*) I remember that evening! I can see you walking up to the platform in your little plaid dress—

FRANCES (*Catching her emotion—she is already keyed up with bride-to-be nerves*): Yes, I remember. (*Sniffs*)

MRS. HILLYER: It had little gilt buttons up the back. (*Sits on downstage end of sofa. Gropes for handkerchief, but can't find it.* FRANCES *gropes for hers, sinks on upstage end of sofa, and unknowingly picks up end of wedding veil which is between them on sofa.*)

FRANCES (*Sob in voice*): Oh, nobody remembers things about you as your *mother* does!

MRS. HILLYER: Oh, "Wunkie," how I am going to *miss* you!

FRANCES: Oh! (*It is a small, sharp cry.*)

Mrs. Hillyer (*Frightened*): What is it?

Frances (*Tragically*): You haven't called me Wunkie since I had chicken pox! (*Wipes eyes with end of veil*)

Mrs. Hillyer (*Diffidently, but earnestly*): I *do* call you—Wunkie.

Frances: When?

Mrs. Hillyer (*Earnestly*): Night and morning, I say, "God bless Wunkie and make her a good girl." (*Wipes eyes with veil, without noticing it.*)

Frances (*Staring at her*): Do you think He has?

Mrs. Hillyer (*Deeply*): I *know* He has.

Frances (*Suddenly noticing veil which they have been crying on, and is concerned. She rises with veil*): I'm—sorry I cried. It's just that I'm—oh, I guess all brides are sort of jittery.

Mrs. Hillyer (*Positively*): I was thinking of that terrible Iris Westmoreland!

Frances (*Earnestly, proudly, as she takes veil, crosses to get workbasket from floor, and goes left to put both on telephone desk*): No, that's one thing she could *never* do!

Mrs. Hillyer: What?

Frances (*Stoutly, proudly*): Make me cry.

Mrs. Hillyer (*Apprehensively*): Oh, don't say that! It's tempting Providence! (*Glances nervously out window*) Look! Is that a car stopping?

Frances (*Glancing out window*): Someone's coming in here.

Mrs. Hillyer (*Alarmed—fearing it may be* Iris): Who?

Frances (*Smiling affectionately*): "*Our* Miss Parminter," Principal of Glendale High School, Educator of Youth. (*Her voice is warm with affection and remembrance.*)

MRS. HILLYER (*Sighing with relief and speaking with love and admiration*): Such a *fine, good* woman! How I remember her!

FRANCES (*Musingly*): Yes. All these years—a Beacon Light to the Young—"Truth, Honor, Honesty!" She taught you, too, didn't she?

MRS. HILLYER: Yes. I was a sophomore at Glendale, her first year there—she taught math.

FRANCES: Did she always look like that?

MRS. HILLYER: What?

FRANCES (*Smiling affectionately*): A Grenadier Guard.

MRS. HILLYER: Yes. "The Three P's," we called her.

FRANCES: What's that?

MRS. HILLYER: "Precision, Perfection, Punctuality." She still fills me with awe and admiration.

FRANCES (*Fervently*): *Me too!* (*Smiles a little*) When she comes in I'll bet we both say, "Good afternoon, Miss Parminter," and stand at attention. (*Musingly*) Do you think she was ever in love?

MRS. HILLYER: Yes. She was engaged to a young lieutenant during the First World War.

FRANCES: What happened to him?

MRS. HILLYER: Oh, when he came back, Miss Parminter's father had died, and she had to teach to support her mother.

FRANCES (*Love and sympathy in her voice*): Poor darling! "Just a little love, a little kiss," in your teens and then—

MRS. HILLYER (*Sighing*): Nobody to kiss her now.

FRANCES (*Sighing, too, and speaking thoughtfully, with a small rueful smile*): No, and I guess now—it would be like—

MRS. HILLYER: What?

FRANCES (*With same small rueful smile*): Kissing the Statue of Liberty.

MRS. HILLYER (*Starting suddenly and looking at wrist watch*): Frances! It's late! Take your new suitcase, go upstairs, and pack! (*Doorbell rings. In a flurry*) No. Wait! Here she is! Open the door! (FRANCES *goes to front door and opens it to admit* MISS MINERVA PARMINTER. *She is a tall, very good-looking woman in her late fifties, straight as an arrow, carrying herself with great dignity and poise. She wears glasses, and carries a plain leather handbag, a furled umbrella, and rather incongruously, a large market basket full of groceries, on top of which reposes a huge bunch of carrots.*)

FRANCES (*Smiling warmly and affectionately*): Miss Parminter! What a nice surprise! Do come in.

MISS PARMINTER (*Enters*): Good afternoon, Frances— (*To* MRS. HILLYER) Constance.

MRS. HILLYER (*In a flurry of ad lib greetings*): So glad to see you! May I take the basket? Do sit down!

MISS PARMINTER (*Calm and unruffled*): I am very sorry to disturb you, but I am getting donations for the Flickenger family, and your name was on my list. (*She retains basket.*)

FRANCES (*Returning from closing front door. Surprised*): The Flickengers? Why I thought the school board expelled Fidelia Flickenger for what she did at the talent show.

MRS. HILLYER (*With morbid interest*): What did she do?

FRANCES (*Excitedly*): Started to dance.

MRS. HILLYER (*Puzzled*): But all contestants sing or dance.

FRANCES (*Darkly*): It was *what* she danced.

MRS. HILLYER: What?

FRANCES (*Dramatically*): The cancan.

MRS. HILLYER (*Shocked*): Oh, no!

FRANCES (*Slowly and dramatically*): She had just started—
up there on the stage. The whole school was holding its
breath—about to erupt in a roar. When Miss Parminter
entered, left, and walked her offstage—by the ear—thus!
(*Holds up thumb and first finger, clenched on an imaginary Flickenger ear*)

MRS. HILLYER (*Sighing in admiration and gazing fondly at
MISS PARMINTER*): Oh, my! (*During this dialogue* MISS
PARMINTER *has been deeply absorbed in placing her
basket neatly on floor, adjusting her glasses, opening her
handbag and extracting a notebook which she consults
with concentration, apparently oblivious of* MRS. HIL-
LYER *and* FRANCES.)

FRANCES (*In a thrilled and admiring voice*): It was the
most dramatic thing I ever saw!

MISS PARMINTER (*Irritated at* FRANCES' *dramatization of
the Flickenger incident which she considers utterly
negligible*): Nonsense! (*Turning to* MRS. HILLYER)
Now, Constance, if you could give me your donation—

MRS. HILLYER (*Still under spell of* FRANCES' *drama, recovers guiltily*): Oh, yes. Of course—the Flickengers!
Mr. Flickenger is—is—

FRANCES (*Falling from grace with a giggle*): The town
bum, darling.

MISS PARMINTER (*Sternly*): Frances! Your *language!*
(*Turning to* MRS. HILLYER) Alonzo Flickenger is indi-
gent, convivial, and—

MRS. HILLYER (*Eagerly, delighted that she can add to the
Flickenger saga*): Musical! He sits on his little front
porch and plays the accordion!

FRANCES (*Unable to resist this opening, grins as she*

sings through her nose): "I'm an old cow hand—"
(*Casts up eyes and pulls out an imaginary accordion to
the full extent of her arms. Drags out "ha—nd-d-d" as
she does this*)

MISS PARMINTER (*Sternly*): Frances!

MRS. HILLYER (*Flurried and apologetic, to* MISS PARMIN-
TER): Please, forgive her, Miss Parminter! You see, she
is getting married next Thursday and—

MISS PARMINTER (*Smiling and interested*): I hadn't heard.
(*Turning to* FRANCES *with warm smile*) Frances, my
dear, may I wish you every happiness?

FRANCES (*Daring and breathless with her own happiness,
to* MISS PARMINTER): Darling, you may! And may I—?
(*She darts over to* MISS PARMINTER *and kisses her
swiftly, lovingly on the cheek, and flashes through
door, left, without suitcase.*)

MISS PARMINTER (*Stands silent for a moment gazing after*
FRANCES, *a hand touches her cheek where the kiss lies,
a quiet joy in her eyes. Then recovering herself, she
straightens her hat and turns to* MRS. HILLYER.): And
now, Constance, may I put you down for a basket like
this (*Indicates basket*), or—

MRS. HILLYER: I'll just make a cash donation. (*Pausing
to consider, frowning a little as she concentrates*) Now,
let's see—I have forty cents in this workbasket—(*Claws
about hopefully in workbasket on desk*)—and a dollar
sixty-five in my bag. That makes— (*Starts to count on
fingers*) One sixty-five and forty make— (*Shuts her
eyes and continues to count on fingers*)

MISS PARMINTER (*In terrible voice*): Constance Appleby!

MRS. HILLYER (*Startled, opens eyes, presses hand to
breast*): Oh, how you startled me! Nobody has called
me that since I was—married!

MISS PARMINTER (*Severely*): Do you mean you are still doing *that?*

MRS. HILLYER (*Staring at her, bewildered*): What?

MISS PARMINTER (*Severe and accusing*): Counting on your fingers! (*Illustrates by counting, grimly, on her own*)

MRS. HILLYER (*Demoralized, speaks pleadingly*): But— but don't you remember, I was never very good at arithmetic.

MISS PARMINTER (*Stern and unyielding*): Yes, I remember, but never let me see you do that again!

MRS. HILLYER (*Meekly and plaintively*): Yes, ma'am. I mean, no, ma'am.

MISS PARMINTER (*Briskly*): And now, Constance, will your donation be a basket or money?

MRS. HILLYER (*Nervously, putting hands behind her*): I—I think I'll just send a—check.

MISS PARMINTER (*Brisk and businesslike*): Very well. I'll cross your name off my list. (*Reaches for handbag and opens it, searching for notebook*)

MRS. HILLYER (*Nervous, seeking something to say*): Isn't school out early today?

MISS PARMINTER (*Leafing through notebook*): Yes, I dismissed school early.

MRS. HILLYER (*Innocently*): On account of the football rally?

MISS PARMINTER: No. On account of an—*incident*. (*Looks up from notebook at* MRS. HILLYER)

MRS. HILLYER (*Slightly apprehensive*): What?

MISS PARMINTER: George Warburton fell down the stairs.

MRS. HILLYER (*Concerned*): Dear, me! Was he hurt?

MISS PARMINTER: No, not hurt. And he didn't exactly fall. (*Slight pause*) He was—*pushed*. (*Looks meaningly at* MRS. HILLYER)

MRS. HILLYER (*Falls back, stricken and speaks in a small voice as she sinks into large chair, left*): You don't mean—Roberta? (MISS PARMINTER *nods grimly and severely.*) Why did she push him?

MISS PARMINTER: Because he was trying out for the part in the school play she wanted. She said he cheated.

MRS. HILLYER: You mean the Irish play?

MISS PARMINTER: Yes, the whole school has turned Hibernian overnight.

MRS. HILLYER (*Suddenly worried again*): Besides pushing Georgie, Roberta didn't do anything else, did she?

MISS PARMINTER (*Severely*): She incited a riot.

MRS. HILLYER (*Appalled*): How?

MISS PARMINTER: Don't ask me; ask her. She can handle a mob scene better than Mark Antony. It was at the pep rally.

MRS. HILLYER (*Eagerly, thankful for a chance to change subject*): Oh, did you raise the final thousand for the new gym?

MISS PARMINTER (*With pride and satisfaction*): Yes, I have the whole ten thousand in my safe.

MRS. HILLYER (*Venturing a small smile*): Well, maybe the riot did some good—it stirred people up. Roberta worked so hard on that drive. Of course, she does throw herself into things with such—

MISS PARMINTER: Abandon? She does. Her enthusiasm is as contagious as measles. (*Briskly*) Well, I must be going. (*Looks again in notebook*) I'll mark on my list that you'll mail your donation. May I borrow your pencil?

MRS. HILLYER (*Eagerly*): Certainly.

MISS PARMINTER (*Severely*): Someone borrowed my pen this morning and didn't *return* it. (MISS PARMINTER *picks up pencil from table, right, hurriedly writes in notebook, and absent-mindedly drops pencil in her bag with notebook.*) I must be going. Good day, Constance, good day. (*She turns to front door, which* MRS. HILL-YER *hurries to open.*)

MRS. HILLYER: Goodbye, Miss Parminter. I hope that Roberta— (*But* MISS PARMINTER *is gone and* MRS. HILLYER *slowly closes door and sighs worriedly.*)

FRANCES (*Entering from left*): Well . . . some little sister I've got. (*Grinning*) I heard part of Miss Parminter's story. How come you produced such a hell-raiser?

MRS. HILLYER (*Picks up veil from telephone table and crosses to sit on chair, left, by desk. Abstractedly, as she frowns in concentration, hunting in workbasket on desk for needle to sew hem of veil*): I think Roberta was some kind of a—mistake. (*Frowns at veil*) Roberta should have been a boy. (*With sudden heat*) How I wish she had been a boy!

ROBERTA (*Offstage*): See you later, Sally.

FRANCES (*Crosses to look out window*): Well, here's the little inciter of riots herself.

ROBERTA (*Bursting in at center, and throwing her small felt hat on upstage end of sofa. She is a very attractive girl of fifteen, abrupt and noncommital as a boy. All her actions are boyish. She throws herself into her interest of the moment with headlong enthusiasm. Just now her absorbing enthusiasm is the drama. All she does is "acted," but there is nothing affected in this. She has strong affections and loyalty; but, like her sense of humor, they are buried deep, and never show except in occasional gleams. All she asks is to be let alone in her own little world where everything is simple and direct and no demands are made on emo-*

tions. She has "visions" but refuses to talk about them. She never "clowns," or shows off, or is smart-alecky): Hey, when do we eat? (*She goes to corner, right, to look at snake. To* Mrs. Hillyer) Hey, did you feed Herman?

Mrs. Hillyer (*Exasperatedly*): I have enough to do to feed *you* without feeding your snake!

Roberta: Well, I have to eat now and get back to school by four-thirty. (*Positively*) Got to!

Frances: That's when they have yours and Georgie's final tryouts for the play?

Roberta (*Moving center*): Yes, and right after that— (*Voice sinks and she stares ahead as if entranced*) they're choosing the cheerleader.

Frances (*Smiling understandingly*): And Roberta Hillyer would rather be cheerleader of Glendale High School than— (*Dramatically*) I can see her now! All in white—with a big orange (*Sketches a "G" in air*) "G" on her sweater—out in front of the whole stadium— (Roberta *stares into space and draws a long sigh of ecstasy.*)

Mrs. Hillyer (*Crosses to desk, puts down veil, and sits on desk chair which she turns to face audience, but keeps close to desk. She takes workbasket in lap, shakes head as she tidies basket and speaks plaintively*): All Roberta can think about is *herself*. She's so *self-centered!*

Frances (*Smiling tolerantly and whimsically*): Well, aren't we all?

Mrs. Hillyer (*Vaguely, as she hunts in basket*): What do you mean?

Frances (*Thoughtfully*): I mean that we all live in our own little worlds, and there's only one thing that can make us forget our own and come out into the other fellow's.

MRS. HILLYER: What's that?

FRANCES (*Under her breath, raptly*): Love.

MRS. HILLYER (*Turning around to* FRANCES): Yes, *love!* (*Turning again to desk to take up basket and look in it*) But Roberta doesn't love us. She—

ROBERTA (*Abruptly*): Hey, where's that pie you made yesterday, Mom?

FRANCES: I ate it.

ROBERTA (*Anxiously*): All of it?

FRANCES (*Grinning at* ROBERTA): To the last lick. (*Illustrates by flicking tongue along first finger*)

MRS. HILLYER (*Goaded to protest, speaks to* ROBERTA, *but continues to search the workbasket*): Can't you think of anything but your *stomach?* Here is your only sister, going off to be married. You don't know *when* you'll ever see her again—*if* you'll ever see her again! You show no more emotion than—

FRANCES (*Grinning*): If she were going to *Tony's* for a double-dip.

MRS. HILLYER (*Looking tragically at* ROBERTA): You never tell us you love us! Why don't you? (ROBERTA *throws herself on back of sofa, stares up at ceiling. She apparently doesn't hear.*) Why?

ROBERTA (*Gruffly, as she continues to stare at ceiling*): I hate a lot of talk.

MRS. HILLYER: Talk?

ROBERTA: Yes, a lot of talk about the way you feel.

MRS. HILLYER (*Turning again to basket*): Why shouldn't families talk about how much they love one another?

ROBERTA (*Speaking gruffly and with reluctance*): Because it isn't *decent.*

MRS. HILLYER (*Bewildered and appealing to* FRANCES): Frances, do you know what she's talking about?

FRANCES (*Smiling at* ROBERTA): It's as if you went in swimming without a suit, eh, Rob?

ROBERTA (*Scowling darkly at ceiling*): I hate the way people do!

MRS. HILLYER: What do you mean?

ROBERTA: I mean they sort of take out their emotions and purr over them.

MRS. HILLYER (*Bewildered*): Purr?

ROBERTA: Yes, like over a stamp collection.

MRS. HILLYER (*Turning tragically to* FRANCES): Frances, do you hear her?

FRANCES (*Taking up hand mirror from table, right, and trying to see back of her gown as she stands with back to mirror on right wall. She speaks abstractedly*): Yes, Mother—?

MRS. HILLYER (*Sighing, but attention still on work-basket*): Only the three of us left! And Roberta has no more family feeling than a changeling—a cuckoo— (*Turning around to daughters, delighted at her own perception*) That's what she is! She's a *cuckoo* in the nest!

FRANCES (*Looking in hand mirror, and stretching neck to see better. Abstractedly*): Oh, if "Push came to Shove," I think Robbie would go to bat for us—"All for one! One for all." Hey, Rob?

ROBERTA (*Sitting up eagerly*): That's what I wanted them to choose for the school play!

FRANCES: What?

ROBERTA (*Animatedly*): "The Three Musketeers"! (*Rises in a bound, leaps on sofa, and makes play with imaginary sword.*)

MRS. HILLYER (*Worriedly and reproachfully*): Oh, Roberta! Isn't the furniture shabby enough without your leaping on it?

ROBERTA (*Lost in drama*): Oh, if I could be d'Artagnan! Gosh! How I would swashbuckle! (*Illustrates with "sword" and "cloak," ruffling cloak grandly*)

FRANCES (*Smiling*): Off the sofa. (*Gives her a slight push from the rear to speed her descent*)

ROBERTA (*Getting off sofa, scowling and disgruntled*): The committee chose that old Irish play. There's only one good part in it. (*Crosses to snake cage, right, and feeds snake with some food from saucer on table, right*)

FRANCES: What?

ROBERTA: The banshee.

FRANCES (*Slight smile*): We heard all about the banshee from Miss Parminter. (ROBERTA *crosses to sofa.*)

MRS. HILLYER (*Sighing and shaking head*): And about poor George Warburton.

ROBERTA (*Ignoring Georgie*): What did the Goddess want?

MRS. HILLYER (*Plaintively*): Roberta, must you call Miss Parminter that?

ROBERTA (*Ignoring the statement about question*): What did she want?

FRANCES (*Suddenly, starting to giggle*): Oh, Mother, I did so want to!

MRS. HILLYER (*Staring at* FRANCES): What?

FRANCES (*Grinning*): Shatter just once that Olympic— that Parminter—calm! (*Her eyes are dancing with mischief.*) What do you think she'd do if I sneaked up to her like this and said— (FRANCES *steals up to* MRS. HILLYER, *seizes her arm and hisses in her ear, then speaks in a deep voice.*) "Minerva Parminter, you're wanted by the F.B.I. for reckless driving!"

ROBERTA (*Delighted*): Hot dog! Do you think she'd faint?

MRS. HILLYER (*Scandalized*): Certainly not!

FRANCES (*Smiling fondly and shaking head*): No, she'd just say "Nonsense! Frances Hillyer, go to the blackboard and write: 'I am an idiot,' twenty times." (*After a pause, thoughtfully*) Still, people do change after a certain age—

MRS. HILLYER: What do you mean?

FRANCES (*Shrugging*): Oh, they change completely— kick over the traces—do something foolish—

ROBERTA (*Turning to* FRANCES *with sudden interest*): What do they do?

MRS. HILLYER (*Warningly*): Frances!

FRANCES (*Carelessly*): Oh, at that age they suddenly stop being afraid of things—of convention.

ROBERTA (*With satisfaction*): Yes. That's why she might give me the part.

FRANCES: The banshee?

ROBERTA (*Violently*): Yeah, and I'm gonna yell like hell!

MRS. HILLYER: ROBERTA!

FRANCES (*Smiling slightly*): But there is still doubt in the official mind as to which is the better screecher— you or Georgie.

ROBERTA (*Indignantly*): He's a dirty cheat!

MRS. HILLYER (*Horrified*): Roberta. If you—

ROBERTA (*Violently*): He is! It's his *voice!*

FRANCES: What about it?

ROBERTA (*Indignantly*): It's changing.

FRANCES: Well, he can't help that.

ROBERTA: Help it! He *loves* it! He can do a screech that sim-pu-ly scares the— (*Absorbed in drama*) Look, Frances! (*Sits perched on the back of sofa, feet on seat*) The banshee sits on the roof and wails. Do you think it should go like this?— (*Gives a bloodcurdling shriek*)

FRANCES: Heavens no! You sound like an Iroquois giving his scalp-yell. It should go like this— (*Throws back head and is about to yell when* MRS. HILLYER *clutches her frantically*)

MRS. HILLYER (*To* FRANCES, *in horror*): Don't you dare yell! Are you crazy? What will the neighbors think?

FRANCES (*Smiling*): Can't a bride have hysterics?

MRS. HILLYER (*Indignantly*): You never had hysterics in your life!

FRANCES: I never got married in my life.

MRS. HILLYER (*Suddenly, tragically*): Yes, you're getting married! And going off to live in the Pacific Ocean!

ROBERTA (*Getting down from sofa and starting towards door, left, hastily*): Is there anything to eat in the refrigerator?

MRS. HILLYER (*Tragically, to* FRANCES): You hear her, Frances! Cold as a fish! She won't sit down with us— just the three of us—and talk. (*Emotionally*) Maybe it will be the last time we'll ever— (*Puts handkerchief to eyes*)

ROBERTA (*Scowling as she stoops to inspect her sock*): Oh, heck, I got a hole in my sock. (*Holds up leg for inspection*)

MRS. HILLYER (*Tragically*): Frances, what do you think of her!

FRANCES (*Smiling at* ROBERTA): I think the cuckoo is just

very *shy*. (*Looks out window*) Oh, Mother— (*Goes to window,* ROBERTA *follows and looks over* FRANCES' *shoulder*)

MRS. HILLYER (*Apprehensively, hand at breast*): What— is it?

FRANCES (*Impressively*): A Cadillac, a chauffeur, and two gorgeous ladies at our gate!

MRS. HILLYER (*Hurrying anxiously to window*): Who— is it?

FRANCES: Mrs. Westmoreland and Iris.

MRS. HILLYER (*Crossing to chair, left-center, and speaking faintly*): They can't be stopping here. They never call on us.

FRANCES: Iris must have heard about the wedding and come to— (*Looking out absorbedly*) There they sit— quarreling as usual. (*Turns suddenly to look at* MRS. HILLYER *who has sunk into chair, left-center, and looks faint. In alarm, hurrying to her, as does* ROBERTA) Why, Mother! What's wrong? Get some water, Roberta. Quick! (ROBERTA *hurries off at left.*) Oh, darling! (*Goes down on knees beside* MRS. HILLYER) You've been doing too much!

MRS. HILLYER (*Rising with effort, summoning all her reserve strength.* FRANCES *also rises. To* FRANCES): You must go—upstairs—

FRANCES (*Bewildered*): But why?

MRS. HILLYER: Because— (*Gets inspiration as she looks at the wedding dress*) —I won't have them know we're making your wedding dress.

FRANCES (*Agreeing anxiously*): Yes, dear. I'll go up and change, then come down and sink Iris.

MRS. HILLYER (*Feverishly*): No, no, you *mustn't!* You must stay up there. I'll get rid of her. I—won't have her coming here and—and—I won't let her hurt my—my— (*Making brave show of defiance*)

FRANCES (*Smiling, love and tenderness in eyes*): Stop fluttering your wings and beating your breast on the ground. (*Pats* MRS. HILLYER'*s shoulder*)

MRS. HILLYER (*Bewildered*): What do you mean?

FRANCES (*Smiling at her*): Like a mother partridge protecting her young.

MRS. HILLYER (*Anxiously, with glance at window*): Please, go!

FRANCES: Yes, darling, I'm going, but I'm coming back and let me find that "our flag is still there." (FRANCES *exits, left.* MRS. HILLYER *crosses to center, as* ROBERTA *enters left, with glass of water which she brings to* MRS. HILLYER *who waves it away impatiently.* ROBERTA *sets glass on desk, left.*)

MRS. HILLYER (*Moving back and forth nervously, speaks tragically*): Oh, Roberta! What are we going to do!

ROBERTA (*Practically*): Let's scald them.

MRS. HILLYER (*Weakly, bewilderedly*): What?

ROBERTA (*Lost in the drama of the thought*): Pour boiling oil on them from the ramparts—I mean the window—as they did in the Middle Ages. (*Makes motion of pouring out oil. Glances out window*) They're still fighting.

MRS. HILLYER (*Unheeding and desperate*): Roberta! I know you're only fifteen, but I've got to talk to you as if you were grown up.

ROBERTA (*Calmly*): Shoot.

MRS. HILLYER: Iris has come here for just one reason.

ROBERTA: What?

MRS. HILLYER (*Earnestly*): To spoil Frances' wedding.

ROBERTA: Why?

MRS. HILLYER: Because she hates Frances—wants to hurt her.

ROBERTA (*Impatiently*): How the heck can she spoil Frances' wedding?

MRS. HILLYER (*Earnestly*): She can take away all the beauty.

ROBERTA (*Disgustedly*): But Frances isn't dumb! She wouldn't let that old heel spoil her marriage.

MRS. HILLYER (*Desperately*): Listen, Roberta! Iris knows something that will ruin Frances' happiness!

ROBERTA (*Calmly*): What?

MRS. HILLYER (*Crossing to window and pulling curtain aside to peer out anxiously*): Ever since Frances told me she was going to marry Richard Gordon, I've been afraid—afraid of what Iris might do if she heard Richard's name.

ROBERTA (*Practically*): What does Iris know? (*Reclines on sofa*)

MRS. HILLYER (*Desperately and apprehensively, instinctively lowering voice*): Something about Richard.

ROBERTA (*Sitting up in sudden interest*): Did he bump somebody off?

MRS. HILLYER (*Sinking into chair, left center*): No, no! Richard went to Annapolis.

ROBERTA: What's that got to do with it?

MRS. HILLYER: Everything. He met Iris there one week end and fell in love with her.

ROBERTA (*Disgustedly*): The poor dope!

MRS. HILLYER (*Lost in the tale, sighing*): He was only nineteen. (*Shakes head and sighs*)

ROBERTA (*Impatiently*): Yes, but what?

MRS. HILLYER (*Very dramatically, lowering her voice and*

speaking impressively and mysteriously—she relishes the drama and the idea of herself as raconteur): Well, Mrs. Westmoreland broke up the affair. Then it seems somebody found Richard with a revolver in his hand, and it got out that he was going to shoot himself because of Iris.

ROBERTA (*Disgustedly*): Baloney!

MRS. HILLYER: Yes, but don't you see what a story Iris could make of that—to Frances? (*Doorbell rings sharply. Both rise,* MRS. HILLYER *in great agitation.*)

ROBERTA (*Goes towards front door stoically*): Here they come. "Pull up your socks."

MRS. HILLYER (*Agitatedly and in a flutter*): I'll go upstairs! I'll tell Frances not to come down! (MRS. HILL-YER *exits at left.* ROBERTA *sinks suddenly into character and dramatizes the moment. She swings front door open slowly, keeping herself out of sight behind it, then slips behind window curtain, directly left of open door. She is completely concealed.* IRIS *and* MRS. WESTMORE-LAND *are seen in open doorway.* IRIS, *puzzled, steps inside and peers about. She is keyed up, tense, and petulant. She is a pretty girl, spoiled, brattish, and at present in a high-voltage temper. She is expensively dressed in the height of fashion.* MRS. WESTMORELAND *is a full-blown blonde (or brunette) of about forty, large, handsome, commanding, dictatorial. She shows every indication of having been dragged here against her will. She also is fashionably but rather flamboyantly dressed.*)

MRS. WESTMORELAND (*Standing regally in doorway and looking about irritably and impatiently*): Apparently they're out. The wind must have blown the door open. Leave our cards and come immediately.

IRIS (*Mulishly*): I'm going to stay right here until I see Frances Hillyer. (*Flounces about, snooping here and there.*)

MRS. WESTMORELAND (*Determined and exasperated*): Well, you can stay by yourself. I'm going back to that meeting you dragged me away from. (*Angrily*) I wouldn't have come one foot if I hadn't been afraid—

IRIS (*Petulantly*): Of what?

MRS. WESTMORELAND (*Exasperatedly*): That you'd make a scene. Blackmail! That's what it is. When you were small you kicked and screamed. Now you—

IRIS (*Petulantly*): Well, you can't go back! You're going to stay right here with me!

MRS. WESTMORELAND (*Coming gradually further into room—she can quarrel better at close quarters*): You want me here for just one reason. (*Stands still in middle of room*)

IRIS: What?

MRS. WESTMORELAND: To make this visit look casual. (*Looking meaningly at* IRIS) Don't think I don't know why you rushed over here today!

IRIS (*Reckless and defiant*): Why?

MRS. WESTMORELAND (*Amused and malicious*): Because you heard Frances Hillyer was engaged to Richard Gordon.

IRIS (*Resentfully*): He was engaged to me first!

MRS. WESTMORELAND (*Contemptuously*): Phooey!

IRIS (*Passionately and resentfully*): If it hadn't been for you, I'd have married him!

MRS. WESTMORELAND (*Practically*): If it hadn't been for me, you'd have made a fool of yourself. You weren't in love! (*Sarcasm in voice*)

IRIS (*Dramatizing self*): I was! I sobbed myself to sleep

night after night. (*Sniffs. Pause*) My heart was broken! (*Sinks down on sofa with sob*)

MRS. WESTMORELAND (*Ridiculing*): You and your broken heart!

ROBERTA (*In sepulchral tone from behind curtain*): "I am thy father's ghost—" (MRS. WESTMORELAND *falls back, stunned for a moment.* IRIS *recoils with nervous squeak.*)

MRS. WESTMORELAND: What was that?

IRIS (*Nervously*): I—don't know— (*Rises and looks apprehensively about.* MRS. WESTMORELAND, *recovering her poise, marches on a quiet hunt for the sound and finally pounces on the window curtain and snatches it aside, discovering* ROBERTA *who is quite unconcerned.*)

MRS. WESTMORELAND (*Sternly*): Roberta Hillyer, what do you mean! (MRS. HILLYER *makes a sudden and flurried entrance, left.*)

MRS. HILLYER (*Feverishly*): Oh, Roberta! What are you doing?

ROBERTA (*Unmoved, still in character*): Hamlet's ghost.

MRS. HILLYER (*Fluttering*): Please forgive her, Mrs. Westmoreland. You see, she's so taken up with dramatics just now— (*Moves nervously to front door and closes it*)

IRIS (*Wasting no time on social amenities*): Where is Frances, Mrs. Hillyer?

MRS. HILLYER (*Catching breath nervously, frantically*): Oh, Frances is very busy—she— (*Trying to change subject*) Have you met my daughter, Roberta, Mrs. Westmoreland?

MRS. WESTMORELAND (*Icily and grimly*): Yes, Roberta and I have met. May we sit down, Mrs. Hillyer?

MRS. HILLYER (*Making violent effort to come out of her

daze): Oh, I'm sorry! Do sit down—here—on the sofa— (MRS. WESTMORELAND *sits on upstage side of sofa.* IRIS *sits on downstage side.* ROBERTA, *who has come out from place in front of window, crosses to desk, left, and stands leaning back against it, facing audience. She has picked up ball of wool from basket on desk and is casually passing it from hand to hand.* MRS. HILLYER *sits in chair, left center.*)

MRS. WESTMORELAND (*Having settled herself with exuberance*): Yes, Mrs. Hillyer, Roberta and I met last night at a mass meeting called to nominate my brother, Oliver Higgenbothem, for principal of Glendale High School.

MRS. HILLYER (*Bewildered*): A campaign against Miss Parminter? But she's so popular!

MRS. WESTMORELAND (*Severely and impressively*): Minerva Parminter has been principal too long.

IRIS (*Fuming*): Mother, we called to see Frances, not to talk about your meetings.

MRS. WESTMORELAND (*Ignoring* IRIS): My brother would have been nominated, if it hadn't been for your daughter, Mrs. Hillyer.

MRS. HILLYER (*Looking worriedly at* ROBERTA): Oh, what happened?

MRS. WESTMORELAND (*Slowly and impressively*): I was making a speech in the town auditorium, and your daughter was there. (*Baleful look at* ROBERTA) With practically the whole Glendale High School—

ROBERTA (*Calmly and literally*): The *whole* Glendale High School.

MRS. WESTMORELAND (*Glaring at* ROBERTA): And every time I mentioned Oliver's name she would cheer.

MRS. HILLYER (*Relieved*): Well, I should have thought that would have helped your brother's campaign.

MRS. WESTMORELAND (*Glaring—emitting a snort*): Helped! Do you know what she yelled? She yelled, "Yo-ho-ho, and a bottle of rum!"

MRS. HILLYER (*Innocently, her mind on* FRANCES): It must have been the association of ideas.

MRS. WESTMORELAND (*Frigidly*): What do you mean, Mrs. Hillyer?

ROBERTA (*Calmly. To* MRS. WESTMORELAND): Everybody knows why you want your brother to get that job.

MRS. WESTMORELAND (*Icily and warningly*): Why do I want my brother to get the—er—position?

ROBERTA (*Calmly and literally*): So you won't have to support him any more. (*Front door bursts violently open and* SALLY GREEN, ROBERTA'*s chum, rushes in. She is a pretty, excitable girl of fifteen.*)

SALLY (*Wildly, in shout that startles everyone but* RO-BERTA): Roberta! (*Goes off into violent coughing fit, clutches throat*)

MRS. HILLYER (*Anxiously*): Sally is choking, Roberta. Pat her on the back! (ROBERTA *crosses to* SALLY *and thumps her violently on the back.*)

SALLY (*Recovering and waving* ROBERTA *away*): No, no, it's nothing. I just—swallowed my g-g-gum— (*Wildly*) Roberta! Come on! You're late! They're choosing the banshee— (*Seizes* ROBERTA *and pulls her towards the front door*) —and the *cheer-leader!* Come on!

ROBERTA (*Excitedly, dashing about searching frantically for her hat*): Where's my hat! (ROBERTA *crosses before* MRS. WESTMORELAND, *looks about, then dives for sofa to look back of* IRIS, *who sits on downstage end of sofa,*

*and who registers acute discomfort and antipathy, and
protests ad lib. The search proving futile,* ROBERTA
*crosses, down, around end of table in transit. Then she
dives frantically across table and drags her soft felt hat
from behind* MRS. WESTMORELAND, *who registers pain
and aversion and straightens her own hat angrily.* RO-
BERTA *slams her hat on head, plunges towards front
door, then at a sudden thought, turns back to rush at
mirror, right. Snatches off hat and starts to slick down
hair in frantic haste with licks-and-promise gestures.
Slams hat on again, then drags* SALLY *left of window,
and is explaining with gestures and detail—in whispers,
what* SALLY *is to do when she,* ROBERTA, *is elected cheerleader.*)

MRS. WESTMORELAND (*After turning to glare at* ROBERTA.
Sternly—voice heavy with disapproval): You seem to
live in an atmosphere of upheaval, Mrs. Hillyer. (*Gleam
of triumph in eyes as she turns to* IRIS) I told you, Iris,
this was no time to call!

IRIS (*Crossly*): But I saw old Parminter coming out of here
as I drove by.

MRS. HILLYER (*Swiftly seizing on any subject not* FRAN-
CES): Yes, she came to ask aid for the Flickenger family.

MRS. WESTMORELAND (*Indignantly and triumphantly*):
There! You see how inconsistent Minerva Parminter is.
Why Fidelia Flickenger has been expelled from her
school, and she's taking her groceries!

IRIS (*Fuming with impatience*): Isn't Frances at home,
Mrs. Hillyer?

MRS. HILLYER (*Nervous and apprehensive*): She's—lying
down. All her friends are coming at five to say goodbye.
She asks you to excuse her— (ROBERTA *during above*

speech has seized SALLY *and rushes to front door*.)

ROBERTA (*Hurriedly*): G'bye—

FRANCES (*Entering, left, on mother's words*): Oh, no, she doesn't. How do you do, Mrs. Westmoreland and—Iris?

MRS. HILLYER (*Staring at her in horror*): Frances! I thought you were going to stay upstairs! (ROBERTA *turns swiftly to stare strickenly at* FRANCES *who is shaking hands with* MRS. WESTMORELAND *and* IRIS *amid ad lib "How do you do's."* FRANCES *sits in chair at desk, left.*)

ROBERTA (*She has stopped dead in her tracks, staring at* FRANCES. *Strickenly, under breath*): Frances!

SALLY (*Panicky with impatience*): Roberta! Are you c-c-crazy! Come on! You're late! You'll be late for the contest! (ROBERTA *registers wild indecision and conflicting emotions. Turns to door and then back to stare at* FRANCES. *Then she deliberately pushes the stunned* SALLY *out front door,* SALLY *resisting bewilderedly.*)

SALLY (*In heart-rending accents as she is pushed out*): But—Roberta! Aren't you coming! . . . Oh, Roberta! (*An agonized wail as* ROBERTA *closes door, shutting her outside.* ROBERTA *stands motionless, back to door— watching company and listening.*)

MRS. WESTMORELAND (*Regally, condescendingly*): We would have sent Frances a present had we known sooner. (MRS. HILLYER *has been in an agony of apprehension since entrance of* FRANCES *and is clasping and unclasping her handkerchief with fluttering hands.*)

MRS. HILLYER (*Unheeding* MRS. WESTMORELAND, *speaks jerkily, in gasps.*): Yes, yes, I'll—pack all her presents and send them to her as soon as she gets settled. You know how it is in the Navy— (*Gives little gasp of dis-*

may as she says "Navy") I mean—how—how— (*Is appalled at "opening" she has given* IRIS.)

IRIS (*Seizing the "ace" with avidity*): Oh, yes, the *Navy!*

MRS. WESTMORELAND (*Sarcastically, looking maliciously at* IRIS): Iris just dotes on the Navy. (*Pause*) You see, Mrs. Hillyer, she caused many a broken heart when she used to go down to Annapolis. (*Sighs expressively.* ROBERTA *drags chair up from left of window and plants it between* MRS. WESTMORELAND *on sofa and* MRS. HILLYER *in chair, left. She sits down, folds arms, stretches feet out in front of her, and silently regards the company. She is the embodiment of watchful waiting. Up to this point,* ROBERTA *has been off-hand and casual; now her eyes are right on the ball. Nobody is going to get by to make a goal on* FRANCES. *In this warfare with the* WESTMORELANDS *she never resorts to wisecracks—but is as direct as a bullet.*)

MRS. HILLYER (*In dither*): D-d-did she?

MRS. WESTMORELAND (*Enjoying herself, a malicious eye on* IRIS): Yes, indeed. She had a fatal effect upon men.

ROBERTA (*Nodding head shortly. Unsmiling—it is simply a fact*): Oh, like Fidelia Flickenger.

MRS. WESTMORELAND (*Indignantly, glaring at* ROBERTA. *After all,* IRIS *is her own child, and only she, herself, is allowed to heckle her.*): What! (*Then deciding to ignore* ROBERTA *and continue civil war on* IRIS, *whose revolt must be squelched at any cost.*) As I was saying, Mrs. Hillyer, Iris produced a furor at Annapolis.

FRANCES (*Indifferently*): I didn't know she ever went to Annapolis.

MRS. WESTMORELAND (*Enjoying herself in her goading of* IRIS): Oh, dear yes! Iris produced the same effect at Annapolis that—

IRIS (*Glaring savagely at* MRS. WESTMORELAND. *Her pent-up emotion flying off suddenly.*): That you did at Yale!

MRS. HILLYER (*Agreeing delightedly at change of subject*): Oh, yes! (*Leaning towards* MRS. WESTMORELAND *and smiling brightly*) They used to call you "The Boola Boola Belle," didn't they?

MRS. WESTMORELAND (*Furiously, and turing to glare at* MRS. HILLYER): Who told you that?

IRIS (*Weary of delay and going into action—eyes on* FRANCES): Yes, I went down to Annapolis and—

MRS. WESTMORELAND (*Swiftly*): And the middies wrote poetry about her— (*Sighs romantically—she is ridiculing* IRIS.)

ROBERTA (*Staring into space. Speaks slowly and with fervor—she is "acting" again.*): "Was this the face that launched a thousand ships—?"

MRS. WESTMORELAND (*At top of her "form" and intent on ridiculing* IRIS's *beautiful, lost "grand passion." This "Navy subject" is an old and bitter feud between herself and* IRIS.): One man wrote:

Iris lovely and serene,

Her voice has a tinkle crystalline,

Her beauty affects us like—

ROBERTA (*Staring into space. No emotion in voice and unsmiling*): Energine.

IRIS (*In fury*): Somebody *did* write poetry about me, Frances, somebody who—

ROBERTA (*Making sudden, headlong dive along floor. Sprawls in swimming attitude at* MRS. WESTMORELAND's *feet. All are startled as she shouts.*): He's loose again!

MRS. WESTMORELAND *and* IRIS (*Rising apprehensively*): Who's loose?

ROBERTA (*Hunting frantically about the feet of the visitors, to their acute discomfort and further alarm*): My snake.

MRS. WESTMORELAND *and* IRIS (*In horror*): A snake!

ROBERTA (*Wagging head warningly*): Everybody better scram. We have no antidote for rattlesnake poison.

IRIS (*Leaps on sofa emitting yelps of terror*): Rattlesnakes!

ROBERTA (*In a yell*): Herman! (*Emits an ear-splitting whistle by putting two fingers in her mouth*)

MRS. HILLYER (*Bewilderedly*): But Herman isn't a rattlesnake— (*Hurries over to snake-box, right, looks in it*) And here he is in his box! (*Smiles reassuringly and delightedly. ROBERTA gets slowly to her feet, draws a long, heavy sigh, and shakes head—her ruse to evict the visitors has failed.*)

FRANCES (*To visitors, hopefully*): Of course, if you're nervous— (*Rises*)

MRS. HILLYER (*Sighing, and staring despairingly at ROBERTA*): Oh, Roberta! Roberta!

IRIS (*Getting slowly off sofa and stepping gingerly on floor. Nervous, but attempting to conceal it*): We're not n-n-nervous—at all. (*All sit as before. IRIS takes compact from bag.*)

ROBERTA (*Rises dramatically and walks slowly down, left. All stare at her as she speaks loudly and distinctly.*): I wonder who will be the next principal of the Glendale High School now that Miss Parminter has—

MRS. WESTMORELAND (*Turning swiftly and eagerly on ROBERTA*): Miss Parminter has done what?

ROBERTA: Sally told me when she came in here.

IRIS (*Seething with impatience. Between her teeth. Turning on ROBERTA*): Told you what?

ROBERTA (*Shaking head sadly and sighing*): What gets

me is all the work I did to help keep her job for her, and the very next day she—

MRS. WESTMORELAND (*Furious with impatience. Turning on* ROBERTA): She what?

ROBERTA (*Virtuously*): Maybe I shouldn't repeat it.

MRS. WESTMORELAND (*Violently*): Tell me this minute!

ROBERTA (*Calmly*): Well, I guess the whole town knows it by now. I don't see why I shouldn't tell you.

MRS. WESTMORELAND (*Eagerly, snorting with impatience*): Yes? Yes—?

ROBERTA (*With maddening deliberateness*): Well—Miss Parminter has taken the ten-thousand-dollar gym fund and eloped.

ALL (*Shrieking in amazement and horror.* IRIS *who has been holding compact in hand, drops it to floor.*): WHAT!

MRS. HILLYER (*In tears, sobbing*): Oh, no! It *can't* be! Why—why, it's just like—the fall of—*Lucifer!* (*Buries face in handkerchief, shoulders shaking with sobs.* FRANCES *looks "sunk" and sad.*)

ROBERTA (*Oblivious of all, sunk in Drama*): It was midnight—she walks into her office (*Pacing slowly like Lady Macbeth*), unlocks safe (*Illustrates grimly, face set, eyes unwinking. She thrusts hand into "safe."*), takes money, and walks out. (*Walks as before, holding "money" straight before her in both hands, at full length of arms*)

IRIS (*Who has dropped compact in her stupefaction, now recovers poise, stoops to retrieve compact and opens it to inspect face in mirror and apply powder to nose. Maliciously, and with a nasty little sniff and shrug*): Well! I always *knew* she was *too good* to be true.

MRS. WESTMORELAND (*Recovering poise, speaks emphat-*

ically): Well, there can be only one explanation: Minerva Parminter has gone *stark, raving mad!* (*A new and exciting thought strikes her. She struggles to her feet, and rushes to phone, left. Excitedly, wildly*) Give me that phone! (*Dials rapidly*) Ollie! Is that you? . . . Ollie! Minerva Parminter has lost her mind! Gone completely ga-ga. She has stolen ten thousand dollars from the high school and eloped! . . . Get to the mayor's office immediately! I'll meet you there. (*Exultantly*) If you're not the next principal of Glendale High School . . . Yes, she has *stolen* it! Tell the Mayor! Hurry! (*Puts down phone in triumph. Cheering begins softly, offstage, at left.* ROBERTA *starts, runs quickly to window and peers anxiously up street, in direction of cheering students. At same time,* MRS. WESTMORELAND *turns triumphantly from phone. Doorbell rings.* FRANCES *and* MRS. HILLYER *rise.* FRANCES *opens door to* MISS PARMINTER. *All stare at her in utter amazement—except* ROBERTA *who still stares out window.*)

MISS PARMINTER (*Standing tall and stately in doorway*): Good afternoon, all. (*To* MRS. HILLYER) I found that I had carried off your pencil, Constance. (*Draws pencil from bag, advances calmly and deliberately to lay pencil on table, right.*)

MRS. HILLYER (*Faintly*): But it was only a *pencil.* (*During scene* MRS. WESTMORELAND *and* IRIS *stare at* MISS PARMINTER *in speechless horror.*)

MISS PARMINTER (*To* MRS. HILLYER): But it was *your* pencil. I also came to tell you that the Flickengers will need your donation more than ever.

MRS. HILLYER (*Faintly, still shaken*): How—do you mean?

MISS PARMINTER: They are quarantined with measles.

MRS. WESTMORELAND (*Recovering from her daze of horror,*

speaking wildly): Iris! We must stop Oliver! He's at the Mayor's office right now! We'll be sued for libel! (*She rushes out of door dragging* IRIS *after her.*)

IRIS (*As she passes* ROBERTA, *she hisses venomous malediction*): You little *viper!* (ROBERTA, *unheeding, continues to stand motionless, staring out windows towards left, where cheering was and has now stopped.* MRS. WESTMORELAND *and* IRIS *exit, center, violently.*)

MRS. HILLYER (*Crossing to sofa and speaking tragically to* ROBERTA): Oh, Roberta! Roberta! I'll never understand you! (ROBERTA *does not look around or move. Cheering starts again, offstage left.*)

FRANCES: What's that?

MISS PARMINTER: It's the students celebrating.

FRANCES: Celebrating what?

MISS PARMINTER: The election of the new cheerleader. They have just chosen George Warburton.

MRS. HILLYER (*Blankly*): George Warb—?

MISS PARMINTER: Yes, his screaming for the banshee was so—overwhelming that he was voted cheerleader. He won easily as there was no competition.

MRS. HILLYER (*Bewilderedly*): But Roberta—? (*All turn to stare at* ROBERTA *who is still staring out window, silently, motionlessly.*)

MISS PARMINTER: Roberta didn't compete. She must have changed her mind. The young are so unpredictable. Good day, all. (*She exits, center, quickly.* ROBERTA *moves very slowly to open door, center. She holds on to the framework with one hand and stares out.*)

FRANCES (*Looking suddenly at wrist watch, is startled*): Oh, it's five o'clock! I must rush— (*She exits, hurriedly, left.* MRS. HILLYER *hurries left to pick up veil from desk.*)

MRS. HILLYER (*To* ROBERTA): Roberta, bring up that suitcase. (*Goes toward door, left, then turns to look reproachfully at* ROBERTA. *She speaks very slowly and tragically—each word is a reproach. She shakes her head sadly at the "Cuckoo."*) Isn't there *something* you can do for *your* sister! (*Exits at left. Down street from left comes rush of cars, blowing horns, and loud cheering young voices.*)

VOICES: Rah, rah, rah! Warburton! Warburton! Warburton! (*As cheers die into diminuendo and distance,* ROBERTA *moves slowly to suitcase, right, picks it up, and eyes straight ahead, goes slowly towards door at left, as curtain falls.*)

THE END

Production Notes

The Cuckoo

Characters: 7 female.

Playing Time: 35 minutes.

Costumes: Modern, everyday dress. Frances wears a wedding dress. Iris and Mrs. Westmoreland are fashionably dressed. Roberta wears a sweater and skirt. Mrs. Hillyer wears a housedress. Miss Parminter is dressed in a plain, tailored suit.

Properties: Wedding veil, lady's new suitcase wrapped loosely for Mrs. Hillyer; hand mirror for Frances, glass of water, felt hat for Roberta, large market basket full of groceries for Miss Parminter, pencil.

Setting: The Hillyer living room is bright and cheerful. The furnishings are not new but comfortable and in good taste. There is a door to dining room and kitchen towards back left. The front door of the house is in the center and opens on a porch. There is a window to the left of this. A desk is down at extreme left, and behind this, facing audience, is a straight chair. On the desk is a phone. A large, narrow mirror is hung at right of door, and in the right corner of the room is a small cage or box in which is supposed to be a snake. There is a fireplace and mantle in right wall. A large sofa is downstage at right, and behind this and touching it, is a long narrow table, and on it a workbasket with balls of wool, etc. There is a large arm chair to left of sofa and a straight chair at left of window.

Lighting: No special effects.

Cry Witch

By Marion L. Miller

Characters

BETTY CANTWELL, *one of the afflicted children*
PRUDENCE CANTWELL, *her sister*
CHRISTOPHER OAKLY, *Prudence's fiancé*
MR. PARRIS, *minister to Salem Village*
MR. HATHORNE ⎱ *magistrates*
MR. CORWIN ⎰
THE SHERIFF
ANN PUTNAM ⎫
MERCY LEWES ⎪ *afflicted children*
ABIGAIL WILLIAMS ⎬
MARY WALCOTT ⎭
MR. NOYES, *minister*
MARTHA COREY, *the accused*
GILES COREY, *her husband*

TIME: *March 21, 1692.*
SETTING: *The meeting house at Salem Village.*
AT RISE: BETTY, PRUDENCE *and* CHRISTOPHER *enter from left.* PRUDENCE *is a pretty girl of twenty,* CHRISTOPHER

is about three years older, and BETTY *is about thirteen.*
BETTY *runs across the stage after dragging her hand
from* PRUDENCE'S *grasp. She looks at every piece of furniture curiously, and then crosses back of minister's chair
and leans against the back of it.*

PRUDENCE: Betty, come away from there. How is it with
you, little sister?
BETTY (*Running a hand along the back of the chair*): 'Tis
very well with me. (*Her voice becomes a whisper.*) I—
like—it—here!
PRUDENCE (*To* CHRISTOPHER): What shall I do? She's
standing where the witches stood. (*To* BETTY) Dost feel
all right? Truly, Betty?
BETTY (*Impatiently*): Yes, yes, yes! Prithee, let me alone!
CHRISTOPHER (*Taking a step toward* BETTY): Guard your
tongue! I'll not permit you to address your sister in that
manner.
PRUDENCE (*Laying a restraining hand on his sleeve*): Nay,
Christopher, don't scold her. She is not herself.
CHRISTOPHER: What's the matter with her? Truly I never
heard her speak so until this day. (BETTY *begins to run
about the stage, speaking softly.*)
BETTY: Swish!—Swish!—Swish!
CHRISTOPHER: What are you doing, Betty?
BETTY (*Continuing the action*): She says I must fly—Swish!
—Swish! (PARRIS *enters from right front, carrying paper,
ink, quill pens and a sand box. He stands watching and
gravely shaking his head.*)
PRUDENCE: Who does, Betty? Who makes you fly?
BETTY (*Pausing beside* PRUDENCE): She says I can stop now.
CHRISTOPHER: What does it all mean?
PRUDENCE: Sh! (*To* BETTY) Who, dear?

BETTY (*Leaning against* PRUDENCE): Don't *you* know?

PRUDENCE: No, little sister, try to tell me.

BETTY (*Rubbing her hands across her eyes*): She won't let me. I—I can't see her any more. (PARRIS *crosses to table and begins to arrange his writing materials at the four Magistrates' places.*)

CHRISTOPHER: Here's Mr. Parris now. What dost wish to ask him?

PRUDENCE (*Trying to free herself from* BETTY *who is clinging to her*): Oh—I would have—do let go a moment, dear—I would ask permission to sit here during the trial —near to Betty, d'ye see.

BETTY (*Hugging her*): You are the best of sisters—best of sisters—and I love you— (*Vehemently*) Don't ever forget that—not ever!

PRUDENCE: Ask him for me, Christopher. She won't let me go. (*Drawing* BETTY *down beside her on the bench*) Hush, dear. I know you love me. I love you, too. Here, rest your head against me. There! There!

CHRISTOPHER (*Crossing to* PARRIS): Good morning, sir.

PARRIS: Ah, good morning, Master Oakly.

CHRISTOPHER: Mistress Cantwell would ask permission that we sit near her sister during the trial.

PARRIS (*Looking at him quietly and then crossing to* PRUDENCE): Mistress Prudence, why dost wish to sit here —unless— (*Worried*) God send the witches have not been molesting you!

PRUDENCE: No, Mr. Parris. I just want to be near my sister, Betty. Mayhap I can comfort her a little—when the fits strike. I've always cared for her, you know, ever since our mother died of the plague when Betty was yet a babe. I believe she regardeth me more as mother than as sister.

PARRIS (*Rubbing his chin reflectively*): Hmm! If the justices, Mr. Hathorne and Mr. Corwin have no objection, you two may sit on the second bench. The first is for the afflicted children. But you must not speak to Betty or any of them when they are giving evidence!

PRUDENCE: I won't, sir. I will be silent, I promise.

PARRIS: And you, Master Oakly?

CHRISTOPHER: I will keep silence.

PARRIS: Very well, Master Oakly. This is a dreadful matter. Only these suffering children can point out the witches that are preying upon our people. Ah, the judges! (CHRISTOPHER *and* PRUDENCE *sit on the bench.* BETTY *climbs over and perches herself at the down-stage end of the front bench.* PARRIS *goes to right front entrance to meet and shake hands with the magistrates. They carry paper, rolled and tied. They take their places at the table during the next few speeches.*)

CHRISTOPHER (*To* PRUDENCE): Surely you don't believe all this about witches and witchcraft?

PRUDENCE (*Laying a hand on his*): Oh indeed, Chris. When you see the poor children, how they writhe and cry out in their affliction, you will understand. Much hath taken place here in the days you were in Boston.

CHRISTOPHER: Evidently. (PARRIS *has been talking quietly to the judges. They glance at* PRUDENCE *and* CHRISTOPHER *and nod.*)

HATHORNE: Prithee, have the remaining children brought hither, Mr. Parris. (PARRIS *bows and exits right front.*)

CORWIN (*Fussily*): Where are my notes? I must have them in order. God in His mercy grant the witches will all be discovered this day. (*Finding his notes*) Ah, here they are.

HATHORNE: Nine, the Negress said—nine evil creatures who have given themselves over to the snares of Satan.

Nine, free to turn their evil power loose on Salem Village.

CORWIN: But we have four of them.

HATHORNE: Aye, and I doubt not Goodwife Corey is the fifth. But four others— (*Shaking his head*) Well, our hope is in the children. If they cannot point out the other witches, no one can.

CORWIN: True! But it is pitiful to see them going through such agony to serve us.

CHRISTOPHER: Who are these "children"?

PRUDENCE (*Starting to tick them off on her fingers*): There's little Betty Parris and her cousin Abigail Williams. They were the first ones.

BETTY (*Interrupting*): And Ann Putnam—

CHRISTOPHER: But these *are* children—not twelve years old yet!

PRUDENCE: That's what I said. It's been woeful hard on Mr. Parris. He's preached so hard against wickedness of all kinds—and to have it start there in his own household! (PARRIS *enters right.*)

PARRIS: The sheriff is here with the afflicted children, your worships. (SHERIFF *enters right with* ANN PUTNAM *and* ABIGAIL WILLIAMS *who are about twelve years old, and* MARY WALCOTT *and* MERCY LEWES *who are fifteen and sixteen. They take their places on the front bench. The two older ones are apathetic, but the two younger girls are gay and lively, full of curiosity, giggling to each other as they cross the stage. At their entrance* BETTY *swings around to face* PRUDENCE *and* CHRISTOPHER.)

BETTY: Go away, Prue. Get out of here. (*Shaking her arm*) Go on, I prithee. Take her away, Christopher, please.

PRUDENCE: Why, dear? What is it? Do you feel ill?

BETTY (*Drawing away*): No—no—I'm all right—but you'd

better go. I—someone might do you harm. Oh, go away
quickly! (*At the end of her speech she is almost in tears.*)

CHRISTOPHER: Do you think we'd better?

PRUDENCE: Leave now? With Betty like this? I couldn't.
They won't let *her* go. And I can't go without her.

ANN (*Looking curiously at* MERCY LEWES): She's going
to have a fit in a minute. (*All the girls look at* MERCY
with interest. ABIGAIL *nods gravely several times.* BETTY
swings around to look.)

PRUDENCE (*Trying to keep* BETTY's *attention*): I'll be
right here if you need me, Betty. Don't you want to sit
back here with us?

BETTY (*She has completely lost interest in* PRUDENCE):
Oh, go away, do! (*She stands up to watch* MERCY *who is
moaning softly and rhythmically.*)

PARRIS (*Approaching* MERCY): Who is hurting you,
Mercy?

MERCY (*Stiffening and throwing hands to her throat.*
ABIGAIL *imitates her*): The dark man— (*Making choking noises*) the—dark—man is—choking me! (*She
slumps completely and is supported by* MARY WALCOTT
or she would sink to the floor.)

CHRISTOPHER: Good Heavens, the child hath fainted.

PRUDENCE: No, Christopher, she is fighting with Satan
himself. God help her to conquer!

PARRIS (*Warning them to silence*): What doth he look
like, Mercy? Hast ever seen him before?

ANN (*Suddenly*): A little yellow bird! Goody's little
yellow bird— (*Dodging and covering her eyes*) It wants
to pick my eyes out—no, no—go away!

BETTY (*Apparently striking at it vigorously*): Away! Away!
There, 'tis gone, Ann.

ABIGAIL (*Shrieking*): She bit me—look! (*Showing her wrist to the judges*)

HATHORNE: But these are the teeth marks of a child!

ANN (*Calmly. Her accusations are all the more terrible because of her matter-of-fact voice*): Goody's brat. There she goes with her mother's little yellow bird.

CORWIN: Doth she mean the Goodwin child? Lord have mercy on us—a child—not five years old!

HATHORNE (*Writing hastily*): But think of her mother— can you doubt her witchcraft? Sheriff, have someone seek out Goody Goodwin's daughter and arrest her. Here is the warrant. And bring in Goodwife Corey. (SHERIFF *exits right rear and* HATHORNE *leans toward* CORWIN) That makes six known to us. There are yet three more.

CHRISTOPHER (*To* PRUDENCE): This is horrible! It's un-believable! How did it all start?

PRUDENCE: Speak softly, Chris. The day you left, little Betty Parris had a fit of crying that she couldn't stop, and it was discovered that the Parrises' cook had been practicing witchcraft with these girls. The awful thing about it is that when she was examined, she told the court that she saw nine names in the devil's black book!

CHRISTOPHER: Nonsense! A frightened woman will say anything she thinks you want her to say!

PRUDENCE: But you don't know. The children have found some of the witches. Goody Goodwin and Goody Os-bourne were tried yesterday—

CHRISTOPHER: Goody Osbourne, that frail old woman! She is no witch, I dare be sworn.

PRUDENCE: But indeed she pinched the children most cruelly to keep them from betraying her.

BETTY (*Turning*): Buzz—buzz—What are you buzzing about?

ANN: They were talking of Betty Parris.

ABIGAIL: Betty Parris is sick. (*The entrance of* MARTHA COREY, *whom the* SHERIFF *leads to the minister's chair, interrupts them.* PARRIS *sits at left end of table. Girls grow quiet.* NOYES *enters and goes to right end of table.*)

CORWIN: Are we ready to begin the examination?

HATHORNE: I believe so. Reverend Noyes, will you say a few words of prayer that this court have the blessing of the Almighty?

NOYES (*Rising and removing his hat which he lays on the table*): Dread and mighty Lord, Thou knowest the evil that hath come over Salem Village. Thou knowest the frailty of these children who battle Satan, his snares, in our behalf. Grant them strength to carry their great burden. Clear their eyes that they may see and know the servants of the Devil who threaten us. If it be Thy will, grant that this court here in session may discover by the end of this day the identity of the nine whose names are inscribed in the black book of Satan, and whose souls are condemned to the everlasting fires of Hell. Amen.

MARTHA: Amen! Your worships, I would like to go to prayer also, with your permission.

HATHORNE: Mistress Corey, this court is not assembled to listen to you pray, but to examine into the witchcraft of which you are accused by these children. (MARTHA COREY *looks at the children who react wildly.* ABIGAIL *begins to howl like a dog and tries to get under the bench.* MERCY *stiffens and falls against* MARY *who is wailing and sucking her fingers.* ANN *puts her hands over her eyes and shrieks that she is being pinched and beaten.* BETTY *puts her wrist across her mouth and then begins to cry hysterically.*)

PRUDENCE: Don't cry, Betty. Please stop! Can't you do something, Christopher?

CHRISTOPHER: The child's hysterical. Move over, Prue. I think I can stop her. (CHRISTOPHER *slaps* BETTY *lightly on both cheeks.*) Stop it, do you hear me? Stop, this minute! (BETTY *sits perfectly still, her mouth a little open. Then she rises and, facing* CHRISTOPHER *and* PRUDENCE, *begins to back away from them slowly, her hand across her mouth.*)

HATHORNE (*Sternly, raising his voice*): Martha Corey, why do you afflict these children? (*At the sound of his voice,* BETTY *turns to look at* MARTHA)

MARTHA: I do not afflict them.

HATHORNE: Then who doth?

MARTHA: I am sure I don't know. How *should* I know? Such a thing would be impossible to me. I am a Gospel woman.

BETTY (*Flinging out a pointing hand toward* MARTHA *and shrieking*): She's a Gospel witch!

ANN (*Chanting loudly and monotonously*): Gospel witch! Gospel witch! (*The other children take up the chant which grows softer but continues under the next four speeches.*)

PRUDENCE (*Wiping her eyes*): What does it mean? Betty hath always been sweetly innocent. What hath brought this on her? Oh, Christopher, is it some sin of mine?

CHRISTOPHER: Of course not. Of course it isn't. You mustn't even think such a thing.

ANN: At my father's house I saw her—when Lieutenant Fuller was there at prayer. I saw her praying to the devil.

And Goodwife Nurse—I think—I am not sure it was Goodwife Nurse, but I think it was so—that's where her prayers were directed.

HATHORNE: Nurse! Did you say Goodwife Nurse? (*There is a sensation at the table.*)

CORWIN: Do you suppose—

NOYES: Another witch! The child has named another!

PARRIS: But Goodwife Nurse is bedridden most of the time.

MARY (*Whimpering*): She pincheth me. Let go of my cap! (*Snatching off her cap and thrusting it into the air*) Give me back my cap. Stop pulling my hair!

ABIGAIL (*With much interest*): Who's pulling your hair, Mary?

MARY: The old woman in a bed. She's gone now.

HATHORNE: So Goody Nurse *is* one of the loathsome band. She must be. Make out a warrant for her arrest, Mr. Parris.

MARTHA: Nay, we must not believe these distracted children.

BETTY (*Pointing a finger at* MARTHA): Gospel witch! Gospel witch! (*This is muttered.*)

PRUDENCE (*Laying her hand on* BETTY's *shoulder*): Betty— Betty, be quiet!

BETTY (*With a dark look over her shoulder, muttering still*): Who are you? I don't know you. Let me alone, *Devil!* (PRUDENCE *hides her face in her hands.*)

MARTHA (*Raising her voice*): I say we must not believe these distracted children.

HATHORNE: Distracted children! Distracted children d'ye say! Who, then, distracted them? Tell me that! Let all who have eyes look and see—

NOYES (*Turning toward* MARTHA): You are the only person here who says these children are distracted. It is the opinion of all here that they are *bewitched*.

MARTHA (*She lifts her hands and shakes her head. The children imitate her motions with great exaggeration*): It was not I, sirs. I swear I had no hand in it. (*She shifts her feet and the children imitate. All of her movements are imitated by the children. They thump their feet rhythmically. She bites her lips and the children do likewise and run to the magistrates' table.*)

MERCY: Look—look how she causeth my lips to bleed!

BETTY: My lips bleed—they bleed!

ABIGAIL: And mine—and mine!

CHRISTOPHER: What those girls need is a good whipping and to be sent home about their business. They bit their lips themselves.

PRUDENCE: But the witch maketh them to do it, don't you see?

CHRISTOPHER: No, I don't.

MARY: You'd better be quiet, Master Oakly. You may find yourself behind that chair. You're a dark man, and you just came from Boston, didn't you? (PRUDENCE *gasps in anger and dismay.*)

CHRISTOPHER: Certainly I just came back from Boston. What do you mean? (*But* MARY *has turned away. To* PRUDENCE) What does she mean?

PRUDENCE: Sh! The Parrises' cook, Tituba, told on her examination that she had been to Boston to a gathering of witches, and there she saw a dark man with the devil's book of names.

CHRISTOPHER: Nonsense. Tituba is a slave. How did she get to Boston in the first place?

PRUDENCE: She rode on a broomstick. (CHRISTOPHER

laughs.) No, don't laugh. 'Tis well known that is the method of travel used by evil spirits. (*The other children return to the bench.*)

HATHORNE: Martha Corey, cease to bite your lips.

MARTHA (*Leaning against the chair*): What harm is in it?

MERCY (*Clutching herself and shrieking*): She pierceth me. Make her stand up! (*Removing her slipper, she throws it at* MARTHA. *The* SHERIFF *picks it up and later returns it to* MERCY.)

HATHORNE: You will refrain from leaning against the chair, Mistress Corey. Sheriff, have you something to report of your visit to the Corey farm? (MARTHA *straightens up with a sigh, and the children quiet down to listen.*)

SHERIFF: Yes, your worship. Young Master Putnam and I went out to see her (*Indicating* MARTHA *with his thumb*) after Ann Putnam did accuse her. But first we went to ask the girl what clothes Goody Corey would be wearin' so's we could be sure Ann was seein' the right one.

ANN (*Standing up*): But Goody Corey, she came and blinded me. She said her name was Goody Corey. She said I wouldn't see her any more till night. Then she'd come and pay me off. (*Sits*)

SHERIFF: That's true, sir. We found Goody Corey all alone in her house. She came to meet us smilin', and the first words she spoke were, "I know what you ha' come for. You are come to talk with me about being a witch."

CORWIN: Ha! You see?

MARTHA: Which I am none! I cannot help people talking about me!

CORWIN: Be silent, woman!

SHERIFF: We told her it was an afflicted person did complain of her, and she asked quickly, "But does she tell you what clothes I have on?" (*The magistrates put their heads together for excited comment.*)

ANN: There, I told you. (BETTY *starts to tap her foot softly, one long beat and two short ones. The others gradually pick up the beat.*)

HATHORNE: Did she say ought else?

SHERIFF: Yes, sir. She told us she did not think there were any witches. And she said if the first three persons were, we could not blame the devil for making witches of them.

MARTHA: And so you couldn't. They were idle, slothful persons that minded nothing of good. But ye've no reason to think so of me. I have made a profession of Christ and rejoice to hear the word of God.

NOYES: Speak not too boldly, Martha Corey. 'Tis not an outward profession that will save you. It hath been so before now that the witches have crept into a church.

BETTY: Gospel witch! Gospel witch!

ANN: Look, look, the black man whispers in her ear! (MARY *turns and looks at* CHRISTOPHER.)

BETTY: Don't you hear it—the drum! The witches' drum! They're gathering. They're gathering for the feast of the black Sabbath!

PRUDENCE (*With a shudder*): No, oh no!

ABIGAIL (*Shrieking and waving her arm toward the back*): Out there! On the meeting house lawn! (*Laughing harshly*) They gather! They fly overhead on broomsticks! (*All the children pick up the foot beats, but softly.* MERCY *waves her arm overhead several times and says softly "Zzz-Zzz!" as though indicating the flight of several witches.*)

BETTY (*To* MARTHA): Don't you hear the drumbeat? Why don't you go, Gospel witch? Why don't you go, too?

MARY: See the little yellow bird suck between her fingers? Don't pinch me. Don't!

HATHORNE: Martha Corey, have you a familiar that sucks between your fingers in the shape of a yellow bird?

MARTHA: Of course not!

ABIGAIL (*On her feet*): Take away your book, Goody Corey. Take it away! 'Tis not God's book! 'Tis the devil's book, for ought I know. Take it away! I won't sign it! Take it away! (*She pushes for all she's worth.* BETTY *and* ANN *help her. This must seem real. All attention must be concentrated on the struggling girls.* MARTHA *does not move, but she looks completely astonished.*)

HATHORNE (*Rising and leaning across the table*): What book are you forcing upon these children?

MARTHA: None—no book at all. I know nothing of any book.

BETTY: Your name hath been in it for six years.

ANN: And you have four more to serve.

MARTHA: It is not true!

HATHORNE: Summon her husband, Giles Corey.

PARRIS (*Rising*): Giles Corey, if you are in this assemblage, come forward and be examined. (GILES COREY *enters from right front, preferably from the audience. He is somewhat stooped and looks older than he is. He is nervous and fumbles with his hat.*)

GILES: I—I be here, your worship, I be here.

HATHORNE: Have you noticed anything odd about your wife these past weeks? Tell the truth on your soul, Giles Corey.

GILES: Odd you said—odd? Last—last Saturday—in the evening it were, sitting by the fire—my wife asked me to go to bed. I—I—told her I would go to prayer— When I w-went to prayer, I could not—d'ye see—I could not utter my desires with any sense—any sense. My wife did perceive it and said she was coming to me. After this—after—I did according to my measure, make the—the prayer.

CHRISTOPHER: If he can't pray any better than he can talk, it's no wonder he had trouble. Even Hathorne is finding him hard to listen to.

PRUDENCE: Sh. (BETTY *is drooping, one hand against her forehead*) How is it with you, little sister?

BETTY: My head hurts.

PRUDENCE (*Standing behind* BETTY *and massaging her forehead gently*): Lean back against me, Betty. There, is that better?

MARY (*Muttering*): Black man from Boston. (PRUDENCE *pauses momentarily and then goes on rubbing* BETTY's *forehead.* BETTY *reaches for one of her sister's hands and draws it down against her cheek.*)

HATHORNE (*To* GILES): Is that all?

GILES: So please you, sir, I fetched an ox—last week it was—of a Thursday—a—an ox out of the woods about noon—he—he laying down in the yard. I went to raise him—to—to yoke him, but he dragged his hinder parts as if—as if he had been hip shot.

HATHORNE: Well, what then?

GILES: He did rise.

HATHORNE: I asked of your wife, not your ox.

GILES: Well there was a night—

HATHORNE: Yes?

GILES: She—I did find her on her knees by the hearth—

HATHORNE (*Impatiently*): Well—well—what was she doing? What did she say?

GILES: Why, nought. D'ye see—she was just kneeling there—all cold and quiet like—by the hearth.

HATHORNE: All right—all right! That's all. Take your seat, Giles Corey. (GILES *scurries from the stage throwing a fearful look at* MARTHA *over his shoulder as he passes her.*)

MARTHA: All this is nonsense!

MERCY: Hold her hands, she is pinching me! (*The other children take up the cry. The* SHERIFF *crosses to* MARTHA, *pulls her hands apart and draws them behind her. The cries of the children quiet down.*)

MARTHA (*Indignantly*): Those things of which you accuse me are false. You cannot prove me a witch.

CORWIN (*Impressively*): Neither can you prove that you are not one.

HATHORNE: Take her to prison and fasten her well with chains that she may not torment these children further. (*As the* SHERIFF *leads off* MARTHA *the girls become completely quiet.* PRUDENCE *sits.*)

CHRISTOPHER: They haven't any right to put her in prison. They didn't have the smallest particle of real evidence against her. She is no more a witch than you are.

PRUDENCE: I don't know what to think. Yesterday it all seemed so real, so dreadful. But you make me doubt the truth of these accusations.

CHRISTOPHER: It's still dreadful. Think of those helpless old women chained up in the jail. Have you ever been inside the jail? It's cold and wet among other things.

PRUDENCE (*Almost in a whisper*): I'm afraid, Chris. Can't we go home?

CHRISTOPHER: Yes. See, the magistrates are packing up their papers. Get Betty's attention, and we'll go.

PRUDENCE (*Taking* BETTY's *hand*): Come home now, Betty.

BETTY (*Snatching her hand away*): I'm not going. They need me here.

PRUDENCE: But the trial is over. Everybody is leaving. It's time to go home and get some rest and something to eat.

BETTY (*Her voice grows louder. The other children show interest*): Let me alone! I won't go! I won't eat it, I tell you.

PRUDENCE: Sh. Don't speak so loudly, Betty. You don't have to eat if you don't feel like it. But you must come home with us.

BETTY (*Backing away toward center stage*): Take your fingers out of my eyes! You're trying to blind me—witch! Black witch! (BETTY *covers her face with her hands. The magistrates begin to pay attention.*)

HATHORNE: Whom doth she accuse?

CORWIN: I think it is her own sister.

PARRIS: But that's unbelievable. Why her sister hath been like a mother to the child.

CHRISTOPHER (*Watching the magistrates*): Come on, Prudence. We must get out of here quickly, before they accuse you of witchcraft.

PRUDENCE: Accuse me? That's silly. Betty needs me. She's ill, don't you see? I can't leave her. Betty! (*The pleading in* PRUDENCE's *voice seems to reach* BETTY. *She comes toward her sister and tries to push her toward the left front exit.*)

BETTY (*Hoarsely*): Go on, sister. Go away while you can.

CORWIN: Here is the warrant for Goodwife Nurse. (*Handing it to the* SHERIFF *as he enters from rear right*) That

makes seven. There are still two more witches to seek
out.

HATHORNE: I think, mayhap, we have found the eighth
one. Give me a blank. (*As* CORWIN *hands him one,*
MARY *starts to laugh. She points a finger at* CHRIS.)

MARY: The black man! The black man from Boston!

CORWIN: Good Heavens! The two—the last two names!
(*He seizes another blank and begins to write feverishly.*)

NOYES: God hath delivered them into our hands.

BETTY: No, no, no! I didn't mean it, Prue, I didn't mean
it!

CHRISTOPHER (*Pushing* PRUDENCE *to the exit*): Come on,
there's no time to lose!

PRUDENCE: I can't—Betty!

BETTY: Go on—go on! (*Running to her*) Say you forgive
me, Prue. I didn't mean it.

PRUDENCE: Of course, dear. But I won't leave you. I'm
not a witch.

CHRISTOPHER (*Bitterly*): Can you prove you're not? You
heard the judge, didn't you? Come *on!* (*He drags her
out as the judges hand the papers to the rather bewildered* SHERIFF.)

HATHORNE: Arrest Prudence Cantwell and Christopher
Oakly on suspicion of witchcraft. Here are the warrants.

SHERIFF (*Looking for them*): I don't see them.

CORWIN: They just left—that way! Hurry! You can catch
them. (SHERIFF *starts out but is stopped by* BETTY.)

BETTY: Too late! She's mounted her broomstick and taken
him with her. Don't you hear them flying over the
meeting house? Abigail, you can hear them. They're
flying over us now—Abigail, tell him! Help me tell
him!

ABIGAIL (*Raising her arm and waving it toward the back*):

Zizz! They go—Zizz! Zizz! (SHERIFF *turns back toward* HATHORNE.)

SHERIFF: It's too late, sir. The children say they've made their escape on broomsticks.

HATHORNE (*Shrugging*): Ah well, we know who they are. Unless they flee the colony, we shall arrest them later.

NOYES: God be thanked, we have found them all—all nine whose names are inscribed in the book of Satan.

HATHORNE: You have forgotten those who met to frolic on the meeting house lawn.

CORWIN (*With a start*): I had forgotten them too. I fear me it will be a long time before peace comes again to Salem Village. (*They prepare to depart and finally leave front right, walking soberly down the aisle and out through the audience.*)

BETTY (*While the judges are gathering their papers, she touches* ABIGAIL *on the arm*): I thank you, Abigail, for helping me. (ABIGAIL *grins at her, looks at the judges and sees that they are not watching, then winks broadly. The children are lead out rear by* SHERIFF. MARY *is supporting* MERCY. ANN *is dancing along by herself.* BETTY *and* ABIGAIL *are hand in hand.* SHERIFF *pauses to speak to the people.*)

SHERIFF: Hear ye! Hear ye! Good people! Tomorrow being the twenty-second day of March in the year of our Lord, 1692, will appear before this court Goodwife Nurse, to answer to the accusation of the practice of witchcraft, brought against her by the afflicted children. (*He follows the children out.*)

THE END

Cry Witch

Characters: 7 male; 7 female.

Playing Time: 30 minutes.

Costumes: All of the characters wear traditional Puritan costumes. The Magistrates wear black clothing and white stock collars.

Properties: Paper, ink, quill pens and sand box for Parris, rolled and tied paper for magistrates, notes for Corwin.

Setting: The interior of the meeting house in Salem Village. Upstage center is a substantial table with two straight chairs behind it and one at either end. Right of the table the minister's chair has been placed, facing diagonally left front. This is the bar of justice behind which the culprits stand. Back of the table at far left is the pulpit, which has been pushed out of the way, and serves only as a reminder that this is a house of religious observance on Sunday. Left front are two benches, one behind the other. They are seats for the bewitched girls. There are entrances at right and left front, and another narrow door at upstage right. Note: This play can be produced without any front curtain. When the audience enters, the curtain can be up, and the stage set. The house lights could dim when the play is about to start, and then come up full again at end. If the play is produced without a curtain, characters can enter from the audience.

Lighting: No special effects.

Sticks and Stones

By Robert Downing

Characters

TOBY COLMAN, *a Sophomore*
ABBIE PRENTISS, *Senior Class Secretary*
BILL GRANT, *Senior Class President*
TOM VERNON ⎱ *Juniors*
JOAN MILLER ⎰
SALLY BOLTON ⎫
NEDRA DAWSON ⎬ *Seniors*
HELEN WALKER ⎭

SETTING: *The Dolly Madison Social Room at the James Madison High School.*

AT RISE: *Music blares from a phonograph. The tune and the arrangement are distinctly jazz. Pushing a mop around the edges of the room is* TOBY COLMAN. *TOBY'S shock of unruly hair tumbles from beneath the dust-cloth he has wound about his head like a turban. He executes a few neat steps, using the mop as his partner. The music comes to an abrupt, "sock" finish.* TOBY *bows low to the phonograph.*

TOBY: Thank you, maestro. (*To mop*) Say "thank you" to the boys in the band, Matilda. (*He punches the mop so that it "nods." Then he reverses the record on the turntable, and listens appreciatively to another "hot" tune as* ABBIE PRENTISS *enters. She carries an armful of record albums, and when she hears the jazz pouring from the phonograph, she stands still and glares at* TOBY. *He wiggles his fingers at her in a friendly wave.*) Hiya, honey.

ABBIE (*Her nose in the air*): Really!

TOBY: James Madison Senior High School welcomes you to another Jive Session in the good old Dolly Madison Social Room. (*A step toward* ABBIE) Would you care to cut a rug with me, beautiful?

ABBIE: Of all the nerve! (TOBY *shrugs, and turns back to his mop.* ABBIE *marches to the phonograph. She puts down her armful of albums on the cabinet, and shuts off the music.*)

TOBY: Hey! Don't do that! You want to ruin my mood for work?

ABBIE: I take it the dean told you to help get this room in order?

TOBY: You *take* it, sister—I've *got* it! (*He pushes the mop around the floor, not too vigorously.*)

ABBIE: I happen to be a senior . . .

TOBY: Congratulations! I hope to be one myself some day. (*He bows.*) Toby Colman, sophomore.

ABBIE: I also happen to be student chairman for special events in the Dolly Madison Social Room . . .

TOBY: Good for you, girl!

ABBIE: *And*—I am senior class secretary . . .

TOBY (*Looking very impressed*): All **this**—and *literate,* too! May I have your autograph? (*He steps forward, fishing for a pencil.*)

ABBIE (*Tossing her head*): Oh—what's the use? You're— you're *incorrigible!*

TOBY (*Gaily*): Sticks and stones may break my bones— but words will never hurt me! (ABBIE *removes the jazz record from the phonograph.*)

ABBIE: Now about this record . . . it doesn't belong in the Dolly Madison collection.

TOBY: You can say that again! That symphony of pep is right out of my private stock. .

ABBIE: Well, you can take it with you when you go. And don't bring it back! (ABBIE *tosses the record to* TOBY, *who makes a desperate, flying leap, catches the record in mid-air, and sprawls on the floor, holding the record tenderly.*)

TOBY: Aw, lady! Have a heart! (BILL GRANT, *wearing a large letter "M" on his sweater, enters. He stands in the door, grinning at the spectacle of* TOBY *on the floor.*)

BILL: Hiya, Abbie—what gives?

ABBIE: Hello, Bill. (*She indicates* TOBY *with disdain.*) This—this *person* has been playing *jazz* on the Dolly Madison phonograph!

BILL (*Tolerantly*): Is that right, Toby? (TOBY *rises, guarding his record carefully.*)

TOBY: Sure, Bill. I didn't know Dolly owned a phono- graph—did you? (*He winks at* BILL, *turns a blank face to* ABBIE.) By the way—what was it that *Edison* in- vented?

ABBIE: *Really!*

BILL: O.K., Toby. You'd better get busy with that mop.

TOBY (*With a smart salute for* BILL): Ay, ay, sir! (TOBY

carefully places his phonograph record on the seat of a chair. He starts mopping with vim.)

BILL: What can I do to help, Abbie?

ABBIE: As class president you're not expected to work, Bill. Thanks anyway.

BILL: How do you think I got to be senior class president? Honey—that was *real* work!

ABBIE: Sally and Nedra have gone to get the flowers. I sent a couple of Juniors for the folding chairs. You *could* help me re-arrange the furniture, Bill.

BILL: Glad to.

ABBIE: I thought it might be nice for the faculty to sit at this end of the room. (*Indicating the place*) We can put the folding chairs for the parents and guests over there. (*Indicating the opposite side of the room*)

BILL (*Crossing to sofa*): O.K. Grab the other end of this sofa, Toby.

TOBY (*Putting down the mop*): Ay, ay, sir! (BILL *and* TOBY *lift the sofa.*)

BILL (*Starting upstage with his end of the sofa*): O.K. How about over here under the portraits—is that O.K., Abbie?

ABBIE (*Vaguely, looking at the records*): Uh-huh . . . (BILL *and* TOBY *lower the sofa into position.* TOBY *suddenly emits a blood-curdling yell.*)

TOBY: Right on my toe! I'm crippled! I'm maimed for life! (TOBY *hops around, holding one foot.* ABBIE *looks at* TOBY *disdainfully.* BILL *grins at* TOBY, *shaking his head helplessly.*)

ABBIE: Bill—do you think Beethoven is appropriate for this afternoon?

BILL (*Goes to* ABBIE): I don't know. Don't you think he's a little heavy?

TOBY (*Limping in a circle*): Only about *two tons!* What's the score, Bill? Some long-hair deal in here this P.M.?

BILL: Annual presentation of the Scholarship Award to the best senior student.

TOBY: That's long-hair for sure! Who hits the jackpot this year?

BILL: That's top secret. Nobody knows the winner except the principal and the faculty award committee.

ABBIE (*With a cautious smile*): *And* a certain Abbie Prentiss!

BILL (*Turns to* ABBIE): What's this? How did *you* find out?

ABBIE: Oh, quite by accident, Bill. And I can tell you I'm a little bit peeved with the committee's choice!

BILL: Now, look here, Abbie. That Scholarship Award goes for merit—pure, simple, unadulterated *merit*. And you'd better not let on if you *do* know who's getting the prize.

ABBIE: Oh, I know, all right. It's that *revolting* Helen Walker!

BILL: Are you sure about that?

ABBIE: I overheard the principal calling Helen's father to make sure that Mr. Walker attends this afternoon. Though I can't see why anyone would want *him* at the presentation. Besides, I'm not sure Helen won the prize fair and square!

BILL: Hey, now! Nobody's ever questioned a Senior Scholarship Award.

ABBIE: I happen to know *my* grades were just as high as Helen's.

BILL: In that case, there'll be *two* prizes. You know that.

ABBIE: Then I'll *refuse* mine! I wouldn't stand up at the same affair with Helen Walker!

BILL: What have you got against Helen? (TOM VERNON *enters with some folding chairs. He is followed by* JOAN MILLER *who struggles valiantly with several folding chairs.* TOBY *hastens to help* JOAN *with the chairs.* TOM, JOAN *and* TOBY *carry the chairs to the far side of the room.*)

JOAN (*To* TOBY): Thanks, chum.

TOM (*To* ABBIE): Where do you want these chairs, Miss Prentiss?

TOBY: *Miss* Prentiss! Get *him!*

ABBIE (*With an airy wave of her hand*): Just put them down over there for the present. (TOM, JOAN *and* TOBY *stack the chairs.* ABBIE *turns to watch them.*) We'll need at least twenty more chairs!

JOAN: Come on, Tom. (*She slumps wearily to the door.*) On the double, buster. (TOM *and* JOAN *go out.* BILL *and* TOBY *arrange the furniture.* SALLY BOLTON *and* NEDRA DAWSON *enter with vases of flowers. One of the vases contains jonquils.*)

SALLY: Hi, Abbie! 'Lo, Bill!

BILL: Hello, Sally. Hi, Nedra.

NEDRA: Greetings! (*To* ABBIE, *holding up her vase of flowers*) Aren't these lovely, Abbie?

SALLY: They just arrived from the florist's.

NEDRA (*To* ABBIE): Where do you want 'em, hon?

ABBIE: Well, let's see. I think one vase will look very well here on the phonograph. This one. (*She takes* NEDRA'S *flowers.*) Sally—yours can go over on the table. (SALLY *places flowers.*) No. That's not quite right. Change 'em around. (NEDRA *and* SALLY *switch the vases.*)

NEDRA (*Looking at the two vases of flowers*): I hope they don't look too skimpy.

SALLY: Honey, these posies set the senior treasury back a pretty penny!

ABBIE: I'm kind of sorry we spent the money.

SALLY: Oh, you've got to have flowers.

NEDRA: The room would look absolutely *naked* without them!

TOBY: Please watch your language, Miss Dawson. There's a sophomore present! (*Elaborately, he puts his hands over his ears.*)

SALLY (*To* BILL, *indicating* TOBY): Hey, Bill—who's your comic relief?

BILL (*With a steady, warning look for* TOBY): A pretty smart sophomore who'd better watch his p's and q's if he knows what's good for him!

TOBY (*Salutes* BILL): Ay, ay, sir! (TOBY *whips off his dust-cloth turban and starts dusting the folding chairs.*)

ABBIE: Well—I guess we can't do anything else till they bring more chairs. (*To the others*) Collapse, friends, and breathe deeply! (NEDRA *and* SALLY *sit.* ABBIE *sits on* TOBY'S *record. She jumps up quickly, gathering up the broken pieces.*)

TOBY (*Rushing to* ABBIE): Now look what you've done! (*He grabs the pieces of the broken record.*)

ABBIE: I told you to get that record out of here.

TOBY (*Surveying the damage, sadly*): Oh, dear! My original, brand-new, second-hand, slightly-used, red, hot and blue, orchidaceous jam pot! (*He scowls at* ABBIE.) I hope you flunk your final exams! I hope you don't get to graduate! On second thought, I'd hate to stay around this school another semester with *you* here! I hope nobody dances with you at the Senior Prom! I hope—

BILL: Easy does it, Toby. Back to work, slave!

TOBY (*Mournfully dropping the ruined record into a wastebasket*): Goodbye! Goodbye forever! (*He begins dusting chairs again.*)

BILL: I'll help the kids with those chairs. (*Turns to* TOBY) Remember what I said, Colman. (TOBY *nods sadly.* BILL *goes.*)

SALLY: Explain your magic touch, Abbie. You've got our prexy jumping through hoops!

ABBIE (*A confident smile*): Just my fatal charm, girls! (TOBY *makes a face.*)

NEDRA (*To* ABBIE): Any scuttlebutt on who cops the prize this afternoon?

SALLY: Of course it'll be Abbie!

ABBIE: Fat chance!

SALLY: Don't be modest, chick.

ABBIE: Modesty, dear Sally, is not one of my virtues.

TOBY (*Muttering*): Name two others.

ABBIE (*Sharply*): What was that?

TOBY: I didn't say a word. (*Holds up the mop*) Did you say something, Matilda? (*He makes the mop shake its head.*) Sorry, Miss Prentiss. You must be hearin' things!

ABBIE (*Confidentially, to* SALLY *and* NEDRA): He doesn't know how right he is!

TOBY (*Softly*): Yes, I do!

ABBIE (*Leans forward to* NEDRA *and* SALLY): Girls, I've heard who's getting the Award today!

NEDRA: You didn't! (ABBIE *nods.*)

SALLY: Who?

NEDRA: It's *you*, Abbie! (ABBIE *shakes her head.*) Well— who is it, then?

SALLY: And how did you ever find out?

ABBIE: Well—I happened to overhear a phone conversation in the principal's office. (NEDRA *and* SALLY *ex-*

change looks.) Prepare yourselves for a shock, girls. The Senior Scholarship Award goes to none other than *dear* little Helen Walker!

NEDRA (*Recoiling*): Helen Walker!

SALLY (*Aghast*): Helen!

TOBY (*To the mop*): You know Helen Walker—the girl with *three heads!* (*The girls ignore* TOBY, *who goes back to work.*)

NEDRA: Abbie, you must be mistaken. Everybody knows *you're* the most *popular* girl in the Senior Class!

SALLY: And the best student!

ABBIE (*With a resigned sigh*): It seems not.

SALLY: But your grades, Abbie! You've been at the top all semester!

ABBIE: You know how they figure the Award. Deportment counts. *And* posture, *and* recitation delivery, *and*—good heavens, who knows *what* else?

NEDRA: But Helen's no better in all that than you are, Abbie.

ABBIE: Thank you, Nedra. Unfortunately, *you're* not on the faculty committee.

SALLY: It's a dirty trick, Abbie! It's real mean!

ABBIE: Oh, I don't mind not getting the prize—

TOBY: Not much! (*Receiving a quick glance from the girls,* TOBY *manages a terrific sneeze. He points apologetically to the flowers.*) It's the daffodils!

NEDRA (*Correcting* TOBY): Jonquils!

TOBY (*Backs away from the flowers*): Jonquils! No wonder! They're my special poison! (TOBY *whips out his handkerchief and ties it around his face like a hospital mask. He returns to dusting folding chairs.*)

ABBIE: As I was saying, it's not losing the prize that upsets me. Why, I'd be tickled pink to see one of you girls get it . . .

SALLY: With *my* grades? No such luck!

NEDRA: Same here.

ABBIE: I wouldn't care *who* got the prize—but I certainly hate to lose it to somebody like Helen!

NEDRA: I don't blame you!

ABBIE: It's just that Helen Walker isn't quite *my* dish of tea. (TOM *and* JOAN *stagger in with more chairs. With* TOBY's *help, they set them up.*)

SALLY: You can say that again!

ABBIE: I don't believe Helen has a decent dress to her name. Goodness knows *what* she'll wear today!

NEDRA: Can it possibly *matter?*

ABBIE: And Helen's father! I can just imagine what *he's* going to be like!

NEDRA: Is Mr. Walker coming? I thought he never got out of work till late at night.

ABBIE: The principal invited him. I heard the conversation myself. I heard every word the principal spoke into that phone!

TOBY (*To* TOM *and* JOAN, *indicating* ABBIE): Miss Listening Post of 1970! (TOM *and* JOAN *stifle giggles.*)

ABBIE: Like father, like daughter . . .

NEDRA: What do you mean by that, Abbie?

ABBIE (*Wisely*): You *know* what I mean! (NEDRA *shakes her head.* ABBIE *beckons the girls into a huddle.*) Listen to this! Helen Walker's father once served a *jail sentence!* (TOBY, TOM *and* JOAN *exchange looks.* TOBY *removes his handkerchief mask.*)

NEDRA (*Shocked*): No!

ABBIE: I ought to know. My father had to defend Mr. Walker.

SALLY: That's *ghastly!*

NEDRA: What had Mr. Walker done?

ABBIE (*Airily*): I can't remember all the sordid details—
(*A wave of her hand*) Disorderly conduct . . . something like that.

NEDRA: That's simply *awful!*

BILL (*Entering with chairs*): I think we've got enough
chairs now, Abbie—huh? (ABBIE *rises, turns to* BILL
with a smile.)

ABBIE: Why, Bill—you shouldn't be doing *menial* work
like that! (*She goes to* BILL, *then turns to* TOM.) Boy!
Take these chairs from Mr. Grant! (TOM *shoots* ABBIE
a grim glance. He crosses, takes the chairs from BILL.)

BILL: Thanks, Tom. (TOM *takes the chairs across the
room.* JOAN *and* TOBY *help* TOM *set up the chairs.*)

SALLY (*To* ABBIE): Does Bill know?

ABBIE: He knows.

BILL: Abbie—you didn't blab about Helen Walker?

ABBIE (*Taking* BILL'S *arm*): It doesn't matter, Bill. You
know—I think there's time for a Coke before the great
event. (*Smiles at* BILL) That is—if you have no other
plans, Mr. Grant.

BILL: Sure. Come on. (BILL *and* ABBIE *start for the door.*
NEDRA *and* SALLY *stand awkwardly in the center of
the room.* BILL *turns to them.*) C'mon, gals. I'm buying!
(*With a glance at* ABBIE) And there's nothing *private*
about this Coke-spree!

ABBIE (*Darts* BILL *a quick glance, then smiles sweetly at
the girls*): Yes—*do* join us, won't you?

NEDRA: You bet we will! (*She starts for the door*)

SALLY: Thanks a lot, Bill! (*She follows* NEDRA *to the door.*
BILL *and* ABBIE *go out.*)

NEDRA (*To* SALLY): Cokes with the Class President! Our stock's going up, hon!

SALLY: You're so *right,* Miss Dawson! (*They go out.*)

TOM: What's all this stuff about Helen Walker?

TOBY: Aw, they're just jealous!

TOM: But why? What are they ganging up on Helen for?

JOAN: She's not a bad egg, that Helen Walker. It wouldn't surprise me if she cops that Senior Award today.

TOM: Naw. Abbie Prentiss has got that prize sewed up for sure!

JOAN: I suppose so. (*She sighs.*) Them as has—*gits!* And Prentiss has got *puh-lenty!* What I wouldn't give for a figure like hers! (*She surveys her own shapeless form, ruefully.*)

TOBY (*Putting his hand on* JOAN's *shoulder with an old-fashioned, gallant gesture*): Never mind, Joan. I think you're solid! Really *solid!*

JOAN: That's my trouble! (*She shakes her head grimly.*)

TOM: I didn't know Helen's father was a jailbird.

JOAN: Yeah . . . how *about* that?

TOM: That's serious! (TOBY *hops onto the sofa. He sits there, cross-legged. He puts his hands first over his eyes, then over his ears, then over his mouth, repeating these moves rapidly.*)

JOAN: And that crack about Helen's clothes! That Prentiss is a real *gone* Lady Macbeth! We ought to pass the word about her.

TOM: And *how!* (JOAN *notices* TOBY's *antics on the sofa. She nudges* TOM.)

JOAN: What's with the sophomore?

TOM (*Peering at* TOBY): Oh-oh, Joan. This boy is telegraphing . . .

JOAN: To us?

TOM: Who else? (TOBY *grins. He nods. He repeats the gestures rapidly.*)

TOM (*Snaps his fingers*): I get it!

JOAN: Well, deal me in!

TOM (*Interpreting the gestures as* TOBY *continues them*): Hear no evil . . . (TOBY *grins. He nods. He puts his hands over his eyes.*) See no evil . . . (TOBY *smiles, nods. He places his hands over his mouth.*) Speak no evil. (TOBY *smiles extravagantly. He "shakes hands" above his head.*) He doesn't want us to spill what we heard in here just now.

JOAN: O.K., chum. We're mum!

TOM: Just the same—the Dean should know what kind of poison that Prentiss dame peddles! (TOBY *smiles ruefully, shaking his head.*)

JOAN: C'mon, Tom—let's go! I could use a Coke, too!

TOM: O.K. (JOAN *and* TOM *start for the door.* TOM *turns to* TOBY.) I know it's bad form for juniors to be seen imbibing Cokes with lower classmen, but would you care to join us at the Coke machine? (TOBY *grins appreciatively and nods.*)

JOAN: Let's go! (*They start for the door.* HELEN WALKER *enters. The trio pauses. They stare at* HELEN, *embarrassed.*)

HELEN (*Smiles at them, amiably*): Hello. I'm Helen Walker.

JOAN (*Gulps*): We *know.*

HELEN: I heard there was some work to be done here in the Dolly Madison Room. I hope I'm not too late to help out.

TOM (*Swallowing hard*): We—we just finished, Miss Walker.

HELEN (*Smiles at* TOM): Oh, for heaven's sake—call me Helen. (*To* JOAN) What's your name?

JOAN: I'm Joan Miller. This is Tom Vernon. We're Juniors.

HELEN: I'm glad to meet you. I've seen all of you in the corridors—now it's nice to know your names. And about time, too. (*She looks at* TOBY, *inquiringly.*)

TOBY: I'm Toby Colman. I'm only a sophomore.

HELEN: We were all sophomores once. Good to know you, Toby.

TOBY (*Pleased*): Likewise, I'm sure!

HELEN: Am I really too late to help out?

TOM: We've just finished.

JOAN: That—that's a lovely dress, Helen. (HELEN *looks at* JOAN, *surprised.*)

HELEN: Why—thank you, Joan.

TOM: Joan's dead right about that dress, Helen. I don't know when I've seen a prettier outfit!

HELEN: Now look. (*She smiles, bewildered*) This dress happens to be more than three years old.

TOM: You'd never know it. Would you, Joan?

JOAN (*Earnestly*): I should say not! I thought it was brand-new!

TOM: I—I understand you're one of the top seniors, Helen. I mean grades—and all that stuff!

JOAN: Everybody in the junior class knows that, Tom! Helen Walker's a straight "A" student from 'way back!

TOM (*To* HELEN): Do I envy *you!* I have a tough time making a bent "C" average.

JOAN (*To* TOM): We'd better shove off.

TOM: Right you are! Coming, Soph?

TOBY: I'll be along.

Tom: Look, Helen—whatever you hear—don't believe *half* of it!

Helen (*Mystified*): Whatever I hear? I don't understand.

Tom: Come what may—you stand by your dad! I know you will! You're O.K.

Joan (*Practically hurling* Tom *out the door*): Blabbermouth! (Tom *and* Joan *go.*)

Helen (*Looking after them*): Stand by Dad? (*She turns to* Toby) What are they talking about?

Toby (*Shrugging, he starts for the door*): Aw, they don't know themselves.

Helen: Wait a minute, Toby . . . you've got an honest face. Do you mind telling a girl the score around here?

Toby (*Scratching his head*): Well—as near as I can figure out—it's nothing to nothing, their favor.

Helen: Whose favor?

Toby: I don't know. Abbie Prentiss' favor, I guess.

Helen: Abbie Prentiss? What has she to do with this?

Toby: Nothing! Forget I mentioned her name, huh?

Helen: All right—but why was Joan going on like that about my dress? I wasn't born yesterday, Toby. This dress is anything but sharp.

Toby: On you it looks good.

Helen: And Tom—all that chatter about my grades. What does he mean?

Toby: He's been workin' too hard. (*He touches his forehead sympathetically*)

Helen: Why did Tom mention my father? Why shouldn't I stand by Dad? I always have. I always will.

Toby: That's the girl! (*Turns to the door*) And now— if you'll excuse me. (Helen *goes to* Toby. *She takes his hand, and leads him back into the room.*)

Helen: Please don't go. Not just yet. There are a few

things here that need clearing up—and I think you can
help me. Will you?

TOBY (*Squirms uncomfortably*): Well, . . . I don't know
if I can!

HELEN (*Sitting on sofa*): I think I need a friend. Are you
willing to be elected? (TOBY *reluctantly sits beside
her.*) Thank you, Toby. Now, what's this all about?

TOBY: It's kind of hard to explain.

HELEN: So I gather.

TOBY: Well . . . Prentiss was in here with some of her
friends—seniors, you know . . .

HELEN: I know.

TOBY: Prentiss found out who's going to get that Senior
Scholarship Award today . . .

HELEN: But *how?* That's practically a state secret!

TOBY: It doesn't matter *how!* She found out! And she's
not getting it! Well—she's kind of burned. *Kind* of?
She's *fryin'!*

HELEN: I can understand that.

TOBY: It's—it's *you!*

HELEN (*Incredulously*): *Me!* (TOBY *nods.*) Why, that's impossible, Toby! I never won a prize in my life!

TOBY: Well—you're going to today!

HELEN: The Senior Scholarship Award! (*Happily*) I never
dreamed.

TOBY: That's about all. (*He rises.*) I—well— (*He grins,
sheepishly*) Congratulations! (*Starts to go*)

HELEN (*Rises*): Thank you, Toby—but wait a minute,
if you don't mind . . . What about the rest of it? All
those other things Joan and Tom were talking about?

TOBY: Hot air! Nothin' but hot air!

HELEN: Toby—did they hear Abbie say something—
about *me?* (TOBY *nods, miserably.*) I see. About my

clothes. That explains Joan's compliments. Well, it was sweet of her just the same. But I still don't get that chatter of Tom's. Did Abbie say something else?

TOBY: Aw, Helen! She's just jealous because she's not going to get the prize!

HELEN: What about my father, Toby? What did they say about Dad?

TOBY (*Hedging*): I don't know, Helen . . . (*Upset*) Does it *really* matter?

HELEN: It matters very much to me. Dad's been through such a lot! He mustn't be hurt more.

TOBY: Sure. After all—he's paid his debt to society. (*He bites his lip, puts his hand quickly over his mouth.*)

HELEN: Paid his debt to—? (*Goes to* TOBY) Toby, what are you talking about?

TOBY (*Unhappily*): You've got me on an awful spot! Believe me, Helen, I don't care whether your Dad's been in jail or not! (HELEN *stares at* TOBY, *shocked.* TOBY *looks thoroughly miserable.*) Now I've gone and put my foot in it! (*Stamps foot furiously*) Glory be, Helen! A man can make a *mistake*! Your Dad served his time. What's past is past!

HELEN (*In a level voice*): My father never spent an hour in jail in his life.

TOBY: But I thought. . . .

HELEN: Dad was arrested once on a traffic charge. Abbie's father knows all about it, but Dad was cleared. He was completely cleared of any blame at all!

TOBY: Helen, you might as well know the rest. Abbie heard the principal inviting your father to come here today to see you get the prize.

HELEN: Good! I *want* Dad here! It's nice of the principal to call him. (*She stops, horrified.*) Oh, Toby!

TOBY: What's the matter?

HELEN: Now the whole school will be thinking that Dad committed a *crime!*

TOBY: But he *didn't!*

HELEN: Just *try* to tell people that after the gossip they've heard!

TOBY: Yeah. Besides there isn't time. (*Snaps fingers*) I've got it! I'll get on the school's public address system —you know . . . that intercom with the loudspeakers in every classroom! (*Grabs mop for an imaginary mike*) I'll open every channel! I'll be just like—like a *stationary Paul Revere!* Now hear this! Now hear this! Helen Walker's old man is *not* a jailbird! (TOBY *looks at* HELEN, *but she has turned away.*) No good, huh? Wrong approach, maybe? Fight fire with fire, huh? (*Grabs mop for another announcement*) Attention! (*Speaks very elegantly, rapping on the mop handle with his knuckles*) Attention! An enormously important announcement! No matter what you have heard to the contrary, Helen Walker's pater has never been in—in-*car*-cerated. He was ex—ex-*on*-er-ated in—in *toto!* As a matter of fact—Mr. Walker is one of our leading citizens. He is all wool, a yard wide—and true, true blue!

HELEN (*Turns to* TOBY, *tears in her eyes*): He is! Oh, Toby! Daddy's the most wonderful man in the world!

TOBY (*Puts mop aside*): Sure. That's what I said . . .

HELEN: When I think what he's been through these past few years—losing the business he worked a lifetime to build up—and losing it through no fault of his own.

TOBY: I didn't know that.

HELEN: We don't talk about our troubles, Toby. Dad

says when you've got a problem, the best thing to do is pitch right in and find the answer.

TOBY: That makes sense.

HELEN: We lost everything—our home—our savings—and then Mother died. Dad went to work to help me finish school. It wasn't easy for a man his age to get a job—but he got one. He got a job as a night watchman. And I went to work, too—part time, to help out. Dad says an education is the most important thing in the world!

TOBY: He sounds O.K. Now what's this traffic deal with the cops and Abbie's old man?

HELEN: At the corner of Main and Elm, another driver sideswiped our car. He said Dad was to blame. Plenty of people saw the accident. Dad was completely innocent—and they proved it! That's all there was to the whole thing, Toby. At the time, Abbie's father was good enough to stand by Dad. Now Abbie's turned this into something awful, just to hurt me! Well—she's done it. I hope she's satisfied!

TOBY: Don't let it throw you, Helen. Sticks and stones may break your bones—but words will never hurt you!

HELEN: One thing's certain—they're not going to hurt *Dad!* (*Starts for the door*)

TOBY (*Following, stops her*): Hey—wait! What are you going to do?

HELEN: I'm not going to accept that prize today!

TOBY: Sure you are.

HELEN: I won't let Dad come here with everyone believing Abbie's story! I've got to reach Dad before he leaves home.

Toby: Helen, you can't back out now. Why, this is the biggest honor you can get at Madison!

Helen: They can't make me go through with it. I'll quit school first.

Toby: But you *graduate* in a few days, Helen! Aw, look, Helen, don't let a few measly gossips spoil things for you and your dad.

Helen: Everything's spoiled now, anyway. I don't want to see any of them again. Not ever! I want to go home! (Helen *breaks for the door, but her exit is blocked by the rapid entrance of* Abbie, Sally *and* Nedra, *who are virtually propelled into the room by* Tom *and* Joan. Bill *follows them in.* Helen *turns away, covering her eyes with her hand.* Bill *goes to her.*)

Bill: Helen, it's me . . . Bill Grant.

Helen: Please go away!

Bill: We've got to have a little powwow with you, Helen.

Helen: No! (Helen *turns, ducks her head, runs for the door.* Bill *puts his hands on her shoulders, restraining her.*)

Bill: Shut that door, Vernon! Stand guard!

Tom: Yes, sir! (Tom *shuts the door. He and* Joan *stand with their backs to the door, their arms folded formidably. They glare at* Abbie, Sally *and* Nedra, *who are looking most uncomfortable.*)

Bill: Helen—I just found out a few things I don't like.

Helen (*Miserably*): So did I.

Bill (*To* Toby): Have you been talking out of turn?

Toby (*Quickly, seriously*): Yes, sir!

Bill: I'll tend to you later!

Toby (*Lowers his head, speaks in a small voice*): Yes, sir.

Helen (*To* Bill): It's not Toby's fault. I made him tell

me. (*Turns to* ABBIE) Abbie, how *could* you? (ABBIE *avoids* HELEN'S *eyes.*)

BILL: Joan and Tom told me the whole rotten story. I already knew some of it. I'm ashamed to say I didn't go to bat for you right away. (*He gives* ABBIE *a sour look*)

HELEN: Why should you?

BILL: I happen to be class president, Helen. I wear this "M" on my sweater. Those things mean something to me. I got to the bottom of this, Helen. I made a couple of phone calls. I think Abbie wants to tell you what I found out. (*He turns to* ABBIE.) Well, Abbie?

ABBIE (*Flaring*): I won't do it! I don't have to say a thing!

TOBY (*Grimly, to* ABBIE): That's exactly what you should have said in the first place! *Nothing!*

ABBIE (*Glares at* TOBY): I don't need any advice from *you!*

BILL (*Steadily*): All right, Abbie . . . Vernon—get the principal. Joan—call the dean. (TOM *and* JOAN *start out.*)

ABBIE: No! Wait! (BILL *signals to* TOM. TOM *and* JOAN *resume their positions at the door.*)

HELEN: Please, Bill! Don't go on with this scene! It's not that important.

BILL: I think it is. The honor of our whole class is involved, Helen. The honor of Madison High is involved, too. It's *got* to be cleared.

SALLY (*Stepping forward to* HELEN): Helen, I said some ugly things about you today. I'm ashamed, and I'm sorry. I don't expect you to accept my apology. I wouldn't if I were in your place. I hope I've learned my lesson.

HELEN: Thank you, Sally. (SALLY *turns away.* NEDRA *looks at* HELEN, *embarrassed.*)

NEDRA: The same goes for me, Helen. I didn't realize what a wicked thing gossip can be. I'm terribly sorry. I *mean* that.

HELEN: Thank you.

BILL: Well, Abbie?

ABBIE (*Looking at* HELEN): All right! I said some mean things, too. I suppose I'm sorry. Bill says I should be. I take it all back. Your father never spent a day in jail in his life!

BILL: I talked to Abbie's father on the phone, Helen. He explained everything. I know what your Dad has sacrificed to keep you in Madison. We'll be proud to see your father here this afternoon.

HELEN: Dad won't be here, Bill, and neither will I. I know all about the prize—but I won't accept it.

BILL: It's yours, Helen—fair and square. That's right, isn't it, Abbie?

ABBIE: Yes. Everything I said was a lie. I was jealous. I admit it . . .

HELEN: You can have the prize, Abbie. I don't want it.

ABBIE: While we're holding true confession hour, I may as well tell you that I said some vile things about your clothes, Helen. I'm sorry about that, too. (*To* BILL) Satisfied, Mr. Grant?

BILL: I'm not the one who has to be satisfied, Abbie.

ABBIE (*Flashing a look at* HELEN): All right, then! Are *you* satisfied? What else must I do? Crawl on my hands and knees?

TOBY: *That* I'd like to see!

BILL: *Shut up, Colman!* (TOBY *silently salutes* BILL.

BILL *turns to* ABBIE.) Have you anything else to say, Abbie?

HELEN (*To* BILL): I don't want Abbie's apologies. I don't want anything from any of you! I just want to go home!

BILL (*Looks at his watch*): It's almost three o'clock, Helen. In five minutes this room will be full of people. Your father will be here—

HELEN (*Miserably*): No! I—I can't go through with it.

BILL: In Madison's whole history a year has never passed without this Award being given. How can we explain it if you fail us now?

HELEN: I don't owe you a thing—any of you! I didn't ask for that prize! I won't accept it!

BILL: Then I'll have to make an announcement. Tell me what to say.

HELEN: I don't care what you say! Say anything you like! Say that Helen Walker couldn't take it! Tell them there comes a time when you can't lead with your chin any more! Say that I tried to believe it didn't matter I was poor—the poorest girl in school! Tell them I pretended for a long time that nobody really noticed my clothes were old and shabby! Say I was fool enough to think it was all right I had to work part time—and that I honestly believed my Dad is just as good a man today as when he had money and position! But I found out! And how do you think I felt? I longed for happiness, too. I wanted to join your clubs and go to the dances and be in the plays and have dates—just like the rest of you. But I couldn't. I didn't have money for all the extras it takes. I couldn't afford a new gown for a dance—or a new dress for a date. Only I didn't have dates. I had to work. Oh, I don't blame any of you for my troubles—but why do you have to make it tougher for me? Why spread gossip and lies? What have I done? What has my father done? Is poverty a crime? What happened to us could happen to any of you. You're just lucky—that's all! But think for a minute! Think, Abbie! What if *your* father lost everything tomorrow—everything in the world? Could *you* take it? Maybe *you* could! But *I* can't! I'm *through!* If that's what you want—you've got it! (*Starts for the door*) Here goes *nothing!* Here goes Helen Walker!

ABBIE (*Going to* HELEN): Helen—wait!

HELEN (*Tries to get past* TOM *at the door*): Please let me go. (BILL *signals* TOM *to stand firm.* HELEN *sinks into a chair, drops her head into her arms. Looks are exchanged.* ABBIE *keeps watching* HELEN.)

ABBIE: Bill—

BILL: Well, Abbie?

ABBIE: About that announcement—

BILL: What about it?

ABBIE: I'm class secretary, Bill. Will you let *me* make the announcement?

BILL: Why?

ABBIE: I'd like to tell the truth for once.

HELEN: You needn't bother, Abbie.

ABBIE: Listen to me, Helen. I've been a fool. Oh, I know that's not news to some people.

TOBY: You said it!

ABBIE: I've hurt you, Helen. I'm sorry.

HELEN: Never mind. It's over and done with.

ABBIE: Not for me. You've made me more than ashamed, Helen—you've made me put myself in the other person's place—in *your* place. And I feel so shabby . . . so humiliated.

HELEN: You don't have to parade your emotions for my sake, Abbie.

ABBIE: I'm not going to. I can't blot out my mistake that easily. But I can stand up here today and tell Helen Walker's story—and that's what I want to do.

HELEN: *My* story?

ABBIE: I want to tell about a girl who reached the top of her class by honest work and perseverance, despite all kinds of odds. I want to speak—with real pride—of a girl who wasn't ashamed to take a part-time job to help earn her education. I want to mention other things, too—your courage and patience—the loneliness and unhappiness some of *us* made you suffer. And I want to speak of a fine gentleman who happens to be your father, Helen. I want to say that we're grateful to this man who has unselfishly helped our school to acquire the one honor student whose record is the highest in Madison history—the very highest scholastic record ever to be achieved in this county—and in this state!

TOBY (*Leaps into the air*): Hoo-ray! (*Looks sheepishly at* BILL)

ABBIE: Those are the facts, Helen. I happen to know. I heard the principal tell your father.

HELEN (*Looks away*): That must have made Dad very happy . . .

ABBIE: He'll be here soon, Helen. Please don't let him down.

BILL: Is it O.K. now, Helen? You'll go through with it?

HELEN: I—I guess so, Bill.

TOBY: Rah! Rah! Rah! Three cheers for Helen! (*Jumps into the air, almost landing on* BILL's *toes*) Beg pardon, sir! (*Salutes, steps back, stumbles, nearly falls*)

BILL (*Looking at his watch*): Hey! It's almost time!

HELEN (*At* ABBIE'S *side*): Abbie, thank you.

ABBIE (*Not looking at* HELEN): Oh—I haven't made that speech *yet,* Helen.

HELEN (*Smiles at* ABBIE): Indeed you have! And you're not going to make it *again!* (ABBIE *turns to* HELEN.) Bill is our president, Abbie. Whatever speech needs making today—*he'll* do the honors. But I don't expect to hear a word of it, Abbie. I'll be hearing *your* speech. And I don't think Bill Grant can possibly be that eloquent. He'd be foolish to try. (HELEN *glances at* BILL, *who smiles and nods. The clock strikes three.* JOAN *takes a quick look out the door, turns to* BILL.)

JOAN: Hey, Prexy! There's a big mob out here waitin' to get in!

BILL: O.K., Joan. (*To* JOAN *and* TOM) Out the other door, you two! (JOAN *and* TOM *scurry for the other door.*)

TOM (*As he darts out*): Happy landings, Helen!

HELEN: Thanks, Tom!

JOAN (*Hurrying out*): Keep a stiff upper lip, you lovely upper classmen! And remember—seniors never cry! (JOAN *and* TOM *are gone.* BILL *looks at* TOBY *and jerks his thumb toward the door.* TOBY *nods. He offers* BILL *a snappy salute. Then* TOBY *goes to the vase of flowers, and picks up a handful of jonquils. He sneezes violently. Holding the flowers in one hand, at arm's length, and pinching his nostrils with the thumb and forefinger of his other hand,* TOBY *marches up to* ABBIE. *With a low bow, he presents* ABBIE *with the flowers. When he speaks, he continues to hold his nose.*)

TOBY: My compliments, madam. They do not do you justice—these daffodils— (*Sneezes, and continues, nasally, with difficulty*) I mean, *jonquils!* (*Another tre-*

mendous sneeze) But, sister—you *earned* 'em! (ABBIE *takes the flowers, smiles at* TOBY. TOBY *starts for the door, pauses by* HELEN.) Helen, you don't need any flowers. You've got a whole garden of posies—right here . . . (*He taps his heart.*) So long, Miss Dolly Madison Walker! (*Winks toward Madison's portrait on the wall*) Give the old boy my love! You're doin' him proud!

HELEN: Bless you, Toby. I won't forget you. (HELEN *gives* TOBY *a warm smile, which he returns. Completely flustered,* TOBY *turns toward the door. He trips over the mop. He staggers. He falls flat. Everyone laughs. Struggling to his feet,* TOBY *regards the mop soberly.*)

TOBY: Gosh, Matilda! I'm awfully sorry! (*He turns, grins sheepishly at the others.*) That's Toby Colman for you! What an exit! (TOBY *blows* HELEN *a kiss and runs out with mop.* BILL *goes to the main door.*)

BILL: Get set, gals. Here comes the thundering herd! (BILL *takes his place by the door.* NEDRA *and* SALLY *cross the room, and sit side by side in folding chairs.* HELEN *crosses to* ABBIE, *gives her her hand. Slowly the two walk to their places in the front row of folding chairs.* BILL *throws open the door, speaks toward corridor.*) Good afternoon, folks! On behalf of the Senior Class of Madison High, welcome. Won't you please come in? (*Smiling genially, he steps back.*)

THE END

Production Notes

Characters: 3 male, 5 female.
Playing Time: 30 minutes.
Costumes: Modern everyday dress. At rise, Toby has a dustcloth wound around his head. Bill wears a sweater with a large "M" on it. Helen should be dressed very simply.
Properties: Record, record albums, mop, folding chairs, two vases (one with jonquils), handkerchief for Toby, watch for Bill.
Setting: A pleasantly decorated room. There are two doors, one at right and one at left. On the upstage wall are portraits of James and Dolly Madison. There are a few pieces of furniture in the room—a sofa, two or three arm chairs, some low tables, lamps, a wastebasket, bookcases filled with books, and a phonograph.
Lighting: No special effects.

Minority of Millions

By Mildred Hark and Noel McQueen

Characters

MR. BROWN, *a high school principal*
MISS JANIS, *his secretary*
CARL SHEPHERD, *head of student committee*
KEN ⎫
GEORGE ⎪
BOB ⎪
SALLY ⎬ *members of the committee*
MARIE ⎪
DORIS ⎭
GLADYS ⎫
NANCY ⎬ *students*
BILL SWANSON, *the maintenance man*
MISS FLETCHER, *a teacher*
REDHEAD, *a student*
MISS HERBERT, *a teacher*
MR. SCHMIDT, *an alumnus*
RUTH, *Carl's girl*
8 GIRL STUDENTS
4 BOY STUDENTS
OTHER STUDENTS

Scene 1

Time: *A school day during Brotherhood Week. Just before 9 a.m.*

Before Rise: *The area in front of the curtain is set to represent* Mr. Brown's *office. At right, a large desk faces left. A little to the left of it, a smaller desk faces downstage. Both desks have chairs in back of them and telephones on them. The large one has some papers and books; the smaller one has a typewriter.* Miss Janis *enters left and sits down at the desk facing downstage. She starts to type as* Mr. Brown *enters right.*

Miss Janis: Good morning, Mr. Brown. You're early this morning.

Mr. Brown: Yes, you know we're having our Brotherhood Week Celebration today, and I'm having a final meeting with the committee before school opens. (*He sits at his desk.*)

Miss Janis: Oh, so the big secret is finally going to come out. All I know so far is that there is a dance tonight and that an alumnus, Mr. Schmidt, is going to speak to the students.

Mr. Brown: Well, at nine o'clock, I'm turning the management of the school over to the Brotherhood Committee for the entire day.

Miss Janis: Mr. Brown, whatever made you decide to do that?

Mr. Brown: I'll tell you. Carl Shepherd, head of the committee, came to me a few weeks ago. He was worried about the amount of prejudice in the student body, and said he thought Brotherhood Week would be a good time to try to get rid of it.

Miss Janis: It's worth a try.

OFFSTAGE VOICES (*Shouting*): Down with redheads! I don't like mustaches! I'm prejudiced against tall people!

MR. BROWN: It sounds as though they are in the corridor now! Will you have them come in, Miss Janis?

MISS JANIS (*Rising*): Yes, Mr. Brown. (*She goes off right. The boys and girls are heard laughing and talking offstage.*)

CARL (*Offstage*): Miss Janis, you are a secretary. You belong to a minority group. Boo! (CARL, KEN, GEORGE, BOB, SALLY, MARIE *and* DORIS *crowd in right and string out across the stage. Each one wears a badge with colored ribbons, and each one except* CARL *carries a sign on a stick.* MISS JANIS *follows, laughing, and takes her seat again.* CARL *stops near* MR. BROWN.) We're all set to go, Mr. Brown. And if the program we've worked out for today doesn't make the whole student body see how silly prejudice is, I don't know what will.

MR. BROWN: I know your main idea is good, Carl, and that you've planned certain penalties for various groups.

CARL: Right! Look at Sally's sign.

MISS JANIS (*Reading*): "Redheads are a minority group."

CARL: Now, turn the sign around, Sally. (*She does so.*)

MR. BROWN (*Reading*): "So redheads can't use the library today. Absolutely no admittance." (*Laughing*) Very good! Very good, indeed!

GEORGE: Boy, are we ever prejudiced against redheads!

BOB: And against girls with freckles. too. (*Holding up his sign, which reads, "We're prejudiced against girls with freckles." He turns sign around.*)

CARL: Yes, you see there's a penalty for girls with freckles. They can't dance with boys who are over five feet nine at the celebration tonight.

Mr. Brown: Very good! What's this? (*Reading* Doris' *sign*) "We're prejudiced against men with mustaches." (*He laughs.*) My, I'm glad I don't have one.

Miss Janis: Isn't Bill Swanson, our maintenance man, the only man around with a mustache?

Carl: That makes it all the better, Miss Janis. Don't you see? He's a minority group of one.

Mr. Brown (*Laughing*): Wait till Bill Swanson hears about this. (*Looking down line at other signs held by* George, Marie, *and* Ken) And I see you're prejudiced against girls with pony tails, and boys with striped ties— (*Then breaking off*) You've certainly worked it out well!

Carl: Maybe our stunt will have an effect on the whole community.

Mr. Brown: Carl, you and your committee have my final O.K. I herewith turn the school over to you for the day.

Carl: Thanks, Mr. Brown. Now, after the first bell rings we're going to station ourselves in the big entrance hall with our signs.

Bob (*Waving sign*): The monitors for the day. (*The bell rings off.*)

Carl: O.K., here we go! Don't forget, we're really prejudiced.

Boys *and* Girls (*As they start off*): We certainly are!

Carl: Remember, if a person belongs to a minority group, he has to pay the penalty.

Mr. Brown (*Laughing*): Good luck! I'll come out later and see how things are going—and find out if I belong to a minority group. Boys *and* Girls *exit, waving signs.* Mr. Brown *turns to* Miss Janis.) Well, Miss Janis, what do you think?

Miss Janis: I don't see how anything but good can come

of it. It's such a clever idea. (*The phone rings.* MISS JANIS *answers.*) Hello? Mr. Brown's office. . ... Who? Who is it? Oh, my goodness. (*Turning to* MR. BROWN) It's Mr. Schmidt, Mr. Brown. He's at the airport.

MR. BROWN: At the airport? (*He picks up his phone.*) Hello, hello, Mr. Schmidt. What's that? You decided to fly so you'd get here earlier? That's fine. We're delighted. . . . Yes. Do you want someone to meet you? . . . Oh, I see. That's fine. . . . Then we'll look forward to seeing you later. (*Hangs up.*)

MISS JANIS: What did he say?

MR. BROWN: He said he'd take the airport bus.

MISS JANIS: Is he coming right to the school?

MR. BROWN: No, he's going to his hotel first. Then he'll be over. I do hope everything goes well, because there's a fair chance Mr. Schmidt will donate some money for our new addition.

MISS JANIS: I think it's a good sign that he's decided to come early.

MR. BROWN: So do I.

MISS JANIS: It shows he's really interested. He'll have a chance to see more of the school and the students.

MR. BROWN: Yes, and also more of our special activities for today. I'm sure he'll be amused and *impressed* with them! (*The lights black out.* MISS JANIS *and* MR. BROWN *exit. The desks and chairs are moved offstage.*)

*   *   *   *   *

SCENE 2

TIME: *Later, the same day.*

SETTING: *The large entrance hall of the school. Doors at right lead to the library and outside; doors at left lead to other parts of the school. Upstage is a long table with seven chairs behind it. At the right end of the table is a large open carton, containing dunce caps and labels.*

AT RISE: CARL *sits at center behind the table.* GEORGE *stands on one side of him holding a sign which reads, "We're prejudiced against girls with pony tails."* MARIE, *on the other side, holds a sign which reads, "We don't like boys with striped ties." The other four signs are leaning against the wall upstage.* DORIS *and* KEN *have lined up three girls with pony tails, and* SALLY *and* BOB *three boys with striped ties. They stand a little downstage from table, the girls facing left and the boys facing right.*

CARL: We are prejudiced against all of you.

GEORGE *and* MARIE (*Waving signs*): Yes! Yes!

1ST GIRL (*Laughing*): But why?

CARL (*Pretending to be serious*): Young lady, this is no laughing matter.

2ND GIRL: Is it because we're a minority group?

CARL: No, in this case it seems it's because you belong to a majority group. We've had fifteen pony tails so far this morning, and I don't know how many striped ties. Too many girls wear pony tails and too many boys wear striped ties.

ALL MONITORS: And we're against them! We're against them!

CARL: You must pay the penalty! (MARIE *turns her sign around and the other side reads: "Wear a dunce cap."* GEORGE *turns his sign around and the other sign reads: "Wear a prejudice label."* DORIS *and* KEN *take labels from carton and put them around necks of the three girls. The labels read: "Pony tails, boo!" and have cords on them so they may be hung around the neck. SALLY and BOB take dunce caps from carton and place them on heads of the three boys. Printed on the dunce caps is: "Striped ties, boo!"*) Now, go to your classes. (*The three BOYS and three GIRLS laugh and start offstage just as three more STUDENTS, a BOY and two GIRLS, enter. The BOY has his coat collar turned up and holds it close to cover his tie.*)

BOY and GIRLS (*Pointing at students with dunce caps and labels*): Boo, boo, pony tails! Striped ties, boo, boo! (*They laugh and point again as students with dunce caps and labels exit. Then they start across stage toward library.*)

CARL (*Calling*): Oh, no, you don't! You with the turned-up collar! Just a minute! (BOY *with turned-up collar stops.*) Grab him, monitors. Don't let him get away. (BOB *takes* BOY's *arm and brings him in front of* CARL. *The two* GIRLS *stand watching and laughing.*)

BOB: I think we're prejudiced against you.

CARL: Yes, what are you concealing under your coat?

BOY (*Laughing. He opens coat and discloses brightly striped tie. Then innocently*): It's just my necktie.

CARL: Aha! Just your necktie, but it's striped! And we're prejudiced against stripes. Give him a dunce cap, Bob. (BOB *puts dunce cap on* BOY *who laughs and starts right. The two* GIRLS *watching point their fingers at him.*)

GIRLS: Boo, boo, we don't want to be seen with you! (*They laugh and rush off through library doorway.* BOY *laughs and follows them.* GEORGE *and* MARIE *stand their signs against the wall.*)

CARL: How are the dunce caps and labels holding out, gang?

KEN (*Peering into carton*): There are still a few left. You were certainly right, Carl, when you said girls with pony tails and boys with striped ties are majority groups.

DORIS: Can you be prejudiced against both majority and minority groups?

CARL: Of course, why not? We are. Besides, the sillier the reason for the prejudice, the better it makes our point. I, for one, think our stunt's going over well.

MARIE: So do I. Everybody's getting a kick out of it.

SALLY: They're all laughing their heads off.

CARL: What's more, they're laughing at prejudice. And that means they're beginning to see how ridiculous it is. (GLADYS *and* NANCY *enter downstage left.* GLADYS *wears a blue dress and giggles a lot.*)

GLADYS: Look at the signs, Nancy.

NANCY (*Pointing to sign*): Yes, look at that one. (*Reading*) "We're prejudiced against girls with freckles." (SALLY *goes to sign and holds it up, turning it around so girls can see penalty:* "They can't dance with boys over five feet nine tonight.")

GLADYS (*Giggling*): Oh, my, and look at the penalty. Girls with freckles can't dance with boys over five feet nine at the celebration tonight. My, I'm glad I haven't any freckles!

NANCY: So am I.

GLADYS: It wouldn't matter so much with you. Your boy friend is short. But if I had freckles, I couldn't dance with Phil at all tonight. He's over five feet nine. (*Pointing at another sign*) Oh, look, they're prejudiced against redheads, too. Well, I'm not a redhead, either. (*Smiling sweetly at* CARL) Carl, I'm so glad you're not prejudiced against me.

CARL: But we are. Hold up your sign, Ken. (KEN *picks up sign which is standing with the penalty side showing. It reads: "They can't use the study hall." He turns it around and it reads: "We don't like girls with blue dresses.")* You see? We don't like girls with blue dresses.

GLADYS: I thought all boys liked blue.

CARL: This school is prejudiced against girls with blue dresses.

KEN (*Turning sign again*): And you see what the penalty is. Girls with blue dresses can't use the study hall.

GLADYS: Well! (*Starts to giggle.*) Isn't that cute? Nancy, I think it's so funny! I didn't feel like studying anyhow. (*They exit giggling.*)

KEN (*Laughing as he puts sign against the wall*): Gladys is certainly pleased. (*He sits back of table and so does* SALLY. *From time to time other* MONITORS *sit down to rest a minute, depending on the business.*)

SALLY: Yes, the only thing that would have bothered her was if she couldn't dance with Phil tonight.

BOB: That's really a tough penalty—that one about the dance.

GEORGE: Say, I just happened to think—are any of these rules going to apply to us?

CARL: I don't know. I hadn't thought.

MARIE: What about your girl, Carl?

BOB: Yes, does Ruth have freckles? You're over five feet nine. So if she does, you can't dance with her tonight.

CARL: Of course Ruth doesn't have any freckles. She has a lily-white skin. Perfection! (*The door right opens, and* BILL SWANSON, *wearing overalls and carrying a tool kit, enters. He has a mustache.*) Oh, look who's here. Grab him, boys. (BOB *and* GEORGE, *laughing, each grab one of* BILL'S *arms and march him in front of* CARL. DORIS *holds up the sign reading: "We're prejudiced against men with mustaches.")*

BILL: Hey, you kids, what do you think you're doing?

CARL: Bill Swanson, you're in disgrace. You're not allowed in this building all day today.

ALL MONITORS (*Laughing*): Boo, mustache! Boo, mustache! (*They point at sign and then shout.*) Down with mustaches!

BILL: Down with mustaches? But I've always had a mustache, ever since I grew up.

CARL: That makes no difference. We're prejudiced against mustaches. That means we don't like them, and your penalty for wearing one is— (*He points to sign as* DORIS *turns it around.*)

BILL (*Reading*): "Not admitted to main school building."

CARL: You see, you can't come in.

BILL: But Miss Herbert called. She says the ventilator fan in her room is rattling. The boys and girls can't hear her.

CARL (*Laughing*): That makes no difference. That's what prejudices do—they inconvenience people. Miss Herbert will have to wait.

BILL (*Belligerently*): Who says so?

CARL: I say so, and I'm the boss. Mr. Brown has turned the management of the whole school over to us for the day.

BILL (*Relaxing and smiling a little*): Oh, I get it—it's all a big joke.

CARL (*More seriously*): Well, Bill, in a way it is a big joke, but there is a serious idea behind it. We are trying to show the boys and girls that it is foolish to be prejudiced against different kinds of people.

BILL: That's good. Then I agree, and I'll go by your laws.

(*He starts right, then he turns grinning*) But Miss Herbert will be awfully mad.

ALL MONITORS (*As he goes right*): Boo, mustache! Boo, mustache!

BILL (*He opens door and turns grinning*): I'll go to the shop and sit and read the paper all day. Boo to you, too. (*He dodges out, closing the door behind him.*)

CARL (*Laughing*): Good old Bill. He started to get burned up, but as soon as I explained it, he was O.K.

DORIS: Yes, and he got the last word on his way out. Boo to you, too. (*They all laugh.* DORIS *puts sign back against wall and sits down as* MISS FLETCHER *enters from library and starts toward left.*)

SALLY: There's Miss Fletcher, and look what she's wearing. (KEN *rises and picks up "blue dress" sign and holds it.*)

CARL (*Calling*): Miss Fletcher, where are you going?

MISS FLETCHER (*Turning toward* CARL, *crossly*): I'm going to the study hall. I'm in charge there this period. (KEN *turns sign around so penalty shows, "They can't use the study hall."*)

BOB (*As he and* GEORGE *go and stand in doorway upstage left leading to study hall*): Oh, no, you're not, Miss Fletcher.

MISS FLETCHER (*Looking at boys in doorway*): Whatever do you mean?

CARL: He's right, Miss Fletcher. You're not allowed in there today. (KEN *turns sign around again.*)

MISS FLETCHER: But this is ridiculous. (*Looking at sign*) Girls with blue dresses. I repeat, it's ridiculous. And besides, I'm not a girl. I'm a woman. I've been teaching in this school for twenty-five years. (KEN *waves sign.*)

CARL (*Laughing*): In our book, you're a girl, Miss

Fletcher. And you're wearing blue. (*Motioning toward sign as* KEN *turns it again.*) No study hall today.

MISS FLETCHER: Carl Shepherd, I don't know what Mr. Brown is thinking of to allow you to behave in this high-handed manner. At the next faculty meeting I'm going to complain. (*She starts back toward library sputtering, then turns.*) You haven't heard the last of this! (*She goes off.*)

MARIE (*Laughing as* KEN *puts sign back against wall*): Poor Miss Fletcher. I think she's prejudiced against us.

CARL: Yes, that's the first sour note we've had. She's plenty mad all right. (REDHEAD *enters downstage left and starts diagonally across the library.*) Just a minute, young lady. Where do you think you're going?

REDHEAD: To the library. (SALLY *picks up sign reading:* "*Redheads are a minority group.*")

CARL: But young lady, don't you realize you belong to a minority group?

REDHEAD: Oh, Carl, what is all this? I'm in a hurry.

CARL: I'm sorry, but it's against the law for redheads to go into the library. (SALLY *turns the sign and it reads:* "*Redheads can't use the library today.*")

REDHEAD: But I simply have to go into the library. I have a theme due next week, and I have to work on it. All the books I need are in the library.

CARL: Sorry, but we're prejudiced against redheads.

REDHEAD: I think it's the meanest thing I ever heard of— just because I happen to have red hair.

CARL: Yes, that's the trouble with prejudices—they are unfair.

MONITORS: Boo, redhead!

REDHEAD: Don't you point the finger of scorn at me! (*She dashes off.*)

CARL: Now we're pointing the finger of scorn. (SALLY *puts "redhead" sign against wall.*)

MISS HERBERT (*Rushes on upstage left*): Carl Shepherd, you listen to me.

CARL: Yes, Miss Herbert.

MISS HERBERT: I called Bill Swanson again and told him to come over and fix the ventilating fan in my room. He says you won't let him in.

CARL: That's right, Miss Herbert. You see, he has a mustache. (DORIS *gets "mustache" sign and holds it up.*)

MISS HERBERT: Mustache or no mustache, I'm going to have my fan fixed. I'm going straight to Mr. Brown. (*She rushes off downstage left.*)

SALLY: That's three we've made mad in a row. Better take it easy, Carl.

CARL: But we can't take it easy. We're committed. (*The door opens right, and* MR. SCHMIDT *enters and stands looking around.*)

KEN (*Going toward him*): Good morning, sir.

MR. SCHMIDT: Good morning.

KEN: I'm sorry, sir, but you can't come in here.

MR. SCHMIDT: What? (*Stepping toward stage center*)

CARL: He's right, sir. You can't come in because you are wearing a mustache, and we are prejudiced against mustaches. (DORIS *holds sign high, then turns it around to show penalty as* CARL *goes on.*) The penalty is no admittance to this building.

MR. SCHMIDT: But I never heard of such a thing!

CARL (*Smiling*): Oh, we're prejudiced against all sorts of things. See the signs. (*Turning and pointing at them*) Redheads, freckles, blue dresses, striped ties—

MR. SCHMIDT: Yes, I see. So I am banned from here even

though I have an appointment with your principal, all because of your silly prejudices.

CARL: But that's the point. The whole idea of our stunt is to show how ridiculous *all* prejudices are.

MONITORS: Boo, mustaches! Boo, mustaches!

MR. SCHMIDT (*Stands frowning for a moment, then bows stiffly to* CARL): Very well, then. I shall go. (*He walks quickly to door right and out.*)

SALLY: Maybe we shouldn't have booed at him.

RUTH (*Rushes on downstage left and straight to* CARL): Carl Shepherd, you're a snake in the grass.

CARL: Well, hello, Ruth, now what have I done?

RUTH: Don't hello me. You know very well what you've done. You planned this whole thing so that I wouldn't be able to dance with you tonight.

CARL: What are you talking about? Of course I'm going to dance with you tonight.

RUTH: No, you're not—look. (*Pointing at her nose*)

CARL: Oh, my gosh, freckles! But you didn't have them yesterday!

RUTH: Of course, I didn't. I only get them when I stay out in the sun too long. And who took me out walking in the sun yesterday? You did, and then you cooked up this whole business. Now you'll spend the whole evening dancing with May Wilson.

CARL: But Ruth—

RUTH: No. I don't ever want to speak to you again—ever! (*She rushes off left.*)

CARL: That's one prejudice that certainly backfired.

DORIS (*Putting her sign back against wall*): Yes, and everything seems to be going wrong. Everyone is getting mad.

MR. BROWN (*Enters downstage left*): Well, boys and girls, how does it go?

CARL: Oh, not so good right now, Mr. Brown. We started out all right. Everyone seemed to get the idea. But now my best girl is mad at me, and one redhead had fits because we wouldn't let her go to the library.

MARIE: And Miss Fletcher is angry, and so is Miss Herbert.

MR. BROWN (*Laughing*): Yes, I know. I had rather a time calming down Miss Herbert.

KEN: And some man came to see you and didn't like it when we wouldn't let him come in.

MR. BROWN: Wanted to see me? When was this?

CARL: Just a little while ago. He seemed quite upset, too. But we couldn't let him in because he had a mustache.

MR. BROWN (*Worriedly*): A mustache? I didn't know he had a mustache, but what did he look like otherwise?

CARL: Oh, a little gray-haired man with glasses. In his fifties, I guess.

MR. BROWN: Gray-haired, with glasses, and about fifty. That must have been Mr. Schmidt.

CARL: Mr. Schmidt? But he wasn't coming until this evening, in time to make the speech at the celebration.

MR. BROWN: No, no, he called earlier this morning. He came by plane. Carl Shepherd, do you realize what you've done? You've turned away the man who might have donated a new addition for our school. Now, he'll be furious.

CARL: But Mr. Brown, he had a mustache. It was the rule.

MR. BROWN: Rule or no rule, you shouldn't have done it. Maybe I can catch him and explain. I have to. (*He rushes out right.*)

KEN: I don't know why he blames us.

SALLY: We're certainly in plenty of hot water now, though.

BOB: The teachers are mad at us. Mr. Brown is mad at us.

MARIE: The students are getting mad at us.

DORIS: And Mr. Schmidt won't give his speech tonight. Everything is ruined.

GEORGE: Yes, I'm beginning to think this whole idea was a bad one.

CARL: Now, wait a minute, all of you— (RUTH *and three other* GIRLS *with freckles enter downstage left looking determined and angry.*)

RUTH: Carl Shepherd, we all have freckles, and we don't like your silly rule for the dance tonight.

CARL: Ruth, I thought you didn't want to speak to me again.

RUTH: I don't want to. I'm not even coming to the dance tonight. I'm just doing this to help the others.

1ST GIRL: Yes, we wanted her to be part of the delegation. We're a committee of four come to protest.

CARL: It's no use protesting—everyone else is obeying the rules.

2ND GIRL: Oh, no, they're not. They're not going to any longer. Everyone's getting mad. The whole student body is angry.

CARL: I don't believe it. They're all better sports than that.

OFFSTAGE VOICES: We don't like Carl Shepherd! We don't like Carl Shepherd!

3RD GIRL: Maybe you'll believe it now. It's another group come to protest. (*A large group of* BOYS *and* GIRLS *enter. Some have dunce caps, some pony tails and signs, some blue dresses, and one or two have red hair. It can include all the boys and girls who have been onstage and as many others as are desired. Others may enter during next lines.*)

BOYS *and* GIRLS: Down with goofy rules. Let's get back to normal! (*Etc.*)

CARL (*Standing and shouting*): Now, wait a minute, wait a minute. This all started out to be a lot of fun, and I thought you'd take the day as good sports, in the spirit in which it was meant.

STUDENTS (*From crowd*): No, no! Down with goofy rules!

MR. BROWN (*Enters right excitedly*): I didn't see a sign of Mr. Schmidt. I'll have to phone the hotel. But I suppose it's too late. He may have been so angry, he went right to the airport. He's probably left town. (*He starts left a little and sees the crowd.*) Why, what's going on here?

STUDENTS: We don't like all these rules. Tell Carl to abolish his day.

MR. BROWN: I'm beginning to wonder if things haven't gone too far. In fact, I know they have. (MR. SCHMIDT *enters quietly right. He has no mustache, and he stands near door watching.*) Carl, I think—

CARL: All right, Mr. Brown, I guess my day is a failure, but I just want to say this. Real prejudice is a serious thing. We've had some instances of real prejudice in this school that have caused great unhappiness. My committee and I thought if we could bring prejudice out into the open and show it up for what it was, we might go a long way toward solving the problem. But I'm disappointed in all of you. You didn't cooperate.

GIRL: But your rules were unreasonable.

CARL: *All* prejudices are unreasonable. We thought we could show this by making up some ridiculous prejudices that would fit most of us. You've been poor sports. Instead of entering into the spirit of the day and doing some real thinking about how ridiculous *any* form of prejudice is, you've all just thought of yourselves and the slight inconvenience you've suffered.

BOY: I still say some of the rules weren't fair—

CARL: Prejudice is never fair, and that's what we were trying to prove. Well, if this day has done nothing else, it shows none of you like being the target of prejudice, not even a silly one that's all in fun. And not even for one day.

STUDENTS: He has a point there. He's right. (*Etc.*)

CARL: So let's try and realize how people who are really the victims of prejudice must feel.

MR. SCHMIDT (*Clapping his hands*): Bravo! Bravo! (*Everyone turns and stares at him. Smiling*): May I come in now? All the way? I no longer have a mustache.

CARL: Mr. Schmidt! You are Mr. Schmidt, of course. (MR. BROWN *rushes right.*)

MR. BROWN: Mr. Schmidt, we can't tell you how sorry we are. I apologize for everything.

MR. SCHMIDT: No need to apologize.

MR. BROWN: I know how inconvenienced you've been. I went out looking for you. I thought you'd gone back to the airport.

MR. SCHMIDT: No, I ducked into that little barber shop down the street to get my mustache shaved off.

MR. BROWN: But Mr. Schmidt, that wasn't necessary.

MR. SCHMIDT: Well, it seemed to be. No admittance for men with mustaches, and I wanted to get back in here and see more of this wonderful stunt your students are putting on.

CARL: Mr. Schmidt, you mean you weren't angry at being put out?

MR. SCHMIDT: Well, young man, I was a little startled. At first I didn't quite get the idea. But then I did, and I couldn't believe it was true. When I was a little boy, no one ever mentioned that there was such a thing as prejudice. It was just there.

CARL: That's still true sometimes, Mr. Schmidt. Why, often people who are prejudiced against others don't even realize that they are.

MR. SCHMIDT: They need to see prejudice in its true light. Why, I couldn't believe, Mr. Brown, that this student body of yours was making an attempt to bring it out into the open and solve the problem. I know I'm going to make a speech later on, but does anyone mind if I tell a little story right now?

MR. BROWN: Why, we'd be delighted, Mr. Schmidt. Of course, of course.

STUDENTS: Go ahead, Mr. Schmidt. (*Applause*) We're listening. (*Etc.*)

MR. SCHMIDT (*Stepping forward a little*): This is a true story about a boy who went to school right here in this building. It happened long ago, during the Second World War. This boy suddenly found that he could no longer have a good time with his schoolmates. They booed at him and hooted at him—and do you know why? It was all because of his name.

STUDENTS: His name? But what was his name?

MR. SCHMIDT: His name was Schmidt.

CARL: You mean you were the boy, Mr. Schmidt?

MR. SCHMIDT: Yes, I was the target of prejudice because my name was Schmidt, and you see, Schmidt is a German name.

CARL: But what difference did that make?

MR. SCHMIDT: At that time a lot of difference because we were at war with Germany, and everything German was supposed to be bad.

STUDENTS: But that wasn't fair. You were in America. (*Etc.*)

MR. SCHMIDT: Yes, we were, and we didn't think it was fair either. We thought of ourselves as Americans, and we'd always tried to be good ones. My father joined the National Guard, and my mother knitted socks for the soldiers, but still, because our name was German, it was bad.

MR. BROWN: To think that that happened here in this community.

MR. SCHMIDT: Yes, here, and in many other communities. (*He smiles.*) But I suppose I should have taken consolation in the fact that people were even prejudiced against something—well, something as American as apple pie.

STUDENTS: As American as apple pie?

MR. SCHMIDT: Yes, and today you can't drive anywhere in this great country of ours without seeing its name emblazoned in electric lights. Each one of you students has eaten it many times.

CARL: Eaten it? But what was it, Mr. Schmidt?

MR. SCHMIDT: I'll tell you what it was. It was hamburger.

STUDENTS: Hamburger? I don't believe it. (*Etc.*)

MR. SCHMIDT: I'm not surprised that you don't believe it, but it's true. Just because hamburger was a German word, people were prejudiced against it, and for years we had to call it Salisbury steak.

STUDENTS (*Laughter*): Salisbury steak. Give me two Salisbury steaks with mustard. (*Etc.*)

MR. SCHMIDT: Yes, it sounds silly, doesn't it? It doesn't make sense. But that's the sort of thing prejudice will do to otherwise normal people. That's why when I saw what was going on here, I knew it was good. The students of this school are showing how stupid prejudice is by bringing it out into the light of day. You are doing a service to the brotherhood of man. I say, more power to you! Now I've talked enough. Tonight I'll have something to say that I'm sure will please you all, but for now, get on with your day. (*All applaud.*)

STUDENTS: Yes, let's keep on with the day. We're back of you, Carl. We'll all cooperate.

CARL: Wait a minute, all of you. I have a feeling that we've pretty thoroughly made our point and that Mr. Schmidt has brought it to a fitting climax. He has told us of a real prejudice just as silly as any we made up, and I don't think we can top it. Let's stop our program right now, and just remember to try to avoid prejudice in school and out.

MR. BROWN: Carl, maybe that's a good idea.

MR. SCHMIDT (*Laughing a little*): You mean there are no minority groups? Not even men with mustaches?

CARL (*Laughing*): I guess that's right.

MR. SCHMIDT: I must admit I'm going to grow another mustache, but I don't think I'll be able to do it by tonight.

CARL: That's O.K. We like you—with or without. (*Turning to* STUDENTS) And I, for one, think Mr. Schmidt deserves a rousing good cheer from all of us.

STUDENTS (*Ad lib*): So do I. Come on, gang. (BOY *leads in cheer.*) Yea, Schmidt! Yea, Schmidt! He's all right! Who says so? We do! Yea, Schmidt! (*There is a big cheer.* RUTH *steps forward from group.*)

RUTH: Carl—Carl—

CARL (*Turning*): Hi, Ruth.

RUTH: I just have to know. Do you really mean there

won't be any prejudices at the celebration tonight? Not even against girls with freckles?

CARL: Well, I don't know. I, for one, am prejudiced—

RUTH: Carl!

CARL (*Taking her hand*): In *favor* of girls with freckles! (*Laughter and quick curtain*)

THE END

Production Notes

Minority of Millions

Characters: 11 male; 18 female; male or female extras as desired.

Playing Time: 25 minutes.

Costumes: Everyday school clothes for boys and girls. Mr. Brown and Mr. Schmidt wear business suits. Mr. Schmidt has a mustache. Miss Janis and Miss Herbert wear dresses or suits. Miss Fletcher wears a blue dress. Bill Swanson wears overalls and has a mustache. Three boys wear striped ties. One boy wears striped tie and a coat with the collar turned up. Three girls wear pony tails. Gladys wears a blue dress. One girl has red hair. Ruth and three other girls have freckles. Extra students wear dunce caps and striped ties, pony tails and signs or blue dresses; some have red hair.

Properties: Six signs, painted on both sides, reading, "We don't like boys with striped ties" and "Wear a dunce cap"; "We're prejudiced against girls with pony tails" and "Wear a prejudice label"; "We're prejudiced against girls with freckles" and "They can't dance with boys over five feet nine tonight"; "Redheads are a minority group" and "So redheads can't use the library today. Absolutely no admittance"; "We don't like girls with blue dresses" and "They can't use the study hall"; "We're prejudiced against men with mustaches" and "Not admitted to main school building." Four dunce caps, reading, "Striped ties, boo!" and three labels, reading, "Pony tails, boo!" Extra labels and dunce caps,

for extra students. Tool kit, for Bill Swanson.
Setting: Scene 1, before curtain, is in Mr. Brown's office.
At right, a large desk faces left. A little to the left of it,
a smaller desk faces downstage. Both desks have chairs
in back of them and telephones on them. The large
one has some papers and books; the smaller one has
a typewriter. Scene 2 is in the main hallway of the
school. Doors at right lead to the library and outside;
doors at left lead to other parts of the school. Upstage
is a long table with seven chairs behind it. At the right
end of the table is a large open carton, which contains
dunce caps and labels.
Lighting: Lights should black out at end of Scene 1.

Anyone for the Moon?

By Elinor R. Alderman

Characters

THEODORIC, *president of the Moon*
CELESTINE, *his teen-age daughter*
CECIL ⎫
NIKKI ⎰ *stowaways*
HEBE, *the president's secretary*
A GIRL FROM PHOBOS
A BOY FROM DEIMOS
SAM ⎫
JOE ⎰ *ring workers*
A VISITOR
WORKERS, *from the cheese mines*

SCENE 1

TIME: *The immediate future.*
SETTING: *Theodoric's office. There is a globe of the world and, hanging on the wall, a large drawing of a man, labelled "Earth Specimen."*
AT RISE: CELESTINE *is sitting on a chair playing "cat's*

cradle" with a piece of rope tinsel. HEBE *sits at her desk, working on a sheaf of papers.* THEODORIC *stands downstage, studying the globe alternately with a large catalogue he holds.* CELESTINE, *trying to loop the tinsel over her fingers, pulls too hard and the tinsel breaks.*

CELESTINE: Oh, Comets! (*She holds up the tinsel.*) Just look at that, Father. Honestly, I think the quality of stardust these days is disgraceful. (*Starts tying tinsel together*)

THEODORIC (*Absorbed, thumbing his catalogue*): Mmm? What's that, dear? (*He looks at her.*) Oh, yes, dear— very pretty. Oh, Hebe?

HEBE: Yes, sir?

THEODORIC: Is that young visitor from Phobos still waiting?

HEBE (*Rising*): Yes, she is, Mr. President. And another one, from Deimos, arrived this morning. They are both very anxious to see you.

THEODORIC: Very well, send them in—even though I'm afraid I can't help them. (*He goes back to his catalogue, shaking his head.*) It's very strange; I can't seem to find rockets listed in here anywhere.

HEBE (*Going to the door*): Is that the new Galaxy Directory?

THEODORIC: No, Hebe, this is called (*Closes book and reads from the front*) a Mail Order Catalogue. I found it in that last rocket, the one that crashed yesterday in the No. 7 shaft of the Big Crater Cheese Mine. It will be a useful addition to my library on Earth data, and I was hoping there would be something in it about rockets. But I'm afraid this won't help me either. (*He goes to desk and puts book down.*)

HEBE (*Sympathetically*): The rockets from Earth are becoming quite a problem, aren't they, sir?

THEODORIC: The rockets from Earth, Hebe, are becoming a menace to space. Somehow we have to find a way to stop them.

HEBE: Won't it stop them when we've finished strengthening the rings?

THEODORIC: *If* we can finish the moon rings. The men are busy every minute reinforcing them, but as soon as we get one section finished—whang!—along comes another rocket through a weak spot.

CELESTINE (*Casually*): There was another one today.

HEBE *and* THEODORIC: Another rocket?

CELESTINE: Mmm hmm. This morning, early. A friend of mine over on Venus saw it go by and called me. (*She sighs.*) She knows rockets thrill me! (*Languidly*) I don't know where it landed.

THEODORIC: Great Stars and Little Planets! Why wasn't I informed? Nobody ever tells me anything around here. Hebe, when you send in the visitors, run out and see if you can get some information on the new rocket. (*He paces up and down.*) This is terrible, terrible! (HEBE *exits.*)

CELESTINE (*Rolling up the tinsel in a ball and tossing it up and down*): I think it's exciting. For simply *ages* nothing ever happened up here. Really, it was too incommunicado!

THEODORIC: Now, Celestine, I've told you before: you simply cannot go around approving of rockets in public. It undermines the Official Attitude. Rockets up here are used for business, not pleasure. (HEBE *enters, followed by the* DELEGATES *from Phobos and Deimos.*)

HEBE: Excuse me, sir—here are the delegates from

Phobos (THE GIRL *steps forward and shakes hands*) and her brother moon, Deimos. (THE BOY *steps forward and shakes hands.* HEBE *exits, with* CELESTINE *trailing her out.*)

THEODORIC: How do you do? Come in, come in. (*He indicates chairs and they sit down,* THEODORIC *behind the desk.*) I'm sorry to have kept you waiting so long. What can I do for you?

GIRL: Well, as you know, Mr. Theodoric, our moons belong to the planet Mars, and we've been getting along fine with the Martians for ages.

BOY: Yes, sir, *we* have, too. With the exception of an extra high tide occasionally—carelessness on somebody's part—we've never had a cross word with Mars.

GIRL: But now! After watching the fun your little planet Earth is having, shooting rockets at *you*—

BOY: The fact is, sir, we have heard, from usually reliable sources, that the Martians are building *sports* rockets.

THEODORIC: No!

GIRL: Yes, sir; some of them are even convertibles! We hear the same thing on Phobos.

BOY: You understand our position, Mr. President, I'm sure. We can't take any chances. If this hit-or-miss rocket shooting becomes a fad among the planets— who knows where it will end?

GIRL: And I'm sure you'll agree with us that a moon shot full of holes is just no moon at all!

THEODORIC: Oh, I do, I do. We're finding that out every day!

GIRL: Couldn't you send them a message down there and explain the situation?

BOY: You could do it tactfully. I understand the Earth people are quite understanding.

THEODORIC (*Doubtfully*): You do? Well, never mind that; the problem goes deeper than reason or tact. You see, it's all rather new for us. Until Christmas Eve of 1969, we never had any real contact with our planet Earth. As a matter of fact, even now, though the astronauts have circled the moon and landed on the moon, they couldn't stay long enough to find out that there is any life up here at all. But they're still studying their findings from those moon missions. They even had giant scrapers on one of the space ships to scrape our surface and find out what it's like. And since they first landed here from Apollo 11, they must have even more specimens to study and analyze.

GIRL: I can see you have a real problem.

THEODORIC: Yes, we do. I've made an extensive study of Earth and Earthmen, and I'm not sure we *want* them here. But they get bolder and bolder, and, I must admit, braver and braver, so I'm afraid there will be more and more of these moon missions.

BOY: I'm sure you'll figure out what to do—but please do it quickly. The future of the Galaxy is in your hands. (BOY *and* GIRL *rise and move toward exit.*)

THEODORIC: You may assure your people we are working on the problem. (*He rises and shakes hands with them.*)

GIRL: (Thank you, Mr. President. (*She exits, followed by* BOY. *A crash is heard offstage, then loud shouts.*)

WORKER (*From offstage*): Easy, man! Watch it there!

THEODORIC (*Running to stage left, calling*): Hebe! Hebe! (HEBE *enters, almost colliding with* THEODORIC.)

HEBE (*Breathlessly*): Oh, Mr. President! That last rocket— there was something on it! A *live* something!

THEODORIC: There, there, calm down. (*Anxiously*) Was it a Man? From Earth?

HEBE: I'm not *sure, sir. (She looks at the chart.*) Would you like to see it for yourself?

THEODORIC: By all means. Have it sent in immediately.

HEBE: Yes, sir. (*She goes stage left and calls.*) Boys? You may bring it in now! (*A group of* WORKERS *from the cheese mines wheel in the stowaway* CECIL *on a red wagon. He is crouched over and lashed to the wagon with rope.* CELESTINE *follows the group, much interested in the new arrival.*)

THEODORIC: Right over here will be fine. (*They wheel him to stage center.* THEODORIC *keeps his distance, eyeing* CECIL *warily and checking him against the chart. The* WORKERS *exit.*) How do you do?

CECIL (*Shivering, but cheerful*): Greetings, Daddy-o! You in charge of things around here?

THEODORIC: I am president of the Moon, yes.

CELESTINE (*Eagerly, going up to wagon*): He's my father— my name's Celestine.

THEODORIC: Not too close, child. We know nothing about him!

CECIL (*Admiringly*): A Moon Maiden, huh? My name's Cecil—my friends call me Cease.

THEODORIC: You are an Earth Man?

CECIL (*Proudly, still shivering*): Man, I *was* an Earth Man. But now I'm *way* out! Real gone! (CELESTINE *giggles.*)

THEODORIC: Are you *sure* you're from Earth?

CECIL: Why sure, man, I'm sure. You don't dig me?

CELESTINE (*Primly*): We dig cheese up here.

CECIL: Cheese? You mean like cheese?

CELESTINE: That's right, green cheese. It's our most important industry.

CECIL: They'll never believe it! Say, Daddy-o—you being in charge and all—how about some more heat in here? Frankly, I'm freezing, like congealed.

CELESTINE: Then why don't you turn up your thermostat, Man?

CECIL (*Impressed*): Say, that's the most! You certainly do have an ear for languages!

THEODORIC (*Sternly*): She is not imitating you, Mr. Cecil. She just doesn't realize that you don't have a thermostat. However, run and fetch our guest a cover, Celestine. (*She runs off-stage.*) Hebe, I think we can untie him now. (HEBE *comes forward doubtfully.*) He seems friendly enough. (*He eyes the chart, shaking his head.*) Perhaps when we unfold him . . . (*They begin to untie* CECIL.) How did you happen to come up here?

CECIL: Well, it's like this, Mr. President. Where I come from everybody was "hip." So I grew a beard and got glasses I didn't need and tried talking crazy, but to tell you the truth, I never was very good at it. They kept saying I wasn't really gone. So, one day, I decided I'd show them who was gone and who wasn't—and here I am! (*The ropes are loose now and he stretches.*) Say, that's better. (*They help him and he gradually straightens up.* CELESTINE *enters with a blanket.*)

CELESTINE: Will this do? (*She sees* CECIL *standing.*) Oh! (*To* THEODORIC) Is he harmless?

THEODORIC: We think so, Celestine. (*He takes the blanket and gives it to* CECIL.) Here you are, Mr. Cecil.

CECIL: Thanks, Dad—I mean, Mr. President. (*He wraps himself up and huddles under it, sitting on the floor.*) Just wait till I get back there; those cats will flip! (*A thump is heard off-stage.*) What's that?

THEODORIC: Probably a clumsy workman. We are busy day and night reinforcing our moon rings (*Severely*) against *your* rockets.

CELESTINE: Maybe Cecil could go back and tell them to stop it, Father.

CECIL: Who, me? You got me all wrong, chick; the rocket racket is *way* out of my line. Besides, I can't afford to get messed up with anything constructive. You have to be beat to compete.

THEODORIC: The question now is, will they believe your story? And, if so, won't they send more rockets to investigate?

CECIL: Oh, you can count on that—they'll investigate, probably with more rockets. Of course, if I were some foreigner, it would be a question of security, and they'd have to shut off their rockets till they figured out what I was up to. But, man, they'll believe *me;* I'll see to that! (*There are noises off-stage.* HEBE *looks out of door. A dog barks, and she is visibly startled and upset.*)

NIKKI (*From offstage; in a deep voice with heavy Russian accent*): She won't hurt you; just take good care of her.

CECIL (*Walking over to* THEODORIC): Sounds as if you have company, Mr. President.

THEODORIC: Who is it, Hebe, can you see?

HEBE (*Nervously*): It . . . it looks like another one, sir! (NIKKI *strides in followed by several of the* WORKMEN.)

NIKKI (*To* HEBE *as he almost bowls her over*): Excuse me! (*He bows deeply and she retreats in alarm.*) I am Nikita Samovarich! My friends call me Nikki. *You* may call me Nikki!

THEODORIC (*Coming forward*): Ahem, did you wish to see me, Mr. ah—sir? (HEBE *runs behind the desk.* CELESTINE *has also retreated.* CECIL *sits under his blanket.*)

NIKKI (*Thrusting out his hand*): You are Premier here, no?

THEODORIC (*Shaking hands gingerly*): Well, no—I'm the president.

NIKKI: President! On the moon a decadent society? I wouldn't believe! (*He spots* CECIL.) Ah, hah! Indians!

CECIL: Say, bud—(*He throws back the blanket and rises.*) Who are you calling an Indian?

NIKKI (*Disappointed*): Is *not* an Indian? Always I wanted to see an Indian—American Indian.

CECIL (*Mollified*): Oh, well, shucks—have it your way. My name's Cecil. (*They shake hands.*)

NIKKI: Is a pleasure to meet you, Mr. Cecil Indian. I am Nikki. My dog is outside; she would be happy to meet you, too.

CECIL: You mean to tell me you came in a rocket and brought your *dog* with you?

NIKKI: Is more other way around: they are sending Olga to the Moon. So I say to myself, Nikki, are you man or mouse? No, I say, they cannot do this to you. The pigs, the cows—everything else they can have for the State— but not your little friend Olga.

CECIL: So?

NIKKI (*Spreading his hands*): So—I am hiding in nose cone. I am what you call "Stole Away"!

CECIL (*Admiringly*): Man, that's the most! How about that, Mr. President?

THEODORIC (*Testily*): Yes, how about it? What am I going to *do* with you?

CELESTINE (*Coming forward*): I could show them around the cheese mines, Father.

NIKKI: Ah! A gorgeous creature! You are from Moon, too?

THEODORIC (*Distractedly*): My daughter, Celestine. Now look here, you two— (CECIL *retrieves his blanket and puts it back on.* NIKKI *bows to* CELESTINE *and kisses her hand.*)

NIKKI: I am delighted! (*To* THEODORIC) I can see you have beautiful country here, Mr. President. Maybe my little Olga and I will settle down for a while.

THEODORIC: Yes, well, we'll see. It might be best that way. Just never send you back at all.

CECIL (*Doubtfully*): Never?

CELESTINE (*Happily*): Never?

HEBE (*Wailing*): Never!

NIKKI (*Firmly*): Never! Is very nice on Moon. Needs maybe a Five-Year Plan. I, Nikki, will see to this! (CECIL *still looks doubtful.* CELESTINE *puts her hand on his arm.*)

CELESTINE: Would they miss you very much?

CECIL: That's what bugs me, baby; they probably won't even know I've been gone! I have to get back there and spread the word. (*He looks at her and brightens. He rises and tucks her hand under his arm.*) But not right away. We won't cut out for a while, will we, Nikki?

NIKKI (*Slapping him heartily on the back*): No cutting! First we go visit cheese mines, then we get to work.

CELESTINE: Is it all right, Father?

THEODORIC (*Pacing up and down*): I think so—I don't know. They can't just stay here, but then again, they can't just go back to Earth, either. Not yet, not until those rings are rocket-proof. I must have time to think. (*He stops pacing.*) You three run along; perhaps Hebe and I can figure out something.

CELESTINE (*Happily*): Yes, Father. (*She offers her other arm to* NIKKI.) Nikki? (*He takes it. She addresses them both.*) Shall we go?

CECIL: By all means! (*With a gesture*) Take me to your Liederkranz! (*Curtain*)

*　　*　　*　　*　　*

SCENE 2

TIME: *Several days later.*

SETTING: *The edge of space. (Played before curtain, at the footlights.)*

BEFORE RISE: SAM *and* JOE, *two ring workers, enter, walking carefully along the edge of the stage.* SAM *carries a curtain stretcher and* JOE, *a piece of netting or transparent curtain.*

SAM (*Leading, with the stretcher*): Watch your step here, Joe. (*He peers over the edge, then closes his eyes and pulls back, shaking his head.*) My, there's a lot of *space* out there!

JOE (*Walking gingerly*): Don't remind me! To think I left a nice soft job in the cheese mines to work out here on the edge of nothing!

SAM: Let's face it: we have a very persuasive president. "Every available man," he says. "Work on the moon rings comes first," he says.

JOE: I know, Sam, I know. I heard the speech. "Double time for overtime," he says, too—so here I am! (SAM *sets the stretcher down halfway across the stage and tests the footing.*)

SAM: Spoken like a true Moon Capitalist!

JOE (*Standing beside him, sorting out his netting*): You've been listening to that crazy Nikki! Did you sign up for his Five-Year Plan?

SAM: Sure, why not? Might as well humor him. The president's going to ship him back to Earth any day.

JOE: I heard they couldn't leave till we get all these rings rocket-proofed. (*They start pinning up the curtain.*)

SAM: I guess that's what old Theo had in mind at first, but now I'm not so sure he's going to wait. Nikki keeps pulling the men off the job to go to his meetings; the president can't lock him up because he hasn't done anything wrong and, besides, he's our guest. But he sure has slowed down the work out here.

JOE: The other one, that Cecil—he spends all *his* time with Celestine. The president doesn't go for *that* too much, either. (NIKKI *appears, walking carefully with his arms out, as if on a high wire.*) Oh, oh—here comes Nosecone Nikki!

NIKKI (*From edge of stage*): Hallo out there! Is all right I coming out?

SAM: Is all right with us. You knowing how to fly?

NIKKI (*Coming toward them*): Hah! Jokes you making on the edge of space. You *very* oppressed! (SAM *and* JOE *exchange looks and shrug, then go back to their work.* NIKKI *reaches them.*) You fellows doing fine job, but now is time for meeting.

JOE: *Another* one?

NIKKI (*Firmly*): Every day we must have meeting. Setting up Five-Year Plan is no—how you say—"snap"!

SAM: What d'you think, Joe?

JOE: Might as well go along and see the fun.

SAM: The president won't like it.

JOE: But, Sam (*Points to* NIKKI), he's our *guest!* Moon manners, you know!

SAM: O.K. Nikki, lead the way.

NIKKI: Good. We go. (*They start to file off-stage.*) Everybody else waiting.

JOE: You mean you have them *all?*

NIKKI: Is necessary all workers unite. Today we make plans for meeting tomorrow. (*They leave as* CELESTINE *and* CECIL *enter from stage left.* CELESTINE *leads. She walks easily and is dressed in blue denims, with her hair in a pony tail.* CECIL *follows on his hands and knees.*)

CECIL: Hey! Not so fast. These moon rings are slippery.

CELESTINE: Oh, you get used to it. I just adore coming out here but, of course, I'm very sure-footed. (*She starts to do a dance step.*)

CECIL (*Hanging onto imaginary ring*): Cut that out! You're jiggling it!

CELESTINE (*Stops dancing and tests the footing*): No, it's steady. This part's been reinforced. (*She points to stretcher.*) See, they're working over there.

CECIL (*Looking*): Yeah? Who is? I don't see anybody.

CELESTINE: No, everybody seems to be gone. But they've left the equipment, so I suppose they'll be coming back. (*She goes over and fingers the curtain.*) You want to see how we fix our moon rings? (CECIL *is almost up to her now. He looks back over his shoulder.*)

CECIL: Couldn't you just show me some more cheese mines?

CELESTINE: But I thought you wanted something 'way out!

CECIL: I never figured on this! Being gone is one thing, but out there (*He looks over the edge, carefully*)— that's gone for *good!*

CELESTINE: Oh, all right. We'll go back. You can teach me some more dance steps.

CECIL: Lady, I'm too beat to bop! (*He looks back over his shoulder.*) And how do I get out of here, anyway?

CELESTINE: Here, give me your hand— (*Gaily*) now, *up* you go! (*He starts to rise and loses his nerve.*)

CECIL: Oh, no you don't! (*He clutches the floor again with both hands.*) I'll *back* out—you can guide me.

CELESTINE: Honestly, Cecil! All right—let's go. (THEODORIC *appears stage right. He is shaking his head and mumbling to himself. He stops short as he sees them.*) Careful now . . . (CECIL *starts backing slowly.*) A little more to the right . . . that's fine.

THEODORIC (*Booming*): And what, may I ask, is going on here? (CECIL *gives a yelp of surprise and flattens on the floor.* CELESTINE *is startled but recovers her balance quickly.* CECIL *thrashes about.*)

CELESTINE: Father!

CECIL: Help!

CELESTINE (*Turning*): Cecil! (*She reaches down and pulls him up by one hand so that he is back on his hands and knees again.*) Are you all right?

CECIL: Thank you. (*Bitterly*) I'm fine. I'm just peachy dandy.

CELESTINE (*Brightly*): Oh, that's good. I thought you looked a little green—it must be all that cheese.

THEODORIC (*Arms akimbo and tapping his foot*): I am waiting for an explanation!

CELESTINE: Oh! Well, Daddy-o, it's like this . . .

THEODORIC (*Ominously*): *What* did you call me?

CELESTINE (*Drawing back*): Daddy? O?

THEODORIC: I'll Daddy-o you! And what is that ridiculous costume you're wearing? And *why* are you out here in the first place? And *where* are all my ring workers?

CECIL: Oh, please, not now—not here! We can explain

everything when we get back onto solid moon! (*He starts backing off.*)

CELESTINE: That's fine, Cecil! I knew you could do it. (*To* THEODORIC, *over her shoulder*) We don't know where the men are, Dad—Father, but I expect Nikki has them at a meeting. He generally does.

THEODORIC: I've just heard about the meetings; that's why I came out here. It seems to be true—there is certainly no work going on. (*Eyeing* CELESTINE) But a great amount of foolishness.

CELESTINE: This is how they dress where Cecil comes from. I think it's the most!

THEODORIC: And I think it's the end! Tomorrow Cecil and Nikki are going back to Earth.

CELESTINE: But the rings—they aren't finished.

THEODORIC: We will have to take the chance. All the rockets we've had so far haven't done half the damage that these two—*characters*—have managed in less than a week.

CELESTINE (*Wailing*): But you can't send Cecil back now! Do you want your daughter to grow up to be a square?

THEODORIC (*Violently*): I don't care if you grow up to be a rectangle! Now get back home and take Cecil with you. I have to find Nikki.

CELESTINE: Yes, Father. Come on, Cecil— (CECIL *stands up and turns,* CELESTINE *behind him. She puts a hand on his shoulder and starts to dance off-stage left.* THEODORIC *starts off-stage right, then looks back and sees her.*)

THEODORIC (*Bellowing*): And Celestine! Turn down your thermostat!

*   *   *   *   *

Scene 3

TIME: *The next afternoon.*

SETTING: Same as Scene 1.

AT RISE: HEBE *is sorting papers at her desk. She has a large wastepaper basket and is rapidly filling it.* THEODORIC *is up on a chair preparing to take down his picture of the "Earth Specimen".*

THEODORIC (*Looking down*): When you finish with that, Hebe, there is more to be sorted out in the library files, under "Earth."

HEBE: Yes, sir. Are you sure you want it *all* thrown away?

THEODORIC (*Firmly*): All of it. As far as I'm concerned, we have had our first and *last* human contact with our planet. (CELESTINE *enters. She drops into a chair.*)

CELESTINE: Well, it's over. They're out of sight. (*She flexes her right arm.*) I have "waver's cramp." (*Pause*) How soon do you think they'll be back, Father?

THEODORIC: Back? Don't be ridiculous, Celestine. They won't be coming back.

CELESTINE: But Cecil promised! He said he would give up being beat and lead the expedition when they come up to investigate his story. (THEODORIC *rolls up the chart and steps down from the chair.*)

THEODORIC: I'm afraid you are in for a little surprise. (*He chuckles.*) For that matter, so are Cecil and Nikki, poor boys!

CELESTINE: Father! You *did* send them back to Earth?

THEODORIC: Of course. But not quite in the directions they came from.

HEBE: Directions? I don't understand, sir. Once the rockets are set for Earth, the direction is automatic.

THEODORIC: That's quite true, Hebe, but you don't appreciate the finer complications of life on Earth. For a small planet, I must say they are very poorly organized! All chopped up—here, I'll show you. (*He goes to the globe and picks it up.* HEBE *and* CELESTINE *join him, one on either side.*) Do you see all of these colors? Each one represents a separate country, each with its own laws and language and customs.

HEBE: My goodness, how very confusing for them!

CELESTINE: Do they like each other?

THEODORIC: Occasionally, but it's a little like the ladies of the Celestial Sewing Circle: friends become enemies and change back to friends again rather frequently. At the moment Nikki's color and Cecil's color aren't getting along too well. I am counting on that to save the Moon. They will refuse to act together because they don't trust one another.

HEBE: Then won't the boys come back separately?

THEODORIC: Not for a while, Hebe; not until the countries investigate every aspect of the boys' stories.

CELESTINE: I don't believe it! Cecil said his people would listen to him.

THEODORIC: *They* might. But Nikki's people won't.

CELESTINE: Nikki? Oh, Father, you know how persuasive *he* is. Remember the ring workers?

THEODORIC (*Shuddering*): Please, don't remind me! No, I meant that Nikki's people won't believe Cecil's story. You see, I sent each one back to the other's country.

CELESTINE: Father, you didn't!

THEODORIC: Oh, the boys won't be harmed, but it will keep them all busy down there for a while, straightening things out. Meantime, we can fix up the moon rings. (*There is a staccato rap on the door, stage left.*) Yes?

Come in! (*A* VISITOR *enters.*)

VISITOR (*Brightly*): I say, old chap, is this the Prime Minister's office? (THEODORIC *is too stunned to speak.* CELESTINE *nudges him with her elbow.*)

CELESTINE (*In a stage whisper*): Is he from *another* color? (THEODORIC *nods his head and looks at the globe in his hands.*)

THEODORIC (*To himself*): Of course—it never occurred to me! (*To the* VISITOR, *pulling himself together*) Please come in. (*A little bitterly*) Welcome to the Moon!

VISITOR (*Briskly*): Thank you! We've come to colonize, don't y' know. Hardly expected to find anyone here ahead of us!

THEODORIC: You'd be surprised! Will you excuse me for a minute? (*The* VISITOR *sits down.* THEODORIC *sets down the globe and picks up the rolled-up chart he has just taken down. He hands it silently to* CELESTINE. *She climbs onto the chair and starts putting it back up again.* THEODORIC *goes to the wastepaper basket and starts stacking the discarded papers back on the desk.*) Never mind the library files, Hebe. Just take a Rocketgram for me, please. (*Slowly throughout, thinking.*) "To the moons, Phobos and Deimos: have given careful attention to our problem, with little success." (*He glances at the* VISITOR.) Better make that "no success," Hebe. "I suggest that from now on it will be a case of— (*He picks up the wastepaper basket and on his last words empties it out onto the desk*) every Moon for himself! (*Curtain*)

THE END

Production Notes

Anyone for the Moon?

Characters: 7 male; 3 female; male extras.

Playing Time: 25 minutes.

Costumes: Modern, everyday dress for Theodoric, Celestine and Hebe. In Scene 2, Celestine wears blue jeans and a pony tail. The visitors from Phobos and Deimos wear leather jackets, and have goggles or dark glasses pushed up on their foreheads. Cecil is dressed in blue jeans and a sweater, as befits a fugitive from the Beat Generation. He sports a small pointed beard and horn-rimmed glasses. Nikki is dressed like a farmer. The ring workers and workmen from the cheese mines wear coveralls. The Visitor is dressed in a conservative suit and homburg. He carries a slim black umbrella.

Properties: Piece of rope tinsel, for Celestine; large "mail order catalogue," for Theodoric; red wagon, rope, and blanket, for Cecil; curtain stretcher, for Sam; netting or transparent curtain, for Joe.

Setting: Scenes 1 and 3: Theodoric's office, on the Moon. At stage left is a large globe of the world, and, hanging on the wall, a large chart showing a picture of a man, and labelled, "Earth Specimen." There is a desk covered with papers, several chairs, and a large wastebasket. Other furnishings may be added if desired. Scene 2: Before curtain. No set is required.

Lighting: No special effects.

Sound: Sound of a dog barking, as indicated.

All This and Alan, Too

By J. A. Sanders

Characters

CORKY
MARGE
BETTY
KAREN
DIANE

SETTING: *Double bedroom of a rather fashionable girls' dormitory at Hayes University.*

TIME: *Late afternoon.*

AT RISE: *At the window, in a somewhat posed attitude, sits* KAREN, *languidly smoothing the back of her page-boy bob with a silver hairbrush. Across the bed lies* MARGE. BETTY *enters with a large bath towel wrapped about her and a shower cap on her head.*

BETTY (*Indignantly*): That goon of a Cleone Davis has been in the shower now for an hour and twenty-six minutes. It doesn't make sense! Nobody's that dirty!

KAREN (*Languidly*): Maybe the gal's drowned.

BETTY: Drowned, nothing. She's taking singing lessons,

and the shower room's the only place she can reach her high notes.

MARGE: Oh, stop stewing, darling. We all have our troubles. Look at me! I just wish a dirty neck were all that stood between me and beauty. I'm scared to death I'll eat something with a calorie in it before the dance tonight, and burst out the seams of my new red formal.

KAREN (*Reaching for a chocolate*): Really, Marge, you're amusing. You think too much of food—that's all. Maybe if you took up music—something cultural— you know—to take your mind off the more material things of life— (*Murmurs*) The inner essence . . .

BETTY (*With a low, dramatic moan*): Ah, Ninotchka—

MARGE: Shades of the prophets, gal, you're balmy. Here I slowly starve to death for weeks on pretzels and carrot juice, on purpose, to get slim and streamlined for the dance tonight, and look at me!

KAREN (*Smoothly*): That's precisely what I mean, darling.

MARGE (*Throws a pillow* KAREN'S *way*): You and your Russian theatre and all the inner essences! Phooey! (*Greedily*) What's that you're eating?

KAREN (*Raising an eyebrow*): Chocolate creams. Have one?

MARGE: Don't be silly. You know me and chocolate creams. I am on a diet. (*Goes over and takes a chocolate and regards it lovingly, then carries the whole box to the middle of the bed, where she sits with it on her knees.* BETTY *is now cross-legged like a Hindu in the middle of the floor, painting her toenails a brilliant red.*)

KAREN: My, how glamorous, darling. May I ask what brand that polish is?

BETTY: Oh, it's Diane's—a dollar a bottle. "Scarlet Passion." She got it to go with her turquoise blue suit.

KAREN (*Taking flower from vase on table, burying her nose in it*): Lovely. (*Sighing*) Ah, que j'aime les belles fleurs! Who sent these? Another of Lady Diane's cavaliers?

BETTY: Darling, how do I know who sent them? It could be any one of twenty love-sick boobs. If you roomed with Miss Elizabeth Taylor Carroll the way I do, you'd give up trying to keep track of her beaux.

MARGE: Some people have everything. Here's Diane with a millionaire papa—and all her clothes from Bergdorf-Goodman—and a Cadillac convertible, and all the men in college ready to swoon with joy if she even looks in their direction. Even Alan Mansfield!

KAREN: Think of it. All this, and Alan, too—

BETTY: The good fairies certainly got in at her christening, all right. The old witch, or whoever she was, must have had fallen arches the day they gave out the gifts for Diane.

MARGE: What do you mean, fallen arches? I thought old witches flew.

BETTY: Oh, all right, then. A terrific case of air sickness. I'm not particular. Anyhow, she has some line. Just looks demure and helpless, and all the men for a mile around come swarming up.

KAREN: And now Alan Mansfield has asked her to the dance.

MARGE: He's one she had to work for! That's something. (*Dramatically*) They can't take that from me. She had to turn on every kilowatt of charm she's got—and she's not sure, yet, she's got him dazzled.

BETTY: Me-ow!

MARGE: Well, it's true. This is the first time I've ever seen *her* get dewy-eyed over any man.

KAREN: Who wouldn't get dewy-eyed over Alan Mansfield? All last term, I slept with his picture under my pillow. You know, the one they published in the "Quill and Inkhorn." (*Hastily*) Not that I ever made a play for him, myself.

MARGE: What! None of the good old essence, even for Alan?

KAREN: Oh, do shut up.

BETTY (*Finishing her nails*): Stop fighting, and I'll show you Diane's formal! She was planning to keep it secret till tonight, and then just lay you out—but she'll never know the difference. (*She picks up her polish, stands it on the dresser, then, as if about to unveil a monument, opens the closet door. They crowd around with awed exclamations.*)

MARGE (*In a whisper*): Shades of Schiaparelli! Where'd it come from?

BETTY (*Enjoying it*): Saks Fifth Avenue or somewhere. (*Displaying the lid of the box in which it had arrived.*)

KAREN: And white, at that. Apparently she's planning to be Juliet tonight or our chaste Diana, setting out to hunt the stag—and how! (*She flings back her bangs. Leaps gracefully to one toe, and, drawing the string of an imaginary bow, lets fly an imaginary arrow. Giggles from the other girls.*)

BETTY: Don't be silly. You haven't forgotten the Mansfield masterpiece—that poem he wrote.

KAREN: What masterpiece? What poem?

BETTY: You know—the one that came out in *The Scribe* —all about a girl in a white dress.

MARGE: You remember—something about some skinny

Winnie of a girl—"white in a mist"—"cool with silver"—all that sort of blah.

KAREN: You've no soul, my child.

MARGE: If I had, I'd sell it for that white dress, darn it. (*Mournfully*) It's gory—that's what it is, gory. Her with a layout like that, and Alan Mansfield, too—and me stepping out with Butch in my sixteen ninety-eight markdown!

BETTY (*Cocking an ear, finger on lips*): Do these old ears deceive me, or was that the shower-room door opening? Quick, quick! My soap! And my Algerian mud! (*She flies to the door. As she reaches it, there is the sound of another door being firmly shut and the click of a latch. She turns back, despair in her voice.*) I see it now, I was a fool to imagine that I should ever again see the inside of that dear old shower room. I know who played me that dirty, low-down trick. It was that Harris girl, the cat. She knows I've been waiting ages to get in. Well, if I die of pneumonia, remind me to haunt her. . . . Everybody in this dorm is going off to the dance tonight, I believe.

MARGE: Everybody? Really?

KAREN: Well, everybody but Lennie, of course. She'll be home getting soulful over the law of diminishing returns or something. Can you imagine—on dance night!

MARGE: I can—Lennie. Lennie—and Jane Eyre—and maybe Elsie Dinsmore.

BETTY: If she wouldn't be so darn bashful. It's just plain silliness to go creeping around corners the way she does. Just about dies if anybody looks at her.

KAREN: You know, the other evening I came down with Diane, and there was Lennie sitting all by herself in the living room. Just sitting. A couple of Sigs had asked if some of us wanted a ride. So Diane asked Lennie if she didn't want to go along. Diane's like that. Lennie looked at us and went pink as the flowers on that bedspread. Then she says, "Oh, no! Please—really—thank you very much—I must do my trigonometry—" Then she turned and ran up the stairs so fast you'd have thought the Board of Education was after her. Queer, that's what!

MARGE: I haven't any patience with her, myself. I don't know what Diane sees in her. She says Lennie's *got* something.

KAREN: If she has, it's not apparent to the naked eye. And she's as different from Diane as a sparrow from a bird of paradise.

MARGE: If you're born a Diane, you can afford to spread around a little sweetness and light. Just let little Lennie get in her way once, and— (*Makes eloquent gesture of cutting her own throat*).

BETTY (*Thoughtfully*): I'm not so sure. When you really know Diane— (*Sound of door banging interrupts. With feverish gleam in her eye*) Was that the door to the shower opening? No, of course; it couldn't have been. (*She tiptoes out into the hall, turns around, and comes back.*) It wasn't. I'll never get in there, never, and I'll look like something out of the gallery of horrors for the dance.

KAREN: Never mind, pet. You'll be in the dark most of the evening.

BETTY: When you say that, smile! Well, I might as well get my facial while I can. (*She sits at the dresser and begins applying cream to her face and neck.*) Don't anybody say anything funny till this dries. I might laugh and crack it.

KAREN: What's that?

BETTY: It's called an Algerian mud facial highball. Wonderful. Full of vitamin D-4.

MARGE: Don't tell me the Algerians use it. They'd scare their camels to death. (BETTY *lies at full length on the bed, face composed to let the mud dry. There is the sound of footsteps in the hallway. A little tap on the door—then it flies open and in bursts* CORKY, *breathlessly, as if she knows some secret too good to keep. In her excitement, she sprawls over a wastebasket. They help her up.*)

CORKY: Where's Diane? Lead me to her, somebody! I have to see her this minute! It's too, too precious! Isn't she here?

BETTY (*From under her towel*): Gone down to the Maxwell Salon for a manicure and hair-do. Why? What's eating you, Corky, my pet?

CORKY (*With a gurgle of delight*): You'd never guess, never, never, never! Not in a million years! I've just unearthed a treasure! (*Waves the book in air*)

MARGE: Hey, quit that girlish gurgling! Calm down!

CORKY: I'm trying to tell you! I was just hunting around for Lennie's lab notes—

KAREN: So that's how you got by in chemistry last term.

MARGE: Be still, Karen. Let Corky alone. So what, Corky?

CORKY: Well, I just ran across it—quite by accident— Lennie always lets me use her notes, and here I was, completely unsuspicious—

BETTY: For Pete's sake, get on with it! How do you expect me to keep a straight face?

CORKY (*Sputtering*): Give me a chance to tell you! The whole thing's too romantic for words—just aflame with emotion!

KAREN (*Teasingly*): What's aflame? Have you called the fire department?

MARGE: You mean Lennie's aflame? She's outside under the elm with a book. (*Looks out window*) I can see her.

CORKY (*Exasperated*): Oh, oh! Stop being silly! The dorm's not afire and neither is Lennie. It's this book. I mean—

KAREN: Do try to articulate.

BETTY: Girls, girls! The directions on the jar say I mustn't get excited.

CORKY: Oh, darn it. Here, read it yourself. I can't wait to see Diane's face! I suppose Lennie just forgot to take it with her.

MARGE: I should hope not—it might be awkward.

CORKY: Don't be silly—Lennie, I mean—until today she must have kept this book—it's a sort of diary—with her. (*Enter* DIANE *from the hall. She is met at the door by the unquenchable* CORKY, *who takes her bag, hat, and belongings, and pushes* DIANE *into chair.*)

DIANE: Gosh! Who let the cyclone in? Is it an accident? What's all the excitement? Has the dean of women run off with the janitor?

KAREN: Corky is simply percolating to tell something that will lay us all low. Something to do with Lennie or a fire, or something.

CORKY: Be still, can't you! I've been trying to tell you all along, if you'd give me half a chance. (BETTY, *unable to bear the suspense any longer, slides off the bed and comes up behind, leaning over* DIANE'S *shoulder. She is a truly weird spectacle.* CORKY *gives an uncontrollable shriek,* MARGE *and* KAREN *wince,* DIANE *half springs from her seat.*)

DIANE: Ye Gods—the Great Stone Face! Take it away, somebody!

KAREN: What are you going to this dance as, Betty? The painted desert?

BETTY: Oh, don't be silly! Anybody'd think I look like Mrs. Frankenstein, to hear you talk. Anyway, I thought somebody was going to tell a secret that would slay somebody.

CORKY: Honest, Di, you'd never guess! I couldn't wait to rush in and tell you. At first, I couldn't believe, that Lennie wrote it. The mouse! But here's her name in the front— (*Opens the book, pointing it out*) "Lennie MacArthur, her book and heart." Isn't that quaint? I couldn't imagine what it was at first. Then I read through it, and it's all romantic confessions! (*Turns pages*) She's perishing—listen, this will kill you, Diane—she's simply perishing of a fatal amour for Alan Mansfield! Wouldn't it slay you? So poetic, too. (*Flips through pages, stops at a passage near the middle*) Here! (*Triumphantly*) Listen to this! (*Opens her mouth for the first words.* KAREN *calmly takes the book from her.*)

KAREN: Let somebody read who knows how. (*Reads*) "Beloved"—Hummm! Nice beginning! "Beloved—there is a thought I have could I but say it—put it in words—set it to burning its brief moment on the winds that blow up from the dark, out to inevitable darkness"—

CORKY (*Tittering*): Sounds just like Edgar Allan Poe, doesn't it?

KAREN (*Withering her with a glance*): Don't interrupt the performer. You've never really lived, Corky. (*She goes on reading*) "Something of warmth, to have with me when the sun is gone; something of light, to shut out darkness when my good days are past."

MARGE: Shades of Shakespeare! Our little petunia has turned out to be a passion flower. (*Laughter*) —Go on. Continue!

KAREN (*Who has been reading ahead*): Now be still, everybody. But first, see if Lennie's still there.

MARGE (*Looking out window*): Still sunk in a book. All quiet on the western front. (BETTY *tries to peer into book.*)

KAREN: Wait—wait! This is too precious for words! A-aahem! "Only to be near you, Alan, to fill my eyes and thoughts with your image—to know that you could love me, no matter how little, how short a time. Believe me, given this much of grace, I could go blind tomorrow, were your shadow the last that came between me and the light—or deaf, were your words the last to break my silence—Ah, that would be something for remembering!" (*Then with a husky sob,* KAREN *begins a variation.*) Ah me! My Romeo! Wherefore art thou Romeo! Here I stand; there you stand—strange, one does not understand. . . . Ah, Pagliacci—ah, Nijinski—ah, the nine muses—the three fishes— (*In an ecstasy of despair*) the itty bitty poo! (*Laughter and applause.* KAREN *beams, bows.* MARGE *and* CORKY *are hugging each other, speechless with mirth.*)

CORKY: Isn't it killing, Di? What are you going to do about it?

DIANE: What am I supposed to do?

BETTY (*Cutting in*): Please let me be there when you tell Alan! (*Fervently*) Please! It's a roommate's privilege. I've got to see his face!

DIANE (*Dryly*): And I'll bet he'd like to see yours. (*Looks at watch*) Do you know what time it is?

CORKY: Oh, oh, it's late! Lennie'll be coming up from

downstairs and miss her book the first thing! (*Picks up the book, gets half-way across the room, then turns around and comes back*) Diane, darling, be a lamb, will you and—the red ones with the rhinestones?

DIANE (*Nodding*): Sure thing, scatterbrain. You'll find them in the closet. (CORKY *comes out with the slippers.*)

CORKY: Thanks a million, Di. (*Kisses her cheek*) I adore you. 'Bye now, kids. (*Exits.*)

MARGE (*Following*): Well, wait a minute, Horsefeathers. (*From the hall*) You've got to help me on with my girdle.—Hey! Betty! Shower!

CORKY (*Off*): Yoo-hoo! Shower. (BETTY *bounds across room like a gazelle. She knocks over a chair on the way, but she makes the shower. We can hear her bursting into song as the door shuts.*)

KAREN: Really, Diane, you shouldn't let people sponge off you like that. That little featherbrain of a Corky'll run holes through those slippers in no time. The last party she went to she started wanting to ride a horse along about two A.M. Climbed a barbed-wire fence, in her blue formal, waded a creek, and got clear out to the stables before Chuck caught up with her.

DIANE (*With a giggle*): Yes, I remember, we were all waiting out by the quadrangle, scared to death. It's a wonder we didn't get expelled.

KAREN: Say, are you using your Black Tiger perfume this evening, by any chance? You know—just a touch with the black velvet . . .

DIANE: Help yourself, Karen. Top drawer. But be careful how you use it. You know what it says. "Not for the timid soul—Black Tiger is for the woman who dares to take her fate in her hands." Don't say I didn't warn you!

KAREN (*Eyes widening*): How thrilling! I'll borrow the whole bottle. Merci beaucoup, cherie. See you tonight. (*Goes out, smelling the lid of the bottle.* DIANE *is silent a moment. Then she gets up, hitting the palms of her hands together with a nervous little motion, and walks over to the window, looking out. Then decidedly, she walks toward the closet, stopping, as she sees the lid of the dress box. She picks it up, looks at it, then drops it to the floor, and walks restlessly to and fro, as if trying to collect her thoughts for a decision. Finally, face set and expressionless, she opens the closet door and takes out the dress. For a moment she holds it to her. It is a beautiful dress—it sweeps to the floor in soft lustrous folds, catching the light here and there in little star-like points. Resolutely she lays it out on the bed, next bringing out the little glittering Juliet cap and the jewelled slippers. She walks with sudden decision to the telephone and dials a number.*)

DIANE: Hello, Jan Maxwell Salon? Please connect me with Department 6. Hello—yes—hello, Clara. Diane Carroll. I'm in a jam and need you badly. No, no—I haven't been fooling with my hair-do. I've left it just as you did it, but I still think it makes me look like the president of the W.C.T.U. Never mind, darling. Don't get excited. I don't need you for me—it's for someone else. We've got to do a Cinderella act and do it fast. What? Oh, never mind. I'll explain when I see you. Just bring everything and hurry. . . . There's a love. You're going to give a friend of mine the works. Yes, up here and just as quick as you can make it—you know the way! (*Hangs up, waits a moment thoughtfully, and dials again*) Hello. May I speak with Alan Mansfield—is he in? Thank you. Hello, Alan. This is

Diane. (*She is trying hard to be casual*) Alan, the most stupid thing—I've come down with a cold and the nurse says it looks like "flu." She won't let me out of the house. Oh, I am, too—I can't tell you how sorry—it's nice of you to say so—You know I do. But listen, Alan, I've arranged something—something really nice. I have a friend, Lennie MacArthur's her name. Well, no . . . I don't think you'd remember her. She's lovely, but very quiet and aloof. Really hard to get, you know. Never goes out unless it's someone special. (*Laughs*) Lennie thinks you are. She admires your poetry, too. Yes, isn't it? Oh, but it's better than that. Wait till I tell you! I happen to know she's even wearing the kind of dress you like—you know, white—and cool with silver—Wait till you see it! . . . Yes, darn it! I'll tell her . . . Of course . . . I'm going to crawl under a mustard plaster, myself . . . Goodbye, now. (*She gets up, goes to mirror and rumples up her hair, wraps a white scarf around her throat, slips a robe over her things, and coughs experimentally once or twice. Goes to window and leans out. Calls in a firm voice.*) Lennie, Lennie! Yes, you! Come up quick. I need you! (*Holds up dress once more, then lays it down and straightens folds of skirt as curtain falls.*)

THE END

Production Notes

ALL THIS AND ALAN, TOO

Characters: 5 female.

Playing Time: 30 minutes.

Costumes: Karen wears lounging pajamas. Marge is dressed in sweater and slacks. Betty has a large bath towel wrapped around her sarong-fashion and wears a shower cap on her head. Corky wears a flowered house-coat. Diane wears a suit and hat with gloves and bag.

Properties: Box of chocolates, nail polish, dress box containing a white evening dress, mud pack cream, diary, red evening slippers, Juliet evening cap, white evening slippers, bottle of perfume, white scarf, bathrobe.

Setting: A dormitory bedroom. Twin beds with chintz spreads stand on either side of a wide, recessed window up center. There is a deep window seat with bright cushions, and a small chest at the foot of each bed. Down left is a dressing table littered with photographs of young men, jars of complexion creams and perfume. Upstage left a closet door stands partly open. A lacy slip hangs on the doorknob. On the opposite wall is a door leading to the hall, and down right is a small table holding a telephone and a vase of flowers. A stuffed panda and a stuffed elephant lie on the floor near one of the beds. Downstage center is a desk with books on it.

Lighting: No special effects.

The Ten-Penny Tragedy

By Josef A. Elfenbein

Characters

ANDREA, *an attractive high school student*
GERALD, *her friend*
MARJORIE, *a talkative, dramatic student*
ALEX, *another student*
MARILYN, *a "creatively imaginative" student*
PHIL, *a student on the basketball team*
DELIA, *a gossipy, close friend of Marjorie's*
MR. FADDLE, *nervous principal of the high school*

TIME: *Afternoon of a school day.*
SETTING: *The "Information Desk" just outside of Principal Faddle's office, bearing several textbooks, an open loose-leaf notebook, a box of tickets, a cash box and a telephone. Behind the desk is a free standing blackboard bearing the message:*

> SPRING CARNIVAL FRIDAY AT 2 P.M.
> Prizes   Contests
>
> TICKETS HERE 10¢ EACH

AT RISE: ANDREA *is sitting on the desk, pencil in hand, talking on the telephone. In front of her are an open loose-leaf notebook, a box of tickets and a cash box.*

ANDREA: Yes, Miss Furbush. Tickets are available today. . . . They're ten cents each. . . . No, *ten* cents. A dime. That's right. . . . Yes, I can take one up to you. Are you in the English office? . . . No, no trouble at all. I'll be glad to. Marjorie Higgins takes over this desk when the bell rings. I'll bring one ticket with me when I come. . . . At the end of the period. . . . Yes, and thank you. Goodbye. (*During this speech* GERALD *enters. He waits until the conversation is over.*)

GERALD: Here's your ten cents, Andrea. I just got my allowance for the week. (*Takes ticket from* ANDREA) Thanks.

ANDREA: Oh, dear! Where will I put it? I have no pockets in this dress. I'll lose the dime.

GERALD: Tie it in your handkerchief. You won't lose your handkerchief.

ANDREA: I shouldn't. It's my mother's best handkerchief. Dad gave it to her for her birthday last month. She lent it to me today. I promised I'd take care of it.

GERALD: It won't hurt the handkerchief. Here, give it to me. (*He takes the handkerchief and ties the dime in it as he speaks.*) This way you'll hang on to your money.

ANDREA: Hurry, Gerald. The period is almost over, and I have to get a ticket up to Miss Furbush. Marjorie should be along any minute.

GERALD (*Giving her the handkerchief*): Here, all fixed.

ANDREA: Thanks. (*She puts the handkerchief in the open loose-leaf notebook.*) We're going to be late. (*Bell rings for end of class.*)

GERALD: There's Marjorie coming down the hall now.

ANDREA: She'll have some good excuse for being late, I know.

MARJ (*Entering in a great hurry*): Sorry I'm late, Andy, but Mr. Burton got caught on a dangling participle, and we were kept dangling with him. You can take off now. Don't forget your books.

ANDREA: I'll just take my poetry book; I'll get the others later. (*Closes the notebook concealing the handkerchief.*)

GERALD: Sell lots of tickets, Marj. The basketball team needs new uniforms. (GERALD *and* ANDREA *exit.*)

MARJ: I'll do my best. (*Telephone rings.* MARJ *goes to desk, sits, takes up telephone*) Hello, Spring Carnival tickets. Ten cents each. A dime apiece. Marjorie Higgins speaking. . . . Oh, yes, Miss Furbush, she just this minute left. She'll get it right up there, I'm sure. . . . Yes, ma'am, all classes after 2 p.m. on Friday are cancelled. . . . Yes, I'm sorry, too. I miss algebra. . . . It *is* too bad. But the team needs new uniforms. . . . The moths got into them this summer. . . . No, there wasn't enough left to sew together. They even ate the numbers off the backs. . . . Oh, they *will* take better care of them next summer. Lots of moth balls. . . . All right, Miss Furbush, if I see her. . . . Goodbye. (*Bell rings signifying start of next period.* ANDREA *and* GERALD *enter looking worried.*)

MARJ: Andrea! Gerald! What are you doing here? Are you cutting English?

ANDREA: No, I'm looking for a handkerchief I lost. It has a dime in it.

GERALD: It was her mother's, and Andy lost it somewhere.

MARJ: A diamond? Lost?

ANDREA: How can I face my mother tonight?

MARJ: It was your mother's?

GERALD: Her father gave it to her mother.

MARJ: I didn't see it.

GERALD: Let's go back and look in the hall.

MARJ: I certainly hope you find it. That's awful.

ANDREA (*Leaving*): I'm worried sick! (ANDREA *and* GERALD *exit.* MARJORIE *gets up and follows them down the hall with her eyes.* ALEX *enters from other side and raps on the desk for attention.*)

ALEX: Cash customer! Cash customer! A ticket to the Carnival.

MARJ (*Turning, slightly dazed, her mind far off*): What'd you say?

ALEX: I want a ticket to the— (*Goes to her*) Say what's the matter with *you?*

MARJ: Poor Andy.

ALEX: What's the matter with "poor Andy"?

MARJ (*Going back to her seat at the desk*): It's terrible, Alex. Awful! Even worse than that.

ALEX: What's so terrible?

MARJ: Andrea . . . Andrea lost her mother's diamond.

ALEX: What?

MARJ: It was the one Mr. Nevins gave to Mrs. Nevins.

ALEX: Their engagement ring! I'll bet it was their engagement ring!

MARJ (*Nodding sadly*): You're probably right.

ALEX: I'll tell the team about it. They'll help find it. Here's my ten cents.

MARJ: Thanks. Here's the ticket.

ALEX: Imagine Andrea losing her mother's engagement ring. Humph. (*He exits as* MARILYN *enters.*) Hi, Marilyn.

MARILYN: Hi, Alex. Hi, Marj. How are tickets going?

MARJ: Who can think about tickets, when there is tragedy brewing right here in this very school.

MARILYN: Tragedy?

MARJ: Andrea lost her mother's huge engagement ring.

MARILYN: So that's it. I knew something terrible had happened.

MARJ: What do you know about it?

MARILYN: I saw Andrea in the halls, and she was crying something awful!

MARJ (*Shaking her head sadly, rises and walks toward comfortable chair*): She says she can't bear to face her parents.

MARILYN (*Following her*): Afraid of her father?

MARJ: Most likely.

MARILYN: He's a big man. He'll probably beat her when he hears about it.

MARJ: Oh, no!

MARILYN: Beat her within an inch of her life.

MARJ: Poor, poor, *poor* Andy.

MARILYN (*Bending over, confidentially*): If I were Andrea, I'd run away!

MARJ: I would, too. Imagine a father beating a girl her age.

MARILYN: I'd better go after her. If she's going to run away, I'll let her spend the night in *my* house.

MARJ: You're a bosom buddy. You're a really true friend.

MARILYN: I'll go right away and find her. (*Exits as the phone rings.*)

MARJ (*Goes to desk, sits, and takes phone*): Spring Carnival tickets. Ten cents apiece. . . . Oh, yes, Miss Furbush. I know Andrea was supposed to take you a ticket but something *terrible* has happened. . . . She lost her mother's diamond engagement ring. . . . Yes, and her father is going to beat her for it. . . . (*Her voice fades as* ANDREA *and* GERALD *return and speak.* MARJ *has her back to them. She does not see them.*)

ANDREA: We've been over every inch of the floor from here to 109. I don't know what to do. (*She has been weeping. She wipes her eyes.*)

GERALD: There's no point crying over a handkerchief and a dime. Here, this is my week's allowance. I'll lend it to you. Run downtown and buy another handkerchief just like the one you lost. Maybe the store has another one just like it.

ANDREA: But, what about my English class?

GERALD: Explain it to the teacher later.

ANDREA: All right. I'll run as fast as I can so I won't miss the next class.

GERALD: It's the only thing to do. Go ahead.

MARJ (*As she hangs up the phone, she is surprised to see* ANDREA *and* GERALD): Andy! Gerald! Haven't you found it yet?

ANDREA: No.

MARJ: What are you going to do?

ANDREA: No time to talk now. I have to run.

MARJ (*Complete misinterpretation*): You have to run?

ANDREA: Yes, Marj, I have to go right now. Goodbye. (*Exits*)

MARJ (*Running after her*): Andrea! Andrea, come back! Don't run off like that.

GERALD: It's the only thing she can do under the circumstances. It's the only way.

MARJ: Oh, Andy! (*Returns to* GERALD) What'll she do for money?

GERALD: I lent her my week's allowance. That'll help.

Well, I'd better get back to English. See you later. (*Exits bumping into* PHIL *who enters*)

PHIL: Watch where you're goin' fella! Hm! Where's he goin' in such a rush. He'll kill himself on the stairs. The dope doesn't even watch were he's going.

MARJ: He's not a *dope*. He's a gentleman. A knight in shining armor.

PHIL: Gerald, a knight in shining armor? What brought all this on?

MARJ: Andy lost her mother's huge diamond engagement ring. Then she was afraid that her father would beat her within an inch of her life. So, she's running away. Gerald gave her his week's allowance so she could escape.

PHIL: No kiddin'? That's a shame. Whew! Her mother would be sick if she knew all this.

MARJ: She'll probably faint dead away when she does hear.

PHIL: Any woman would.

MARJ: Imagine a furious father, a fainting mother—no wonder she's running away from home.

DELIA (*Rushing in, tingling with excitement*): Is it true what I heard about Andrea?

MARJ (*With great dramatic emotion*): Unfortunately—yes!

DELIA: I saw her running out of the building—hair flying, tears flowing, and her face as white as chalk.

PHIL: Sounds sick to me.

MARJ: She said she was sick about it.

DELIA: She must be sick. She was wild-eyed!

PHIL: Do you think she is really sick?

DELIA: Phil, I said she was chalk-white and wild-eyed.

PHIL: She's sick as a dog.

DELIA: What do you expect? All this trouble. Nervous tension. Besides, there's measles going around.

PHIL: If she has the measles, she should have a doctor.

MARJ: Instead she's all alone, running through the streets.

PHIL: I wonder where she caught the measles.

DELIA: Her kid brother, of course. All the kids have them now.

MARJ: I could weep for Andy.

DELIA: What about her mother? Think of it! A cruel husband who beats his daughter. A son down with the measles. A treasured diamond engagement ring lost. And a loving daughter sick and running away from home.

PHIL: It's enough to give a person a heart attack.

DELIA: That's no joke. She might very well have a heart attack over this situation.

MARJ: My heart is racing right now, and I'm not even related to her.

PHIL: My health teacher says that more people die of heart trouble than anything else.

DELIA: Don't say another word, Phil. It's all too tragic.

MARJ: Something ought to be done.

DELIA: Yes, our principal should know about it.

MARJ: You're right. Phil, go tell Mr. Faddle all about it before Mrs. Nevins gets any worse.

PHIL: I don't know if I should, but I will. (*Exits*)

DELIA: Exactly what did Andrea say when she left?

MARJ (*Rising to the occasion and acting out the drama*): She stood right . . . here, like this. Her hand clutching her neck. She smiled sadly, but sweetly and whispered in husky tones, "I have to run."

DELIA: "Have to run?" I see, she felt the pressure on her. She knew the beating her cruel father would give her

. . . she knew about her sick brother . . . and her mother with the bad heart.

MARJ (*Dreamily*): Gerald was magnificent through it all.

DELIA: What did he do?

MARJ (*Again the actress*): He stood strong and generous. He gave her his week's allowance. He knew her problem; he understood.

DELIA: Did he say anything?

MARJ (*Pointing with flourish*): As Andrea fled through the hall, he called me back, saying wisely, "It's the *only* thing she can do under the circumstances. It's the *only* way!" (*Pauses for dramatic emphasis here.*)

DELIA (*Thoroughly engrossed, thoroughly moved by the tragedy of it all*): Beautiful, Marjorie. Beautiful and sad.

MARJ: It was like a great movie. A movie right here in the main hall. And I . . . I was a part of it all.

DELIA: I only wish I had been part of it myself.

FADDLE (*Dashing in*): This is incredible. Simply incredible!

PHIL (*Entering behind him*): They felt you ought to know.

FADDLE: And they were absolutely right. Now, then, Marjorie, call Andrea's father at this number. (*Hands her a piece of paper*) It's his business address. (MARJORIE *phones.*)

DELIA: I'm glad you're doing something about this, Mr. Faddle.

FADDLE: It's my duty. Just part of my job. Just part of the job of a school principal. All in a day's work, you know. Give me the phone, Marjorie. (*He takes phone*) Hello, is Mr. Nevins there? . . . Who? . . . Who? . . . Miss Furbush? What are you doing in Mr. Nevins' office? . . . Oh, you're in the English office. . . . What?

. . . No, I'm not selling Spring Carnival tickets. This is Mr. Faddle. Now get off the wire. . . . Call back later. . . . I don't care, Miss Furbush! Hang up! I'm trying to make a very important phone call. Hang— up. Thank you. . . . Operator, give me 3400.

MARJ: Miss Furbush is still after her Carnival ticket.

FADDLE: She can wait. . . . Hello, Mr. Nevins. . . . This is Herman Faddle, principal at the high school. . . . Yes. . . . I have some distressing news to discuss with you that needs immediate attention. . . . I know you have a business to operate, but this is more important. . . . Well, I hate to discuss it over the telephone. It's about your wife's heart attack, and your daughter losing Mrs. Nevins' engagement ring, and running away from home, and you threatening to beat her. . . . No . . . I am not crazy.

DELIA: If you ask me, he's the one who's crazy.

PHIL: Sh, I can't hear.

FADDLE: I do not choose to argue over the phone. I shall expect you in my office at once. Goodbye. (*Puts phone down*)

PHIL: What did he say?

FADDLE: He denied the whole thing.

DELIA: Pretense. That's what it is. Plain out-and-out pretense.

FADDLE: He used very strong language. (*Mops head with pocket handkerchief*)

MARJ: Trying to cover up for himself.

FADDLE: Are you *sure* you have the facts straight?

DELIA: Mr. Faddle, there are three of us here who are witnesses.

PHIL: The entire school knows about it by now.

FADDLE: Oh, my!

MARJ: I hope the newspaper downtown doesn't hear about it.

FADDLE: We must keep it out of the newspaper. Bad publicity for the school.

DELIA: It's almost a *scandal!*

FADDLE (*Shocked by the thought*): A scandal?

DELIA (*Dramatically, with gestures*): I can see the headlines now. "High school girl runs away from home to escape beating by brutal father."

FADDLE: Heavens!

DELIA: "Mother suffers heart attack."

FADDLE: Oh!

DELIA: "Priceless diamond ring lost near principal's office."

FADDLE: Please, Delia, please. That's enough.

MARJ: But, it *could* happen, Mr. Faddle. It could happen.

FADDLE: Not if we keep it to ourselves.

PHIL: Keep it to ourselves? With the whole basketball team looking for the ring.

DELIA: Besides, Miss Furbush knows all about it.

FADDLE (*This is too much*): Not Miss Furbush. . . . Excuse me, everyone. I'm going to lie down in my office. I don't feel well. (*Exits*)

MARJ: I still feel that something should be done to bring Andy back. The poor girl doesn't know what she's doing.

DELIA: Yes, someone should find her and bring her back.

PHIL: You can't bring her back until you know where she's run *to.*

ALEX (*Enters*): Any news about the great diamond loss?

DELIA: It's no joke, Alex. Andrea has run away because of it.

ALEX: Andrea ran away?

MARJ: We have to bring her back. We have to locate her.

ALEX: There's only *one* way to locate a missing person.

PHIL: What's that?

ALEX: Call the police.

DELIA: The police?

ALEX: The only way.

MARJ: Alex is absolutely right. I'll call the police right away.

PHIL (*Restraining hand on phone*): Now wait a minute, Marjorie. We ought to check with Mr. Faddle before we call the police.

MARJ: He's lying down resting. (*In telephone*) Operator, give me the police. Hurry, this is an emergency. A life is at stake.

DELIA: Make it sound real urgent so the police will get right out.

PHIL (*Sadly, but thoughtfully*): Somehow, I'm beginning to regret this whole mess.

MARJ: Hello? Police department? . . . This is Miss Marjorie Higgins at the high school. . . . Yes. . . . One of our students, a Miss Andrea Nevins, has run away from home. She lost her mother's valuable diamond ring and her father has threatened to beat her within an inch of her life. . . . Yes, and her mother has had a heart attack and her brother is down with the measles. . . . Sure I know what I'm talking about. It's serious. . . . Sure. . . . Our principal had a terrible argument with Mr. Nevins right on this phone. Yes, and he nearly collapsed. . . . Mr. Faddle nearly collapsed. He's lying down right now. . . . We'll give you the details when you arrive. Better bring some of your men. . . . We're right in the main hall. . . . Yes. Goodbye.

DELIA: Now we'll get some *real* action.

PHIL: I wonder how Mrs. Nevins' heart attack is.

DELIA: Quite severe, I'd guess.

MARJ: Should I call and check?

ALEX: Might as well. You've called everybody else.

PHIL: I think I ought to go home.

DELIA: Stay right where you are. We'll need you when the police arrive.

PHIL: I was afraid of that!

MARJ (*Phone in hand*): 3223-J, please.

ALEX: Who's she calling?

DELIA: Andy's mother.

ALEX: Oh.

MARJ: There's no answer.

DELIA: Call her doctor and see what he says. Their doctor is Dr. Fine at 1002.

MARJ: Operator, try 1002, and push it, please.

PHIL: I think you ought to hang up.

ALEX (*Offering a package*): Anybody for chewing gum?

DELIA: Honestly, Alex, how *can* you chew gum at a time like this.

MARJ: Hello, Dr. Fine? . . . This is Marj Higgins. I called to ask about Mrs. Nevins and her heart attack. . . . Her heart attack. . . . Nobody called you? . . . Didn't you even know about it? . . . Yes, this afternoon. I just tried to get her on the phone but there was no answer. . . . No, nobody's home with her. . . . Yes, you certainly ought to get right over there. . . . Billy is sick too . . . and Mrs. Nevins may be unconscious. Perhaps you ought to get the ambulance from the hospital . . .

MARILYN (*Entering in a hurry*): For heaven's sake, Marjorie, get off the phone. Miss Furbush has been trying to call down here for the last ten minutes. She's furious.

MARJ (*At phone*): If Mrs. Nevins needs any help, tell her to call on me. . . . Thank you. Goodbye.

DELIA: For one measly ticket, Miss Furbush can wait. This is tragedy here. Pure Greek tragedy.

MARILYN: Miss Furbush will make a tragedy of you, if you don't send up a ticket soon. (*Telephone rings.*)

MARJ (*At phone*): Hello, Spring Tragedy . . . I mean, Spring Carnival . . . Miss Furbush? That ticket is on its way up any minute now. . . . No, Andrea isn't back yet. . . . No, I don't know why she was wearing her mother's ring. . . . Yes, it was foolish. . . . No, he's still resting. . . . Yes, we'll let you know what happens. Goodbye. (*Hangs up phone*)

PHIL: I never realized before how important a ticket to the Carnival is.

MARILYN: She's very much interested in student affairs.

PHIL: That's one way of saying "nosey." (*Telephone rings.*)

ALEX (*Picking phone up*): I have it. You rest, Marj. Hello, Spring Carnival tickets. . . . What, the editor of the newspaper downtown.

PHIL (*Mournfully*): Uh-oh.

ALEX: About what? . . . The girl who ran away after her father beat her? . . .

DELIA: Oh, no—Mr. Nevins found her and already beat her . . .

ALEX (*Still at phone*): Yeah, the police got that. Yes. . . . Yes. . . . Well, if you want to speak to the principal you'd better come down here. . . .

PHIL: This gets worse . . . much worse.

ALEX: He's collapsed in his office . . . collapsed. . . . We're in the main hall. All right. We'll be here. . . . G'bye. (*Hangs up*)

MARILYN: I'm sure Mr. Faddle will be glad to talk to the newspaper.

PHIL: Yes, delirious with joy.

GERALD (*Entering*): Andrea back yet?

MARJ: Back *here?* After her father found her and beat her?

GERALD: Found her? Beat her?

MARILYN: That's what the newspaper editor said.

GERALD: What's going on here?

DELIA: Sh! Look down the hall. There!

MARJ: It's Andy!

PHIL: She doesn't look beat up to me.

MARILYN: She isn't even crying.

ALEX: Looks rather happy for someone in trouble.

ANDREA (*Enters, cheerful, smiling*): Hi!

MARJ (*Shocked . . . something is all wrong here*): Hi?

DELIA (*The little mother*): Now, don't get hysterical, dear. Bear up.

ANDREA: Bear up? About what?

ALEX: Your brother's measles.

ANDREA: My brother is in school, and he doesn't have the measles.

MARILYN: (*Weakly*): But your mother's severe heart attack.

ANDREA: Heart attack? My mother is perfectly well. I just met her downtown in the department store.

DELIA (*Even more weakly*): Didn't your father beat you within an inch of your life?

ANDREA: My father doesn't beat me. And I haven't seen him since breakfast.

PHIL (*Endeavoring to find some firm ground*): You *did* lose something?

ANDREA: Yes, but when I was downtown, I suddenly remembered where I put it. Where's my notebook?

MARJ: Right here. (*Gives it to* ANDREA)

ANDREA: Just when the bell rang I put it on my notebook. And the notebook was open right here to my
French lesson . . . and (*Holds up the handkerchief*)
here it is.

MARJ: The diamond ring in the handkerchief!

GERALD: Diamond ring?

ANDREA (*Undoing handkerchief and holding up the
dime*): It's not a diamond . . . it's a *dime.*

DELIA (*Faintly*): A dime . . .

ANDREA: Wrapped in my mother's best handkerchief.

GERALD: The one her father gave her mother.

PHIL: Which you couldn't bear to lose?

DELIA: Which if you lost, you couldn't face your mother
without?

ANDREA: Yes, this is it. Everything is all right now.

MARJ: And you didn't run away from home at all?

ANDREA: No! What's wrong with all of you?

FADDLE (*Enters; he speaks in a calm, patient fatherly way*):
Andrea, poor child. Let me help you. Let me offer my
sympathy.

ANDREA: Mr. Faddle, do you feel well?

FADDLE (*Smiling wistfully, knowingly*): It's all right,
child. We know all. We will help you in your great
distress. Trust us. We are your dear friends.

GERALD: Something is mighty strange here.

ANDREA: Mr. Faddle, I don't know what's been going on.
But, I didn't run away. I didn't lose a diamond ring.
My brother doesn't have the measles. My mother did
not have a heart attack, and my father didn't beat me.

FADDLE: What?

ANDREA: All I lost was this dime and this handkerchief.

FADDLE: Somebody help me to a chair. (ALEX *guides* MR. FADDLE *to the comfortable chair at left.*) But they said . . . I called your father . . . Miss Furbush. . . . Get me a glass of water my nerves are gone. . . . I . . . I . . .

PHIL (*At window*): Wow, look at the commotion outside.

FADDLE (*Hardly daring to ask*): What commotion?

PHIL: There's an ambulance, the editor of the newspaper with a photographer, Mr. Nevins, Dr. Fine, and a whole car full of police. And they're all rushing up the front steps of the school!

FADDLE: No, no, no! (*Collapses with head on arm of chair. He is sobbing hysterically.*)

PHIL: I think we'd better go now.

ALEX: Yeah. Our work is done.

FADDLE: Don't leave me. Don't leave me. You got me into this. Stay and share the blame. Oh, my nerves. My poor taut nerves. (*His head is back on the arm of the chair again. The students all tip-toe out except* DELIA *and* MARJ.)

DELIA (*Softly, suggestively*): He doesn't look at all well.

MARJ: He kept complaining of his nerves.

DELIA: Probably won't last another week.

MARJ: We can expect a new principal on Monday.

DELIA (*It has begun again*): He was such a *nice* man. (*Telephone rings.*)

MARJ (*Returns to get phone as curtains begin to close gradually*): Hello, Spring Carnival tickets. . . . Miss Furbush? . . . I'm bringing your ticket up myself. . . . What? . . . You decided not to go? We're awfully sorry. . . . Oh, by the way, Miss Furbush, is it true Mr. Faddle is leaving school because of a nervous breakdown. . . . I mean who will be our new principal? . . . well, it's like this . . . (*Curtain*)

THE END

Production Notes

THE TEN-PENNY TRAGEDY

Characters: 4 male; 4 female.

Playing Time: 30 minutes.

Costumes: Modern, everyday dress. Mr. Faddle wears business suit.

Properties: Several textbooks, loose-leaf notebook, box of tickets, cash box, telephone, handkerchiefs, two dimes and some small change, package of chewing gum; bicycle bell for sound of telephone ringing, several magazines.

Setting: The "Information Desk" just outside Principal Faddle's office. Stage left, there is a comfortable chair and end table with magazines. Stage center is the "Information Desk," bearing several textbooks, a loose-leaf notebook, a box of tickets, a cash box, and a telephone. Behind the desk is a free-standing blackboard bearing the message:

SPRING CARNIVAL FRIDAY AT 2 P.M.
Prizes   Contests
     TICKETS HERE 10¢ EACH

Lighting: No special effects.

235

The Nerve of Napoleon

By Juliet Garver

Characters

FATHER, *Jim Bowen*
MOTHER, *Louise Bowen*
CAROLINE ⎤
AMY   ⎬ *their children*
PEGGY   ⎟
CHARLIE ⎦
MISS STEWART
JOSEPHINE
SHARPY WILLMAN
NAPOLEON

TIME: *One evening, after dinner.*
SETTING: *The Bowen living room.*
AT RISE: FATHER *is reading the paper.* MOTHER *is sewing.* CAROLINE *is reading a movie magazine and chewing gum enthusiastically.* PEGGY *is playing with a lump of clay, rolling it into different shapes.* CHARLIE *is reading a big, heavy book, obviously fascinated and in another world.* AMY *walks over and stares at* CHARLIE *a moment, shaking her head.*

236

AMY: I see it but I don't believe it.

CHARLIE (*Without looking up*): Go 'way.

AMY: You still reading that book about Napoleon?

CHARLIE (*Looks up, defiantly*): Yes, I'm still reading it. I happen to like this book. Napoleon Bonaparte was a great man . . . a—a man of daring.

PEGGY: Well . . .

FATHER: So just because they call you "Boney" you've become interested in the life of Napoleon.

CAROLINE: Hypnotized is more like it. Maybe it's because of his sudden interest in Josephine.

CHARLIE: You be quiet!

FATHER: Napoleon's wife, Josephine?

CAROLINE: Oh, no . . . Charlie has a Josephine of his own.

FATHER (*Pleased*): Hey . . . you've been keeping something from me, son.

MOTHER: I didn't know you had a girl, Charlie.

PEGGY: He doesn't really.

AMY: He just wishes he had the nerve to ask her for a date. He just sits and looks at her longingly . . . ah me . . . across the aisle in geometry.

CHARLIE (*Upset*): It's just a lot of silly talk. I—I just sit across the aisle from her in geometry, and I . . . sometimes I help her with the problems, and I . . . uh . . . (*Phone rings. CHARLIE looks at it, relieved.*) I'd better answer the phone. (*Goes to phone*) Hello? Yes . . . speaking. What? Oh no! . . . You sure you mean *me?* No . . . well, I couldn't! . . . I couldn't possibly run for Student Council president! . . . Why not? I have a dozen reasons! In the first place, I don't like to make speeches. And in the second place, I don't want all that responsibility. . . . O.K., so I'm scared!

. . . Sure I realize it's an honor to be Student Council president. But I'm not your man!

CAROLINE (*Looking up from magazine*): He's not a man —period.

CHARLIE (*Into phone*): No, no . . . I don't want to run . . . no . . . uh . . . thanks anyway. . . . See you Monday in school—oh and thanks again. 'Bye now. (*Hangs up phone*) Gosh! They want me to run for Student Council president.

PEGGY: We're all just as surprised as you are.

AMY: Everybody else must have turned it down. (*Phone rings. AMY dashes for it.*)

CHARLIE (*Amused but scornful*): She ought to be on the track team.

AMY (*Into phone, breathless*): Hello? Oh, yes . . . uh huh . . . (*Giggles*) Oh, you . . .

FATHER: That takes care of our phone for the evening. Nobody'll be able to break through the sound barrier now.

AMY (*Into phone*): You really think so?

MOTHER: Charlie, why didn't you want to run for Student Council president?

FATHER: Yes, I've been wondering about that too.

CHARLIE: Well—I . . . look, if they want me to help with the campaign, O.K. And I don't mind plugging the other candidates or working behind the scenes. That's it . . . I like staying behind the scenes.

FATHER (*Shakes his head*): I don't know. He doesn't get that from my side of the family.

AMY (*Into phone*): Now I call that a real shame.

CHARLIE: Look, is there any law that says I have to run for president?

FATHER: No law, but . . . well . . . I'd be kind of proud of you, Charlie, if you ran for president.

CHARLIE: Dad, it's just not for me, that's all. I'm no politician. (*Goes over to table, takes a candy from bowl, takes off gold foil wrapper, pops candy into his mouth*) Mm . . . this is good candy. (*Takes another piece and eats it.*)

AMY: (*Into phone*): Uh huh . . . I sure will. . . . 'Bye now, Buddy. (*Hangs up. To others*) Well, according to Buddy Warren, the Student Council election's practically in the bag. It looks as if nobody has the nerve to stand up against Sharpy Willman and his gang.

MOTHER: Sharpy Willman—that bully I always see slouching around the school yard?

CHARLIE (*Despondently*): Yes, that's the one.

FATHER: But you can't let him be president, Charlie.— You *have* to run—it's your responsibility.

CHARLIE: Dad, I just can't—(*Doorbell rings.*) I'll get it. (*He goes to door.* MISS STEWART *enters.*) Oh, Miss Stewart . . . come on in. . . .

MISS STEWART (*Enthused*): Charles, I came to tell you the good news! I didn't want to wait till Monday. (*She walks towards the others.*)

FATHER: Good news? What good news?

MISS STEWART: Charles won the composition contest— "What Makes A Good Citizen"! Charles won first prize! I'm so proud of him. I was one of the judges, and we just reached a decision a few minutes ago.

MOTHER: Why, Charlie! How wonderful!

MISS STEWART: Let me be the first to congratulate you.

CHARLIE (*Overwhelmed*): Well, gee . . . thanks . . . thanks a lot!

MISS STEWART: And next Monday night in the school auditorium, Charles will be awarded first prize, a $50.00 United States Savings Bond.

PEGGY: Now you can pay me back the two dollars you owe me, Charlie.

MOTHER: Peggy . . .

MISS STEWART: Of course, Charles will have to make a speech.

CHARLIE: A speech! Me? Oh no . . . I mean, couldn't the judges mail me the award? It might save them a lot of bother . . . might save everybody a lot of trouble.

MISS STEWART (*Smiling*): My, did you ever see such modesty?

CHARLIE (*Looking sick*): Do I have to make a speech?

MISS STEWART: Just a short one, Charles, about five minutes.

CHARLIE: Five minutes is like a lifetime out in front of an audience!

CAROLINE (*Dramatically*): I wish I had that chance. I'd love to play to an audience, hold them enthralled . . . look into a sea of faces . . .

CHARLIE: I'm at sea all right. What am I going to talk about? What am I going to say? I—I think I'm getting laryngitis.

MISS STEWART: Oh, don't worry, Charles. If you want some help on your speech, I'll help you Monday after school. Well, I'll be running along . . . congratulations again.

CHARLIE (*Unenthusiastically*): Thanks.

MISS STEWART: Goodbye, everybody! (*She exits.*)

CAROLINE: Say, maybe Josephine will sit in the first row.

CHARLIE (*Moaning*): Everything happens to me!

PEGGY: Yes, this is your bad day all right. First, they ask you to run for Student Council president, and now you've won the composition contest. I wonder what horrible thing is going to happen to you next.

CHARLIE: Never mind the sarcasm. (*Goes over to candy bowl, helps himself*)

MOTHER: Charlie, if you don't stop eating candy, you're going to upset your stomach. You can't possibly be hungry after all that dinner. (CHARLIE *eats another piece.*)

AMY: No, but he gorges himself on candy, anyway. (*Phone rings.*)

PEGGY: It's probably Washington calling. They probably want Charlie to be the first child president.

CAROLINE: I'm sure he'll turn them down. (*Phone rings again.*)

MOTHER (*Answers phone*): Hello? Oh yes—just a minute. It's for you, Caroline . . . a girl calling.

CAROLINE (*Obviously disappointed*): Oh, all right. (*She goes to phone.*) Hello? Hi, Josephine . . .

CHARLIE (*Upset*): What's she calling here for?

PEGGY: Why are you so green around the gills?

CHARLIE: Who? Me?

CAROLINE (*Into phone*): Sure, Josephine, I'd be glad to be on the dance committee, and Peggy and Amy would too. Sure. We'll help all we can. Uh huh. . . . All right. . . . We can meet over here later this evening. . . . Oh, don't worry about that. Charlie can walk you home if it gets late. . . .

CHARLIE: Hey, wait a minute—

CAROLINE (*Into phone*): O.K., Josephine, see you later. 'Bye. (*Hangs up*)

CHARLIE: What's this about my walking Josephine home?

CAROLINE: You just don't appreciate what I'm trying to do for you.

CHARLIE: I sure don't!

PEGGY: It'll be much more romantic walking home with Josephine than sitting across the aisle from her in geometry. . . .

AMY: Yes—you and thirty-eight others.

CHARLIE: I guess you're right. (*Takes piece of candy, hands it to* AMY) Here's a Spanish doubloon, to show my appreciation. (AMY *takes candy laughingly, pops it into her mouth.*)

MOTHER: C'mon, girls, I need a clean-up crew in the kitchen if we're to be finished before Josephine arrives. (MOTHER *and the three girls exit.*)

CHARLIE: Dad, I've been wanting to ask you something . . . uh . . . man to man . . .

FATHER: Sure. Go ahead.

CHARLIE: Did you feel like this when you were growing up?

FATHER: Like what?

CHARLIE: I don't know. Sometimes I wish I could crawl into a nice, dark cave and stay there.

FATHER (*Getting angry*): What kind of attitude is that?

CHARLIE (*Discouraged*): Forget it—forget I said anything.

FATHER: Charlie, I never felt like that in my entire life —like a mouse—and I don't understand it in you. We Bowens were always out in front—real leaders.

CHARLIE: I guess you're right.

FATHER (*Shakes his head*): Charlie, I don't know . . . I just don't know. You must take after your mother's side of the family. They're all scared of their own shadows.

CHARLIE (*Goes over and picks up book on Napoleon, sits down, opens book*): This is a terrific book . . . Napoleon . . .

FATHER (*Yawns*): Think I'll go take a short nap. Always get sleepy after dinner. (*Exits*)

CHARLIE (*Looks at book, then closes it with a sigh*): What did he say? Scared of my own shadow . . . I'll bet Napoleon wasn't scared of anything, ever. . . . (*Opens book and reads aloud*) "He could personally direct complicated military maneuvers and at the same time control the press, the detailed French police system, the intricate foreign policy and the home government of the people." (*Whistles in admiration*) What a man . . . what a man! (NAPOLEON *struts onstage.* NOTE: *If possible,* NAPOLEON *should be given special lighting, to suggest that he is invisible to everyone except* CHARLIE.)

NAPOLEON: You were, of course, speaking about me.

CHARLIE (*Puzzled*): Who—who are you?

NAPOLEON: I am the great Napoleon . . . Napoleon the First . . . you do not recognize me?

CHARLIE: Yes, I—but you can't be! I mean . . . I don't understand. . . .

NAPOLEON: Many strange things in the world, yes? One minute I am peaceful in my grave under the dome of the Hotel des Invalides in Paris, next to my son, Napoleon II —next minute, I am here . . . a different country, a different century, no?

CHARLIE: No—I mean, yes. I've been reading about you so much I must be dreaming about you now!

NAPOLEON: Dreams and reality are so closely related . . . like cousins. (*Shrugs*) But no matter. I have come to give you the courage.

CHARLIE: Courage?

NAPOLEON: Forgive me, Monsieur, but you are timid like the rabbit. I have been peeking into your life.

CHARLIE: You have?

NAPOLEON: And why not? Have you not been peeking into mine (*Points accusingly to book*) in that book?

CHARLIE: Yes, but . . .

NAPOLEON: There you are. Now what you need is a personal advisor, like the great Napoleon I.

CHARLIE: I do?

NAPOLEON: But *absolument*. We have a great deal in common, *mon ami*.

CHARLIE: We do? Golly, I never suspected it. Like what, for instance?

NAPOLEON: For one thing, we are both—shall we say— slightly under six feet? And then, there is our nickname.

CHARLIE: You mean "Boney"?

NAPOLEON: Exactly, "Boney"—my family name was Bonaparte, you know.

CHARLIE: But they call me "Boney" for quite another reason.

NAPOLEON: No matter. We have the same name, and that is reason enough for me to help you. First, before I proceed, I must sit down. Even a personal advisor's feet can hurt. (*Goes over to chair*) Ah, 'tis only a common chair—nothing for me.

CHARLIE (*Apologetically*): Mom's been wanting to get new furniture for a long time.

NAPOLEON (*Musing*): Strange . . . I used to look at

thrones. My words are famous. I said, "When I see an empty throne, I feel the urge to sit down on it."

CHARLIE (*Eagerly*): And you did! (*Suddenly flustered*) I mean, you ruled Europe.

NAPOLEON: Yes, I did. Young man, I came here to give you courage—courage to run for your election, to make your speech.

CHARLIE (*Alarmed*): Oh no, I wish you wouldn't! I mean . . . I'd really rather not.

NAPOLEON (*Drawing himself up*): What? You say this to Napoleon?

CHARLIE (*Looking down at his shoes*): Yes . . . I'm sorry, but you've never crossed swords with Sharpy Willman and his gang.

NAPOLEON: Many are the battles I have fought, but never did I have so much trouble with my soldiers as I have with you.

CHARLIE: I'm sorry.

NAPOLEON: Almost I feel as bad as I did at Waterloo in 1815. Almost, I am ready to sail for England again as prisoner.

CHARLIE: I guess I'm just another Waterloo.

NAPOLEON: Please . . . let us no more mention Waterloo! It was my biggest—how you say—defeat. (*Raises voice emphatically*) But I didn't give up!

CHARLIE: I know, I read about it.

NAPOLEON: *You* give up before you make the start! Today, when you hear you should make the speech in school, what do you do? You dream up lar—yn—gitis!

CHARLIE (*Defensively*): I often get laryngitis and—and they can keep their old award. I just can't make that speech!

NAPOLEON: Why not? You must have the nerve—nerve

like Napoleon. Nothing stopped me. Why, I even escaped from Elba!

CHARLIE (*Wearily*): I know . . .

NAPOLEON: The great Napoleon does not give up. I do not give up now. (*Reaches into pocket*) Here . . . I am going to give to you my own lucky coin. (*Holds up gold coin for audience to see*) A gold Napoleon.

CHARLIE (*Interested*): A gold Napoleon?

NAPOLEON: Yes, named in honor of Emperor Napoleon I. (*Bows low*) At your service. (*Gives* CHARLIE *the coin with a flourish*)

CHARLIE (*Looks at coin in palm of his hand, flustered*): Oh, I . . .

NAPOLEON: This is no ordinary coin. I never told anyone, not even my Josephine, but this coin . . . this is where the nerve of Napoleon comes from.

CHARLIE: What? I mean, I don't get it.

NAPOLEON: You rub the coin. Go on.

CHARLIE (*Rubs it*): Like this?

NAPOLEON (*Nods*): Now you will have the courage. With this magic lucky coin, I defeated the Austrians at Ulm in 1805. I marched into Vienna in triumph. A month later, I beat both the armies of Russia and Austria in that great battle of Austerlitz. And all because I carried that lucky gold "Napoleon"! Now I give it to you.

CHARLIE: Well, gee . . . thanks! I . . . you think it'll work?

NAPOLEON (*Angrily*): You are questioning the word of a man who dared to change the map of Europe?

CHARLIE: No, I—I didn't mean anything, your Imperial Highness. Maybe I could run for office, after all . . . (*With resolve*) With your permission, I'm going right upstairs to work on my campaign—with the help of my lucky gold "Napoleon."

NAPOLEON (*With imperial dignity*): Permission granted. (CHARLIE *exits.* NAPOLEON *turns and faces the audience.*) A foolish boy . . . he does not know yet that the courage comes from inside, not from lucky coins or a rabbit foot or hocus pocus. Yes, I gave him a gold Napoleon . . . my face is engraved on the one side (*Bragging now*), a handsome likeness. And on the other side is engraved "Empire Français . . . twenty francs . . . 1813." Yes, Charlie has a gold "Napoleon" but it is not my lucky coin—it is not even lucky. How could it be? Was I so lucky? I was exiled like a criminal to that miserable island, Saint Helena. (*Laughs bitterly*) Ha . . . the luck of Napoleon. I think the coin will help Charlie, though. I have the feeling, right here. (*Puts his hand in his jacket in the typical Napoleonic pose.* CHARLIE *enters smiling, confident.*) You are back so soon?

CHARLIE (*Very confident*): Oh, I just jotted down a few ideas. I'm not going to write any speeches ahead of time. When I get on that stage, I'll know what to say— whether it's for my campaign or for my composition award.

NAPOLEON: So? The gold Napoleon is working?

CHARLIE: I guess it must be working. I—I feel altogether different. . . . (*Doorbell rings.* CHARLIE *goes to door.* SHARPY WILLMAN *enters.*) Sharpy Willman!

SHARPY: I guess you're surprised to see me.

CHARLIE: Well, I . . . (*Looks nervously back and forth between* SHARPY *and* NAPOLEON)

NAPOLEON: Do not worry. Only you can see me, Charlie.

SHARPY: I can tell by the look on your face.

NAPOLEON: This young man is so sure of himself. I don't like it . . . reminds me of some men in France who opposed me.

SHARPY: I won't keep you in suspense. I came because I heard you had some idea about running for president.

CHARLIE: It . . . uh . . . wasn't my idea, and I . . .

SHARPY: What makes you think you could win? Listen, kid, you don't even have a ghost of a chance! You listen to me!

CHARLIE: Sure, I—you didn't let me explain . . .

SHARPY: What's there to explain? You want to run for president.

CHARLIE: But I . . .

SHARPY: Well, you're sunk before you start. My candidate, Bill Brookfield—he's going to win by a landslide. I've got it all set up, buddy—a real political machine.

NAPOLEON: You have maybe forgotten the gold Napoleon?

CHARLIE: I . . . yes . . . (*Reaches into his pocket quickly, rubs the coin*) Now, Sharpy Willman, you keep quiet and listen to what *I* have to say!

SHARPY: Well . . . gee whiz! I mean . . . gee whiz!

CHARLIE: I wasn't going to run for president, but now my fighting blood's aroused. (*Scornfully*) Political machine! I'm going to fight for what I believe is right!

SHARPY: I've never seen you like this before. What's got into you, Charlie?

CHARLIE: Did anything have to get into me?

NAPOLEON: Go on, tell him!

SHARPY: Ha! That's a laugh!

CHARLIE: Maybe it won't be so much of a laugh when this election business is over. I'm going to fight—you hear me?

SHARPY: I can hear. I'm not deaf.

CHARLIE: Then listen to this. I'm going to expose you and your whole machine! I'll show the school what's going on.

SHARPY: Hey, take it easy, pal! I never thought you had it in you. I laughed when I heard you were running. You quiet guys are funny. Maybe you've got dynamite inside you all the time, and all you need is a match to get going.

CHARLIE: Yes . . . I think I found the match, all right. You can go back to your campaign headquarters and tell your friends they're going to have a fight on their hands.

SHARPY: I heard you the first time—but we can fight, too. You'll see.

CHARLIE (*Coolly*): So long, Sharpy.

SHARPY: I . . . so long . . . (*He exits.*)

NAPOLEON (*Bows*): I bow to the future president of the Student Council.

CHARLIE (*Smiles*): Not so fast, Napoleon. I can't just march in and take over.

NAPOLEON: Why not? It has been done. I was a great believer in surprise tactics. (CAROLINE, AMY, *and* PEGGY *enter, chattering.* NAPOLEON *bows.*) Ah, the young ladies. . . . Too bad they can't see me.

CAROLINE: Josephine ought to be here any minute.

CHARLIE (*Goes over to candy dish and helps himself*): Josephine? I'd better get out of here.

AMY: And don't eat up all the candy. We won't have anything to offer our company.

CHARLIE (*Puts candy back*): Is that all you're going to serve? This miserable candy?

CAROLINE: Which you've been devouring as fast as Mom can put it in the candy dish.

CHARLIE: I mean, aren't you going to have cake and milk . . . something like that?

AMY: It's only a meeting.

PEGGY: However, if you want to take Josephine out afterwards, for chop suey or pizza or something fancy . . .

CHARLIE: No, I—I didn't mean anything like that.

NAPOLEON: Why, what is wrong with this Josephine?

CHARLIE (*To* NAPOLEON. *Defensively*): Listen, Josephine is the most wonderful girl in the world!

AMY: Well!

CAROLINE: May we quote you on that, Senator? (*Doorbell*)

PEGGY: Don't get panicky, Charlie. You can run upstairs.

AMY: With your laryngitis.

CAROLINE: Yes . . .

NAPOLEON: You have again forgotten the gold Napoleon?

CHARLIE (*Reaches into his pocket*): I'm not going anywhere. (*Rubs the coin*) What am I? A coward?

PEGGY: With a capital C.

CHARLIE: Not any more, I'm not. (*Puts coin down on table and reaches for a candy, which he unwraps and puts in his mouth as he goes to the door. As* CHARLIE *goes to the door, the doorbell rings again and* NAPOLEON, *in full view of the audience, takes the magic coin, puts it in his pocket and with a wink, substitutes a gold-foil-covered candy from the candy bowl.*)

CHARLIE (*At door*): Hi, Josephine!

JOSEPHINE (*Entering*): Oh, hello, Charlie.

CHARLIE (*Stuttering because he doesn't have his coin*): Uh—it's uh . . . nice to see you here, Josephine.

PEGGY (*Teasing*): Beau Brummell Bowen . . .

AMY: In person.

NAPOLEON: Your Josephine is beautiful—almost as beautiful as mine.

CHARLIE (*Emphatically*): Never you mind . . . (*Goes over to table and picks up what he thinks is the magic coin*)

PEGGY: We can have our meeting upstairs where we'll have some privacy.

CHARLIE (*Rubs coin*): No, wait a minute . . .

NAPOLEON: With so many women around, you are a brave man.

CHARLIE (*Rubs coin. Boldly*): I want to talk to Josephine, alone.

CAROLINE: Well!

AMY: That beats everything.

PEGGY: It can't happen here . . . but it did.

JOSEPHINE: What is it, Charlie? Do we have homework in geometry?

CHARLIE: This has nothing to do with geometry. I want to talk to you . . . just you and me.

PEGGY: This can't be for real!

AMY: I thought I knew all about men, and here I don't even know my own brother.

CHARLIE: Girls, please . . .

CAROLINE: All right, but don't take forever. (*They exit.*)

JOSEPHINE (*Puzzled but confident*): Charlie, what was it you wanted to see me about?

CHARLIE (*Rubs coin*): I want you to be the first to know. I'm going to run for Student Council president.

JOSEPHINE: That's wonderful, Charlie! Thanks for telling me. (*Starts to leave*)

CHARLIE: Wait, don't go yet.

JOSEPHINE (*Turns and looks at him*): There's something else?

CHARLIE: Yes. (*Rubs coin*) I'm going to make a speech next week in the auditorium.

JOSEPHINE: For the composition contest award?

CHARLIE: Yes . . . when they give me the award. I—I won the contest.

JOSEPHINE: That's terrific, Charlie! (*Gives a little laugh*) I'm talking to a real celebrity!

CHARLIE (*Modestly*): Well . . .

NAPOLEON: Goodbye, Charlie. I see you don't need me any more. (*He exits.*)

JOSEPHINE: I never thought you were the type to run for president and make speeches. But you seem different today.

CHARLIE: You don't know me very well, just from geometry class . . . (*Rubs the coin*) Josephine, I want to take you to the Spring Dance.

JOSEPHINE: I . . . I sort of have a tentative date.

CHARLIE (*Rubs coin*): You can break it. Please, Josephine, it's very important to me. A dance is just a dance . . . but if I can go to the Spring Dance with you, it'll really mean something . . .

JOSEPHINE (*Surprised but pleased*): Why, Charlie! I guess I really didn't know you . . . the real you.

CHARLIE: Then you'll go to the dance with me?

JOSEPHINE: Yes . . . yes, I think I will.

CHARLIE: Josephine, you don't know how happy that makes me! I—I want to tell you something. My whole life has been changed by this (*Opens his hand*)— lucky coin (*Looks at her*) a gold Napoleon.

JOSEPHINE (*Staring*): But, Charlie, this isn't a coin. It's just a piece of candy. (*Takes it from him, unwraps it, pops it into her mouth*) Mm . . . it's good.

CHARLIE (*Alarmed*): No, don't! Why . . . it *is* candy. But I thought . . .

JOSEPHINE (*Smiling*): You were just kidding me.

CHARLIE: No, I thought it was responsible for everything. Strange . . .

JOSEPHINE: Responsible for what?

CHARLIE: It's a long story. I did have a French coin, a gold Napoleon. I thought I needed it (*Smiles*), but I don't. (*Takes her arm*) C'mon, Josephine, let's seal our new friendship with a Coke.

JOSEPHINE: I'd love to, Charlie, but the meeting . . .

CHARLIE: Never mind the meeting. Let's go. . . . (*They exit together.* NAPOLEON *strides to center, faces audience.*)

NAPOLEON: Such ingratitude! (*Shakes his head*) Great men are never fully appreciated. Now Charlie thinks he did it all by himself. Ha . . . where would he be without the nerve of Napoleon? Just dreaming about the things he wants to do. (*Shrugs*) Well, *c'est la vie*— that's life. And now, I must be on my way for there is a boy in *Napoleon,* North Dakota, who needs my services. (*Bows*) Until we meet again. (*Straightens up*) Maybe I'll be seeing (*Points to audience*) *you* one of these days. You never can tell. . . . (*Curtain*)

THE END

Production Notes

THE NERVE OF NAPOLEON

Characters: 4 male; 6 female.

Playing Time: 30 minutes.

Costumes: Father may wear slacks and sport shirt. Mother may wear cotton dress and apron. Charlie, Caroline, Amy, Peggy, and Josephine wear everyday school clothes. Sharpy Willman might wear sloppy dungarees and leather jacket. Napoleon wears blue and gold uniform and three-cornered hat.

Properties: A large impressive-looking book, and bowl filled with candy coins (gold-foil-covered chocolate) for Charlie; a movie magazine for Caroline; modeling clay' for Peggy; newspaper for Father; sewing materials for Mother; a large gold foreign coin for Napoleon; telephone; bicycle bell for sound of telephone ringing.

Setting: The Bowen living room. Stage left is an armchair. Upstage center is a table on which stands a lamp and bowl of candy coins. Upstage right is a small telephone table holding a telephone. Other furnishings, chairs, small tables, etc., may be as simple or elaborate as desired. At right is an exit which represents the front door. At left is an exit leading to kitchen.

Lighting: No special effects necessary. If possible, Napoleon may receive special lighting to suggest that he is invisible to everyone except Charlie.

Society Page

By Joan and Pearl Allred

Characters

VIOLET PEMBERTON, *a society editor*
JANICA REED, *her assistant*
A BRIDE
A BRIDE'S MOTHER
JIMMY HARPER, *a photographer*
BARBARA LAKE, *a career girl*
SALLY SUMNER, *a society girl*
CLIFTON DWYER, *her fiancé*

SETTING: *The society office of a newspaper.*
AT RISE: VIOLET *and* JANICA *are sitting at their desks.* JANICA *is typing a story, while* VIOLET, *engrossed in a telephone conversation, is taking notes on a pad.*

VIOLET (*At telephone*): Oh, yes. Yes, of course. Naturally you don't want to cause any hurt feelings, so we won't mention how many guests came. Or let's just say "a few intimate friends"—that way nobody can feel bad about being left out. Something like this: "Japanese lanterns and masses of roses formed a gala summer setting when Dr. and Mrs. Howard Norbert entertained for a few intimate friends at their charming home on Hillcrest Heights last Thursday evening. The refreshment table, set in the garden, featured a pink lace cloth over satin . . ." But we've been all over that, haven't we? Yes . . . oh, yes, of course. We'll give it a good place at the top of the personals. (*During the last part of this conversation, a* BRIDE *and her* MOTHER *have come in and stand waiting, upstage left.* JANICA *notices them after a moment and motions them downstage.*)

JANICA: May I help you?

MOTHER: Are you the society editor? We were told to go to her.

JANICA: She's busy at the telephone right now. I'm her assistant. Is it something I could take?

MOTHER (*Suspiciously*): Well—(*She gropes through her purse and finally produces a small, dog-eared picture.*) We wanted this put in the Sunday paper.

JANICA: I see. Won't you sit down? (*They sit, but only on the edges of their chairs.*) Hmm. It's a little dim, isn't it? Is that the bride to the left there?

MOTHER (*Insulted*): It's not the bridegroom.

JANICA: Oh, yes. I can see, now. There's the bridegroom sort of behind a basket of ferns.

BRIDE: We had Verl's cousin take the pictures. He does very nice work, but it was a little bit dark in the church.

JANICA: Are you the bride? Well, we'll see what the engravers can do with this, but I can't promise it will be very clear. If you have the wedding information written down, I might as well look it over to see if it's complete. (MOTHER *fumbles through purse again, and*

hands scrap of paper to JANICA, *who reads haltingly*)
"In one of the most gorgeous affairs of the season, Mr.
and Mrs. Joe Jesperson wish to announce the marriage
of their daughter Florence Smith to Mr. Verl Gerber
of this city." (*Furrows brow*)

MOTHER: We want it put in just like that. Sometimes
these articles come out in the paper full of mistakes,
just because people went and changed them.

JANICA: Well, it's just a little confusing. Is it *Miss*
Florence Smith, or have you been married before?

BRIDE: No, I—

MOTHER: No, this is the first time. That's why we went
all out for the wedding. It was so beautiful.

JANICA (*Persisting*): But if her name is Smith and yours
is Jesperson—

MOTHER: *I* am the one that has been married before.
Twice. (*Primly*) We don't mention Florence's first two
fathers. They're best forgot. Mr. Jesperson has been
like a father to Florence, so put it down like that.

JANICA (*Dubiously*): Well, all right. (*Makes pencil mark*)
I see you've left out the name of the bridegroom's
parents.

BRIDE (*Accusingly*): See, Mother, I told you they'd want
to know that.

MOTHER: Well, don't come crying to me about it, Florence. It's your own fault for not finding out things like
that before Verl went off on his fishing trip.

BRIDE (*Near crying*): Well, I can't think of everything.

JANICA (*Curious in spite of herself*): You mean he went
off on a fishing trip right after his marriage?

MOTHER: Yes. He said he had to rest up from the wedding. Think hard, Florence. Try to remember if Verl
ever said anything.

BRIDE: I know he must have mentioned them, but it's just slipped my mind. (*Hopefully*) He said he used to live in Nebraska. Do you know any Nebraska people?

JANICA: I'm afraid not.

MOTHER: Never mind. Just leave them out.

JANICA: I suppose we'll have to let it go. (*Reads*) "The happy couple stood in front of a fireplace; holding potted palms and lighted candles in branch candelabra." Oh—I see, you mean, the *fireplace* was holding the palms and candelabra. Well—everything else seems to be here. (*They rise, collect their belongings, and turn to leave.*) Oh, just a minute. What's this word here?

MOTHER (*Peering*): That's what the bride's bouquet was made of, streptococcus.

JANICA: Streptococcus?

MOTHER: Those real little white flowers, like wax.

JANICA (*Relieved*): Oh, you mean stephanotis.

MOTHER: That's what I said. One of those fancy kinds of flowers. Hurry up, Florence. You'd stand here talking all day. (*They go out. During the scene, VIOLET has busied herself with dialing numbers and getting the busy signal, thrusting pencils into her hair, typing short items, cutting and gluing papers.*)

VIOLET: Oh, my goodness, that makes twenty-four brides already this week. I can't imagine where on earth we'll find the space to put them all. June is such a lovely, romantic month; but the brides keep us almost too busy to enjoy it. (*Sighs*)

JANICA: Romantic! I think it's hilarious—if it weren't so pathetic. Next year by this time, all these starry-eyed little brides will be bogged down in a routine of dirty dishes and grumpy husbands, with dozens of screaming

little children hanging on to their skirts. (*Shuddering*)
Not for me!

VIOLET: Now, Janica. You'll come to it yourself. I've
heard that kind of talk before.

JANICA (*Laughs*): Oh, you're impossible, Violet. You must
have written up five thousand weddings since you
joined this paper, and you can still get excited over
an engagement.

VIOLET: I like to see people happy. Especially young people, in June. It's unnatural not to be in love in a
month like this. (*Thumbs through papers*) How do you
think this is going to be for the front page? (*Holds up
large sheet of paper*) Pine View Lake in the background
with that nice young Bob Turner helping Laurel Evans
into the canoe.

JANICA: I thought you were using Millicent Walker in
that picture. (*Warningly*) Her mama isn't going to like
this. Uh-uh! I hear she hand-picked Bob for her daughter long ago, and she hasn't let him out of her sight
since he got home from Yale.

VIOLET (*With unexpected spirit*): You're telling me! But
I just don't care. Millicent's had her share of the limelight and I'm going to turn a little of it in Laurel's
direction. She's a dear, sweet child and much more
Bob's type than Millicent. (*Dreamily*) Who knows? Pine
View on a Sunday afternoon—all that scenery—nice
boy—pretty girl—

JANICA: Violet, you're incorrigible! I thought you always
said marriages were made in heaven. Heaven, my eye!
Someone should warn them up there they've sold out
to a society editor. Aren't you afraid to engineer romances in this high-handed way?

VIOLET: Not at all. (*Serenely*) I don't believe in leaving

these things up to chance. (*She has been dialing during her last speech and as she speaks into the telephone her voice becomes amiably mellow. After the first few words her conversation is merely monosyllabic with long pauses between "Yes" and "I see," etc.*) Hello, Ruby? This is Violet Pemberton. How are you? Oh, you have the lists all ready—fine! All the officers and new members. . . . Go ahead . . . (*Enter* JIMMY, *with a camera, tripod, and other photographic equipment. He deposits a pile of galley sheets on* JANICA's *desk and perches beside them.*)

JIMMY: Just a few galley sheets, darling. They're not half pretty enough for you. I wish I could afford emeralds.

JANICA: They're beautiful, Jimmy dear. Just the kind of galley sheets I've always wanted. But please—you're sitting on a bride. (*Pulls a story from under him*) As you can plainly see, I'm simply surrounded with work this morning; so please don't be charming and distract my mind. This is June, the season of love and romance and marriage—and nervous breakdowns in the society department.

JIMMY: Now don't start screaming before you're bit, as they say in the back room. I have no intention of being charming to you. In fact, I am rushing to an important assignment right now. (*Pats camera*) But I had to stop off to contribute a little story for your Sunday page.

JANICA (*Groaning*): Not another wedding!

JIMMY: Just an engagement. Put a piece of paper in the typewriter, and I'll dictate it. (*She complies, and he walks around to look over her shoulder, contemplatively*) The season's loveliest and most radiant bride—

JANICA: Oh, stop. They all begin that way.

JIMMY: You're interrupting my train of thought. The

season's loveliest and most radiant bride (*Pause*) . . . will exchange her heart and hand near the end of the month. (*Another pause while* JANICA *types*) Friends learned today of the engagement of Miss Janica Reed to James C. Harper, Jr. Announcement is made by parents of the bride-elect, Mr. and Mrs.—Hey—you've stopped typing!

JANICA: Oh, Jimmy, you lunatic! (*Snatches paper from typewriter, crumples it, and throws it in wastebasket*) You left out one important thing. Quote, "This announcement comes as a total surprise to Miss Reed, who has not yet said 'yes' "! Unquote.

JIMMY: That's a mere formality. But I guess you get that way working in a society office. I won't let you stay here after we're married.

JANICA: Jimmy. Jimmy, dear—please get this straight. I have no intention of becoming a bride this year. Or next year. Or maybe any year.

JIMMY (*Complaining*): Why do you want to be so unreasonable? Why don't you cooperate and be a good sport? *I'm* engaged. I feel extremely engaged. But there should be two of us.

JANICA: The thing for you to do is go find some sweet, young girl who hasn't been over-exposed to love and youth and spring. (*Makes a wry face, puts a fresh sheet of paper in the typewriter, and resumes work. The telephone rings and* JIMMY *answers.*)

JIMMY: Society. Yes . . . well, just a minute, madam, and I'll see if I can help you. (*To* JANICA) She wants to know if there's anything special the bridegroom's father is supposed to do at the reception.

JANICA: Look it up in *Emily Post,* would you, Jimmy? I'm not going to make my deadline if I don't rush.

(*Goes on typing while* JIMMY *thumbs through the book she has indicated.*)

JIMMY: Hello. Well, let's see. It says right here that the bridegroom's father can wander at will through the crowd. He doesn't have to stand at the door, or pass the frappe, or anything like that. What do you know— (*Surprised*) It says, "Guests need not speak to him." That's what it says. . . . Yes, ma'am. You're welcome. (*Hangs up*) How do you like that! Right here in *Emily Post*—guests need not speak to the poor cuss. (*Thrusts book under* JANICA's *nose*) Look there!

JANICA: Well, I didn't write the book. Complain to Emily.

JIMMY (*Muttering and gathering up equipment*): There's some discrimination some place. Getting the poor guy all dressed up in this rented tuxedo, and then nobody even talks to him.

VIOLET (*Between telephone calls*): Hello, Jimmy. How are you?

JIMMY: Fine, sugar. Only I'm not gaining any ground with your assistant here. What she feels for me isn't love!

JANICA (*Primly*): It's a much more stable emotion, Jimmy.

JIMMY: Don't tell me. Let me guess. (*With exaggerated innocence*) Could it be friendship?

JANICA: The lad's precocious!

VIOLET: Never mind, Jimmy. Friendship often blossoms into you-know-what. (*Lowering her voice*) Janica's allergic to the word love. All my assistants get that way in June.

JIMMY: Well, you work on it, Vi, honey; I trust you. You want to know something in strict confidence? At heart I'm a rovin' cowboy, but the unyielding little woman over there has done things to me.

VIOLET (*Amused*): Like what, Jimmy?

JIMMY: It used to be that nothing more than the whistle of a train would start me hitting the trail. Now I'm a changed man. All I can think of is a house and garden and the patter of little feet. Pathetic, isn't it?

VIOLET (*Laughing*): June's got you, too, Jimmy!

JANICA (*Plaintively*): Why don't you just steal quietly away, Jimmy? I've got to concentrate on my hearts and flowers.

JIMMY: I will if you'll give me one little kiss to sweeten my journey.

JANICA: The answer is "no"!

JIMMY: I was afraid not. Well, so long. (*To* VIOLET) If you see me after a while minus a scalp, it'll be because I kept one of your society dames waiting to get her picture taken. (*He waves, then saunters out singing, "Friendship, just a perfect blendship."*)

VIOLET: That Jimmy is the cutest thing. There's something about him—

JANICA (*Absently*): What?

VIOLET: Oh, I don't know. Maybe it's the way his hair grows or the way he sort of lopes when he walks. He makes me think of somebody I knew once. (*A pause*) A long time ago, of course. He didn't believe in careers for women, either. But I was determined I'd prove I could resist him. (*Dryly*) I did.

JANICA: And a good thing, too. If you'd married him, by now you'd be one of those frustrated housewives with nothing to do but call the society editor and complain because your bridge club got a small headline instead of a big one. Or else you'd be home tending the children, while your husband went off on a fishing trip.

VIOLET: I wonder.

JANICA: Well, you heard the new Mrs. Gerber, didn't you? Instead of all that, here you are: a happy, well-balanced individual, able to do what you want with your own money—go where you want to—nobody to tie you down.

VIOLET: Nobody at all. Yes, Janica, you're right about that.

JANICA: That's for me—the free life. I'm not going to let sentimentality lead me into any traps.

VIOLET: How old are you, Janica?

JANICA: Twenty-one. Old enough to know a good lesson when I see one—and this department is full of good object lessons. (*Telephone rings and she answers.*) Hello. Society. (*Long pause*) Is it an article we already have, Mrs. Snively? (*She says the name with a short "i" as in "snivel"*) Oh, I'm sorry. Snively—long "i." You'd just like a correction? All right; I'll make a note of it. (*Talking as she writes*) "Miss Lulu Snively will marry David H. Butler on the evening of June 21." That is instead of "Miss Lulu Snively will marry J. G. Welthorpe." Right? Oh, that's quite all right. It's no trouble. . . . Every girl has a right to change her mind. Goodbye, Mrs. Snively. (*Hangs up*) Yea, Butler!

VIOLET (*Gathering up papers*): Jannie dear, will you hold the fort for a few minutes? I'm expecting Barbara Lake.

JANICA: Oh, is Barbara back in town?

VIOLET: Yes. Just yesterday. If you'll ask her to wait—(*Rummaging*) Now where did I put those proofs? Here they are. (*Pauses and looks at watch*) And there's something else. Oh, dear, I'm afraid I've made a terrible faux pas—

JANICA: What's the matter?

VIOLET: I completely forgot that Sally Ann Sumner and

her fiancé are due here any minute to give me the plans for the wedding. It could be awkward.

JANICA: How do you mean? I could take Barbara on till you're through. We could go into the old hidey-hole over there and—

VIOLET: That's not the point. Maybe you didn't know, but Clifton Dwyer, Sally's fiancé, used to be engaged—or so everyone thought—to Barbara before she went East to study music, and they say she never got over him.

JANICA: Probably a lot of nonsense. A girl with Barbara's talent wouldn't be satisfied just settling down to being a housewife.

VIOLET: Don't be too sure. If ever I saw two people simply *made* for each other, it's Cliff and Barbara.

JANICA: Oh—oh. Here we go again. Arranged in heaven, I suppose.

VIOLET: I mean it. Here's Cliff Dwyer within a year of his Ph.D., and you watch—if he marries Sally Sumner he'll never make it.

JANICA: Why not? The guy sounds namby-pamby to me.

VIOLET: No, you don't understand. I hate to sound catty, but Sally Sumner's a spoiled brat, and she only wanted Clifton Dwyer because he was a change from the Country Club set, and must have been a little harder to get than most. Sally a professor's wife! The whole idea's fantastic.

JANICA: Even so, what are you going to do about it?

VIOLET (*Deflated*): Write the wedding up pretty, I suppose. But my heart's not in it. All that girl wants is novelty. And Cliff's a novelty.

JANICA: She'll soon find out that marriage is no novelty. Anyway, it's their affair, not ours.

VIOLET (*Sighing*): I suppose you're right. The announcement's practically in the paper. If Barbara had only come home sooner. (*Regretfully*) I'm afraid it's too late now to do anything.

JANICA (*Suspiciously*): Violet Pemberton! I believe you deliberately planned this meeting. Faux pas, indeed!

VIOLET (*Innocently*): Oh, no. I swear it's pure coincidence. (*Looks at watch*) But if they do just sort of—well, happen to run into each other here, be a lamb and use your tact, won't you? (*Goes out*)

JANICA: Tact, she says! (*Runs hand through her hair and goes to water cooler for drink. As she stands, back to main door,* BARBARA LAKE *enters. She extends hand cordially as* JANICA *turns and speaks.*) Barbara! How wonderful you look!

BARBARA: If I do, it's because I've just had my first vacation in three years. (*Laughingly*) But now it's back to the salt mines.

JANICA: I've heard about your opening a music studio.

BARBARA: Yes, keep your fingers crossed for me, will you? Is Violet about? She was going to do an item for me— "Local girl makes good"—that sort of thing.

JANICA: She'll be back soon. Won't you sit down? (*Begins straightening desk and speaks with mock resignation*) Brides! June brides!

BARBARA: Sounds like battle fatigue.

JANICA: Worse than that.

BARBARA: Anybody I know taking the fatal step?

JANICA: Well, let me see. Margaret Blaine—did you know her? And Patricia Lester—of course you've heard that the big splurge next week is the Sumner doings— Sally Ann and Clifton Dwyer. (*She watches* BARBARA *closely.*)

BARBARA: Oh. (*There is an uncomfortable pause.*) I didn't know it was that—that final. I used to know him—but of course that was over long ago. Just a high school romance. (*Slowly*) I suppose she's awfully pretty?

JANICA: Her picture's around somewhere. (*Finds it and hands it to* BARBARA *who studies it*) You may even see her in the flesh. (*Wanting to warn* BARBARA) She's due here any time now, Violet tells me.

BARBARA (*Hastily*): Oh, in that case I think I really should go and come back another time, don't you? (*Gets up as* VIOLET *enters*)

VIOLET (*Cordially*): Barbara Lake! (*Grasping her arm*) Come right over here and tell me all about yourself. We're quite excited about your new venture, and I'm giving you a good spot in Sunday's paper even if I have to throw out a bride to do it.

JANICA: Don't you believe her, Barbara. If anyone threw out a bridal picture around here, it'd have to be over Vi's dead body.

VIOLET (*Laughing*): I suppose I am a little touchy about them. Now, let's see—I have some of the facts already— a year in Paris—

BARBARA: Let's not make it sound too dashing. People might expect too much.

VIOLET: Don't you worry. We'll have Jimmy do a picture of you at the piano—that sort of thing. And now, if you don't mind, I'm taking you into the "hidey-hole"— that's what we lovingly call our inner office—and we can plan the campaign.

BARBARA (*As they leave*): You're making it sound fright-fully impressive. (*Voices are heard outside the main door and there is the sound of a dropping package, accompanied by an exclamation.* JANICA *stops writing to listen.*

*After a moment a tired young man, laden with parcels,
and a decidedly chic young woman appear.)*

SALLY: Mother's not going to like your dropping that perfume.

CLIFTON: Your mother's not going to like me, period. She
never has. *(He walks to* JANICA's *wastebasket and drops
crumpled paper and broken bottles into it, and smiles
at* JANICA.*)* I'm afraid I'm the bull in the china closet all
right, but there's no use crying over spilled Chanel.

JANICA *(Getting up and reaching for some of his parcels)*:
May I? *(Begins helping him unload them onto a chair)*

CLIFTON *(Moving tired shoulders and grinning)*: The
bridegroom shoppeth! Thanks.

JANICA *(Amused)*: Sounds like something out of Eugene
O'Neill, doesn't it? Won't you both sit down? Violet
will be with you right away.

SALLY *(Peevishly)*: You sit down, Clifton, if you want to
. . . I don't like to be kept waiting, Miss—it *is* Miss
Reed, isn't it?

JANICA: That's right. Janica Reed.

SALLY: After all, this wedding is Violet's big story, and if
she can't keep appointments, I'll just have to leave her
some lists or something and let her make the best of
it. I have them with me. . . . That's funny. I haven't
my handbag.

CLIFTON *(Wearily)*: Probably in that booth where I
warned you not to leave it.

SALLY: Be a love, Clifton, and run out and get it for me.
(To JANICA*)* It's only next door. *(She takes a chair by
desk as she speaks.* CLIFTON *raises his eyebrows, shrugs
a little, and gets wearily to his feet and goes out.)*

JANICA *(Sweetly)*: It must be nice to have someone go

about with you to take care of all these last-minute details. So few men are that way.

SALLY (*Also sweetly*): Oh, do you think so? I find most of them quite—shall we say—tractable?

JANICA: You're lucky.

SALLY: You might look at it that way. Oddly enough, it's the men I've gone around with who usually describe themselves as—*lucky*.

JANICA: I see. (*Irritated in spite of herself*) I've been hearing nice things about your fiancé—his work in science. He's getting close to his Ph.D. now, isn't he?

SALLY: Oh, that. No, he's not close at all. He has fully a year to go. A year too long. Even if he finishes, what has he got?

JANICA: I always thought a Ph.D. and a college professorship were rather nice, myself.

SALLY: It might satisfy some. Can you see me as the wife of an impoverished professor?

JANICA: Frankly, no. Nor any other kind. Forgive my curiosity, but why are you marrying one?

SALLY: As long as I'm unburdening myself, I might as well tell you I have a strong idea Clifton will change his vocation—for me. Dad's going to offer him an executive post in Sumner Bottling Works, Inc.—and I imagine he'll accept.

JANICA (*Amazed*): You mean after all these years of working for something he loves he'd change over—just like that?

SALLY: I told you I always found men (*Pausing just perceptibly, with downcast eyes*) tractable. (*Telephone rings, and as* JANICA *answers,* SALLY *picks up newspaper from desk*)

JANICA: Society. Oh, yes. Just a moment, Mrs. Cartwright. The annual breakfast. . . . I understand. The Country Club, Thursday, one o'clock. . . . Just a brief notice now and the story later. . . . Yes. . . . You're quite welcome, I'm sure. (*During last part of* JANICA's *telephone conversation* VIOLET *and* BARBARA *emerge from the inner room.*)

VIOLET: I'll let you know, dear. Either Alex or Jimmy will do a good job on pictures of the interior—

BARBARA: You've been awfully sweet. This ought to give my enterprise a real shot in the arm. I can't thank you enough. Now I'll run along.

VIOLET: No, wait. (*Putting a restraining hand on her arm while she greets* SALLY) Sally, how are you?

SALLY: A little shopworn at the moment.

VIOLET (*Cordially*): Do you two know each other? Sally Sumner—Barbara Lake. (*They murmur politely, and* VIOLET *goes on*) Miss Lake's setting up a music studio here in town.

SALLY (*Bored*): How nice. (CLIFTON *appears carrying* SALLY's *handbag which he hands to her.*)

CLIFTON: They found it under the table.

VIOLET: How are you, Cliff? You remember Barbara Lake?

CLIFTON (*With genuine pleasure*): Barb—it's you! (*Clasping her hand*)

BARBARA (*A little shakily*): I didn't expect to see you here.

CLIFTON: It's not my natural habitat. Sally—you must have known Barb. You were both at Westover.

SALLY (*Sweetly*): I think Miss Lake was a little before my time.

BARBARA: Eons, I imagine. Westover is part of my long-ago past. My dead past.

VIOLET (*Briskly*): Sally dear, I've kept you waiting long

enough. Will you all excuse us if we retreat to the hole?

CLIFTON: The hole?

JANICA: The hidey-hole—short for the black hole of Calcutta. It's where we go to escape our public when the deadline's close.

VIOLET (*Beaming*): We'll not be long. (*She has been gathering up a few odds and ends to take with her.*) Oh, a— (*She is obviously trying to think what to do with* JANICA *in order to leave the coast clear for* BARBARA *and* CLIFTON) Jannie, be a love and bring in that layout. We'll consult together. We can hear the telephone in there.

JANICA (*On to her*): O.K., but it'll be a squeeze. (*To* BARBABA *and* CLIFTON) The hole was originally designed for the city editor's clothescloset.

VIOLET: Barbara, you might be thinking whom you'd like to have pour at your opening. Mrs. Porter's a dear—always so nice about the arts—but you be thinking, and we'll get everything down while you're here. (*Exits, pushing* JANICA *and* SALLY *ahead of her.*)

CLIFTON (*Uncertainly*): We might as well sit down since we have to wait.

BARBARA: I suppose so. (*He holds chair for her and then sits beside her.*)

CLIFTON: It's been a long time, Barb.

BARBARA (*Formally*): Yes, hasn't it?

CLIFTON (*After a pause*): I don't think you've changed at all since the last time I saw you.

BARBARA (*Lightly*): How disappointed my father would be to hear you say that—after all the money and hopes he's lavished on me the past years! The least he could expect would be that old friends would stand back in amazement.

CLIFTON: Old friends. Yes, I suppose we are. Only it sounded a little strange.

BARBARA (*Getting back to safe ground*): I've been hearing interesting things about your research. Fancy getting into *Scientific Monthly*.

CLIFTON (*Pleased*): You saw that? I don't know many women who bother.

BARBARA: I daresay I'll soon be saying I knew him when!

CLIFTON (*Suddenly serious*): When what, for instance?

BARBARA: Oh, lots of things. The day when he first discovered those lines from Bertrand Russell, for one. You brought the book to lab, remember? I learned some of it by heart. (*She clasps her hands and recites*) "Mathematics, rightly viewed, possesses not only truth but supreme beauty—a beauty cold and austere, like that of sculpture, without appeal to any part of our weaker nature, without the gorgeous trappings of painting or music,"—let me think—

CLIFTON (*Picking it up*): "—yet sublimely pure, and capable of a stern perfection such as only the greatest art can show."

BARBARA (*Continuing*): "The true spirit of delight, the exultation, the sense of being more than man, which is the touchstone of the highest excellence is to be found in mathematics as surely as in poetry."

CLIFTON: Funny. I never think of those lines that I don't recall the way you looked that winter afternoon in the half-dark lab, with the Bunsen burner making a little glimmer of light on your face—

BARBARA (*Agitated*): Cliff—please— (*She gets up and tries to speak lightly, but does not look at him.*) Bridegrooms are supposed to look forward—not back.

CLIFTON (*Standing*): I guess you're right. (VIOLET *and* SALLY *emerge from the "hole."*)

VIOLET: That's that, then. Just one more thing, Sally. I'm so disorganized—your bridesmaids—

SALLY (*Looking into purse*): I've the list right here somewhere. (*Enter* JIMMY. *He saunters in, whistling between his teeth, and pauses at* VIOLET's *desk.*)

JIMMY: I got the pictures O.K.—all except the one with your pal Mrs. Andrew J. Plympton of the Plympton-Plymptons. She said to tell you she was so sorry, but she has a case of hives that made her look like a blimp. She got them from excitement. Today she made a hole-in-one at the bridge tournament.

VIOLET: Oh, the poor thing. Well, what'll we do now? I know—maybe we could get the art department to air-brush in some silhouettes for that empty space. Oh, Sally, have you met Jimmy?

SALLY (*Turning on her charm*): I certainly have. He's my favorite photographer. I don't know anyone else that has his finesse unless it's Michael. Hollywood, you know.

JIMMY: Hear, hear! (JANICA *comes out of inner room bearing papers in wire basket in time to hear the last of* SALLY's *remark.*) You hear that, Janica? Me and this Michael of Hollywood are just like that. (*Holds up two fingers*)

JANICA: You shouldn't spoil him, Miss Sumner. He's conceited enough already.

JIMMY (*To* SALLY, *who is smiling at him*): You see? I'm not appreciated around here. I'm leaving. (*Gathering up equipment*)

SALLY (*Laying a hand gently on his arm*): Jimmy, would

it be possible—do you suppose I could see how the garden tea turned out?

JIMMY: Not yet. I'm sorry—they're not developed yet. I'm going to work on them right now.

SALLY: You are! (*Eagerly*) Could I watch? I've always wanted to see inside a darkroom.

JIMMY (*Quickly*): You wouldn't like it, believe me. It's just well—dark, with noises of water dripping. And a good healthy stink of chemicals. I'll show you the pictures tomorrow.

SALLY (*Pouting*): Wait—don't go. (*Looking up at him*) I'm not used to having men say no to me, Jimmy. (JANICA *gives her a withering look and bangs down a paperweight.*)

JIMMY (*Grinning in* JANICA's *direction*): And I'm not used to having my art admired like this, either. But you see, Sally, that darkroom is strictly bachelor's quarters, and there's only room for one bachelor at a time, at that.

SALLY: You can't scare me, Jimmy. I'm coming with you.

CLIFTON: Just a minute, Sally. We're—

SALLY (*Cutting him off*): Oh, don't be stuffy, Clifton. I won't be long. You wait right here. (*Exits.*)

BARBARA (*Looks at* CLIFTON *as if questioning whether he will accept such treatment. As he picks up a newspaper and resigns himself to waiting, she crosses to* VIOLET's *desk*): I don't know how I can thank you, Violet. This publicity is just what we need. I'll see you again soon, I hope—and you, Janica—

VIOLET (*Abruptly*): Oh, Barbara—

BARBARA: Yes?

VIOLET: I was wondering, my dear—I know you're busy. But the thought just struck me—could you spare a few

minutes more? I'd like a silhouette to go with the
photos on the front page, and you have such a nice pro-
file.

BARBARA (*Hesitating*): You mean—right now?

VIOLET: If Alex is free, I certainly would appreciate it.
(*Picks up receiver*) Photography, please. . . . Hello,
Alex? Would you have time to take a quick shot for me
there in the studio? One of our pictures failed, and
we've got space for a little art work. . . . Well, in keeping with the theme of midsummer evenings, it would
be nice to have a silhouette of two heads, with a few
stars montaged around—a man and a girl. Looking as
if they were about to—well, heads close together, you
know. Rather romantic. . . . Five minutes? (*To* BAR-
BARA) Just five minutes? (BARBARA *nods.*) Thanks,
Alex. (*Her expression is one of great self-satisfaction as
she hangs up. She glances almost slyly toward* BARBARA
and CLIFTON, *who are conversing in a polite undertone,
then goes back to work.*)

CLIFTON: It *is* getting late. I guess I should really— (*Gets
up and goes out. Sounds of his knocking on darkroom
door can be heard as he calls*) Sally! You're going to miss
your mother if you don't hurry.

SALLY (*Muffled*): Don't bother me right now, please. I
can't possibly come out. The film's developing. (CLIF-
TON *re-enters, looking quietly angry.*)

BARBARA: She's very enthusiastic about learning new
things, isn't she?

CLIFTON (*Grimly*): She is.

BARBARA: At least she'll never let you stagnate, Cliff. She'll
probably keep you from turning into one of those ivory-
tower professors.

CLIFTON (*Wryly*): She'll probably go farther than that and

keep me from turning into any professor at all.

BARBARA: Now's the time to find out.

CLIFTON: Now or never.

BARBARA (*Quickly*): I didn't mean it like that—just, now's the time to find out whether you want to go on teaching, or not. That's what I meant.

CLIFTON (*Impulsively*): It seems we both have a few stray minutes. Would you care to squander them with me having a long, cold drink?

BARBARA: Well—if we have time—Violet?

VIOLET (*She has been delightedly eavesdropping*): Go ahead, dear. There's no hurry. (BARBARA *and* CLIFTON *exit.*)

JANICA: Violet Pemberton! If you shouldn't be ashamed of yourself!

VIOLET (*Amazed*): Ashamed of myself? Why?

JANICA: If I ever saw anybody simply run herself ragged with match-making schemes! And here one of the couples is practically married.

VIOLET (*Firmly*): Not until next Wednesday evening. Until then, all's fair.

JANICA: What I don't understand is why you should care so much. You never get any thanks for your pains.

VIOLET: I have to care. I have to care about other people's weddings, because I'll never have one of my own. (*Suddenly*) What do you think I'll do tonight when I get home, Janica?

JANICA (*Surprised*): Why, I don't know. Anything you want to, I guess.

VIOLET: Did it ever occur to you that a whole lifetime of planning little things to amuse yourself could get monotonous? (*Pause*) I don't know whether I can make you understand about this—but sometimes after I'm through here at the office, and I stand outside my door with the apartment key ready to open it—I think, what if I should find the living room all messed up—toys on the floor—a coat thrown on the couch—maybe model airplanes perched around on the lamps. And somebody there to hurry me into getting dinner ready. Isn't it silly? That seems like the most wonderful thing in the world. Then I open the door. It's all so neat; just the way I left it. So quiet. Once I thought I'd like it that way. (*More briskly, with a smile*) Ideas are bound to change, though, as you get older. Now I guess I've turned into a sentimentalist. I've lost my sense of perspective.

JANICA (*Subdued*): I don't know, Violet. I guess I never thought of it just that way.

VIOLET (*Brightly*): But you're a stronger personality than I was at your age, Janica. Maybe you'll be able to make your own life work out exactly as you expect. Maybe you'll be too sensible to be lonely.

JANICA (*Desperately*): It's just seeing the foolishness—the futility—of most of these little weddings, Violet. It's just looking ahead and realizing what the marriages will be like next year or the year after. Common—tiresome —nothing left of all the plans.

VIOLET: But it's the people, Janica, not the marriages. If you're going to be common and tiresome and bored, you can do it just as well alone.

JANICA: Oh, I guess you're right. I just wish I *knew*. (*Sits perplexed and wondering for a moment; nibbles a fingernail, and glances unhappily in the direction of the darkroom. The telephone rings.*) Society. Oh, Mrs. Sniv—I mean Snively, it's you. Yes, I remember the article. No, I haven't made the correction yet. Now let's see—how do we stand? Whom is your daughter engaged to this time? . . . J. G. Welthorpe? Well, that straightens us out again, then. We'll just let the story go as we sent it out in the first place. . . . Yes, I understand. Young girls are a little fickle that way. . . . It's quite all right. (*Hangs up*) Yea, Welthorpe! He finally came out on top. (*Crumples up the correction note. Enter* BARBARA *and* CLIFTON. *He goes directly across stage, exits, and can be heard once more knocking on the darkroom door.* BARBARA *seats herself right.*)

BARBARA: Is the photographer ready yet?

VIOLET: Alex hasn't called me yet, but I imagine he won't be more than a minute longer.

CLIFTON (*Offstage*): Sally! Are you coming?

SALLY (*Offstage*): Go sit down a minute, Clifton! (*Re-enter* CLIFTON *with an expressionless face but a purposeful step. He picks up some of* SALLY'S *packages and one drops with a clink, as of bottles breaking. He picks it up and throws it with an angry gesture in the wastebasket.*)

CLIFTON: The rest of the beauty treatment, I suppose. (*He makes a sudden decision and puts down the rest of the packages where he found them, brushes his hands together with a gesture of finality. Reaches for his hat.*) I'm through being a Boy Scout for today. (*Turning to the others*) It's been pleasant seeing you—and thanks for everything, Barb.

VIOLET (*Taking the plunge*): Cliff—I know this is imposing on you terribly, but I'm having an emergency. Could you wait just a few minutes and let Alex take your silhouette with Barbara's? (*Cajolingly*) I don't think there's another good-looking man in the building at this hour—except Jimmy—and (*Wickedly*) he seems to be quite busy.

CLIFTON (*Dubiously*): Oh, I don't know, Violet. What's it for?

VIOLET: Just a little art work for a week from Sunday's front page.

BARBARA (*Being a good sport*): Oh, come on, Cliff. Be a little art work with me.

CLIFTON: Well, all right, all right. The afternoon's shot, anyway.

VIOLET (*Almost purring*): Thank you so much. (*Picks up receiver*) Photography, please. . . . Alex, aren't you almost ready? Yes, they're both here. I'll send them right in. (*To* BARBARA *and* CLIFTON) Three doors to your right, just down the hall. It'll be quite painless, really. (*They exit, and she sits smiling to herself a moment as she raps with her nails on the desk top.*) And don't you say a word, Janica.

JANICA: I won't. Not a word. (*Begins to gather photographs from her wire basket and put them in large envelope*) Well, almost the end of another crazy day. I'll dispatch these little brides, here, to the engravers, and that should just about finish up. (*Glances furtively toward the darkroom*)

VIOLET: I'm still swamped, but I'm going to have to leave everything on my desk and run.

JANICA: Party tonight?

VIOLET: No, a band concert. Somehow I can't seem to work up much enthusiasm. Just tired, I guess. (*Takes purse and gloves from bottom desk drawer*) Don't you stay too long, Jannie. We've turned out enough copy to keep them busy in the composing room. (*Ready to leave*) Oh, on second thought—if you don't mind, I *would* like you to stay just long enough to give Jimmy a message for me. I—

JANICA: The thing I like about you, pet, is that you're never transparent. You've done your share of good deeds today without working on me. I love you dearly, but I won't let you trick me. Just as soon as I get in the clear I'm leaving, and Jimmy Lucky-boy Harper can— (*Enter* SALLY, *followed by* JIMMY, *rolling his sleeves down*)

JIMMY: Who's lucky?

JANICA: Ask Miss Sumner. She can tell you.

SALLY: It must be Miss Reed's idea of humor. (*Intimately, to* JIMMY) It's been a wonderful little interlude, Jimmy. (*Suddenly conscious of others' absence*) Where's everybody? Whatever's happened to Clifton?

JANICA: He left quite a while ago.

SALLY: Left? Just went?

VIOLET (*Airily, putting on her hat*): Just went.

SALLY: Didn't he say anything? Leave any message for me?

VIOLET: No. Not anything I can recall.

SALLY (*Shrill*): Of all the—and he didn't even bother to help me get these packages home.

JANICA: They're not always completely—tractable, are they? (SALLY *gives her a "look."*) Don't forget your purse.

SALLY: Oh. (*Goes back and retrieves it from the chair. To* VIOLET, *in a voice with an edge to it*) I think you'd better hold all this up awhile. I may have to teach someone a little lesson. (*Warmly, to* JIMMY) Jimmy dear, I *might* have time on my hands, and I'd love some lessons in photography. How about it?

JIMMY: Oh, sure. Any time.

SALLY (*In a meaningful voice*): You've been so terribly nice. . . . I'll go along with you, Violet. (*Coldly, to* JANICA) I'll have Mr. Dwyer pick these up.

JANICA (*Sweetly but pointedly*): I wonder! (VIOLET *and* SALLY *go out.*)

JIMMY (*Sitting on* VIOLET's *desk*): There goes a girl who should be put in cold storage for about a hundred and fifty years.

JANICA (*Coldly, typing fast*): I don't know. She seems to do pretty well.

JIMMY (*Reminiscently*): Well, along certain lines—certain lines. (*Conversationally*) That seems like quite a nice guy she snagged. (JANICA *pointedly says nothing, typing briskly and keeping her eyes on her copy.*) Now, listen—you're not that busy.

JANICA: You are probably not the best judge in the world of what it means to be busy.

JIMMY: What do you mean by that?

JANICA: Just that *I* don't have time to entertain friends during working hours or give them little lessons on how to be a society assistant. It would be pleasant, but we can't all have those privileges.

JIMMY (*Laughing and coming over*): Janica, baby, you're jealous. Give me a kiss.

JANICA (*Furious*): Jealous? Of her? That's the funniest thing I ever heard. (*Turns her head away*)

JIMMY: All right. You're not jealous. You're just cross because she spent a half hour or so in the darkroom with me. Let me put your troubled little mind at ease. I did not invite her. She pursued me. She thinks I'm cute.

JANICA (*With sarcasm*): "Oh, Jimmy, you've been so-o nice. Let's have some more lovely little interludes, shall we?" I certainly don't care whether she comes back or not. I just don't want you to think I'm being taken in by your innocent attitude. (*Jerks paper out of the type-writer and rolls in a new sheet*)

JIMMY: You're being childish and silly now, and in a few minues you'll be ashamed.

JANICA: Ashamed! I'm certainly not the one that makes dates with other people's fiancés in darkrooms!

JIMMY (*Aroused*): All right, Janica. Have it your own way. But let me make one thing clear. I take just as much interest, just as much pride, in my work as any-body around here. I couldn't help what happened this afternoon. But there is a sign on my door—it says in big black letters, No Admittance. That means her—you—everybody. Just in case anybody wants to come and visit, you can quote me in those two words.

JANICA: I doubt that anybody will ask me.

JIMMY: And speaking of signs marked No Admittance, how about that one you carry around with you?

JANICA (*Startled*): What do you mean?

JIMMY: As long as I can remember, you've had it hanging on your heart. Big black letters. And you keep the rule pretty well enforced. Unfortunately, I can't seem to catch you off guard and rush in, like Sally rushed into the darkroom today.

JANICA (*Looking away*): I'm sorry.

JIMMY: It's O.K. Rules of the management or something, I guess. Well—(*He slaps the desk with the flat of his hand, straightens up, and walks quietly toward the door. JANICA sits with her cheek on her hand, staring at her typewriter. Suddenly she turns, opens her lips to speak, changes her mind; then calls abruptly.*)

JANICA: Jimmy! Oh, please—just a minute. (*Looks at*

him for a moment, then goes on quickly and nervously) Before you go, would you do something for me? I haven't quite finished the stories to go out. If you'd add this last one to the pile on Bert's desk, it'll just barely make the deadline. *(He sits in the chair nearest the door as she begins to type. Suddenly she stops, and looks hesitantly around.)* I'm sorry to keep you waiting. I just can't seem to think of the right words. Isn't that funny—it should be automatic.

JIMMY: You've probably just run out of formulas. It's the end of the day, kid. *(Comes over and leans over her shoulder to read)* Let's see what you've got so far. "June 30 is the date set for the marriage of Miss Janica Reed. Her engagement to James C. Harper is made known to-day by—" *(His voice breaks abruptly and he lifts her from her chair and turns her around. They look at each other briefly; then he kisses her.)* What more do you want to say? What more do we need?

JANICA *(Shakily)*: I guess it really is enough. It says quite a lot.

JIMMY: Enough for now, maybe, but don't think there isn't plenty more I'm going to say to you. Tonight. To-morrow. Next year. It might take the best years of my life. *(Kisses her again. The telephone rings two or three times before* JANICA *disengages herself.)*

JANICA *(Coming down to earth)*: Hello. Oh, yes, this is Society. Oh, yes. I thought you sounded familiar, Mrs. Snively. It's a good thing you didn't call five minutes later—I almost missed my deadline. *(Looks at* JIMMY*)* Yes, I remember the article. *(Long pause)* I see. Your daughter Lulu has decided to take Mr. Butler, after all? She's not going to marry Mr. Welthorpe. *(Long pause)* Yes, I think you're perfectly right; it never does any good trying to stand in the way of true love. Oh, it's perfectly all right. I'll tell them to kill the story. You're welcome. Goodbye, Mrs. Snively. (*She hangs up, and turns and smiles radiantly at* JIMMY)

THE END

Production Notes

Characters: 2 male; 6 female.

Playing Time: 30 minutes.

Costumes: Modern dress.

Properties: Pencils, pads, paper, pictures, purses for the mother, Violet, and Sally, glue, camera, tripod, photographic equipment, galley sheets, book, wrapped parcels (some of them containing bottles), newspapers, hat for Clifton, hat and gloves for Violet.

Setting: A newspaper office. It is pleasantly untidy. Two large desks are placed diagonally at center, with a number of leather-covered chairs near them. The desks are equipped with telephones, typewriters, wire baskets with papers, glue pots, photographs, and other typical miscellany. There are several wastebaskets in need of emptying. Upstage right of center is a large window, draped with brightly figured material and revealing a backdrop of a city skyline. Upstage right is a door to the main office, up left is a door leading to the photography department, and downstage left another door leading to a tiny private office. Upstage left, near the corner, is a water cooler.

Lighting: No special effects.

Jimmy Six

By Robert Downing

Characters

Mrs. Cynthia Abbott
Pam, *her daughter, 16*
Jimmy, *her son, 12*
Pete White, *Jimmy's friend*
Susan White, *Pete's cousin, 17*

Setting: *The Abbott living room.*
At Rise: Mrs. Abbott *sits at a desk, consulting a book, making notes.* Pam *enters from the dining room.*

Pam: Mother . . .
Mrs. Abbott (*Concentrating on her work*): Yes, dear?
Pam: What time *is* lunch around here anyway?
Mrs. Abbott (*Without looking up*): Why, at noon, dear. You know that.
Pam: Well, it's almost one-thirty, and I can't get my kitchen work done!
Mrs. Abbott (*Cheerfully, her nose in the book*): Well, just keep at it, Pam. Remember the Abbott family watchword—*Persevere!*

286

PAM: *I* know that, Mother—and *you* know it . . . but does *Jimmy* know it?

MRS. ABBOTT (*Turns to* PAM): What's Jimmy got to do with it?

PAM: He won't eat his lunch. He's just sitting at the table —*moping!* I can't finish my work!

MRS. ABBOTT (*Sighs*): I do wish you and your brother would try to be a little more cooperative . . .

PAM: That's what I want! Cooperation! Jimmy knows I'm entertaining my History Club girls this afternoon. He knows that Susan White, the celebrated author, is going to be my guest. (*Wails*) Oh, Mother—Jimmy's *sabotaging* my whole day!

MRS. ABBOTT: Darling, Susan White is not a *celebrated* author. She's simply a very promising young lady.

PAM: Susan White may not be Jane Austen, Mother, but she *did* have her essay published—the best essay in the whole country in the History League contest—and she was written up in all the papers. I wish *I* could write about history like that.

MRS. ABBOTT (*Smiles*): Well, dear—remember the Abbott watchword . . .

PAM: I know—*Persevere!* Mother, don't you see how important today is to me?

MRS. ABBOTT (*Making notes*): Every day has its vital moments, darling.

PAM: Here's Susan White coming to Maple Valley to live —to make her home right here in this grubby old town . . .

MRS. ABBOTT (*Looks up*): Thoreau found charm at Walden, Pam. Mark Twain came from Hannibal . . .

PAM: But I didn't know *them!* Susan White turns out to be the cousin of our very own next-door neighbors!

Why, she's sitting over there right now—just *waiting* to come to *my* party! Imagine that!

MRS. ABBOTT (*Smiles absently*): Authors have relatives, too, dear . . .

PAM: But it's such a *privilege!* To be able to present Susan White in her first Maple Valley appearance! My History Club girls are simply *wild* with envy! Think of it! A real, live author right here in this room! (*Storms*) And I can't even get the place decently cleaned up! All on account of Jimmy!

MRS. ABBOTT (*Rises, crosses to bookcase*): Pam, I simply can't cope with these difficulties between you and Jimmy. Not today.

PAM (*Following*): If you'll just cope with Jimmy, I'll be satisfied!

MRS. ABBOTT (*Gets a book, returns to her desk*): You know I'm working on my book review for the Ladies' League. It has to be finished by tomorrow. I promised you that you could have the living room this afternoon for *your* meeting. That means I'll have to take *my* material upstairs. I'm delighted to do this for you, dear —but *please* settle your problems with Jimmy yourself. (*Sits at desk*)

PAM (*Goes to her mother*): Jimmy's impossible! He's pouting because he has to stay in and help me. He wants to play baseball! (JIMMY *enters in time to hear this. He is finishing a wedge of apple pie.*)

JIMMY: Darn right I want to play ball! We have a heavy game set for this P.M. My Maple Valley Tigers versus the Elm Street Polecats!

PAM (*Starts for the dining room*): *Now* maybe I can clear the table! (*Goes out*)

JIMMY (*Goes to his mother*): Mom, I just *have* to make that game this afternoon!

MRS. ABBOTT (*Absorbed in her work*): Yes, dear . . .

JIMMY: You mean I *can?* Hot ziggety! (*He bolts the last bite of pie, and dashes to the French doors.*)

MRS. ABBOTT (*Turning to him*): Jimmy, where are you going?

JIMMY: Over to the vacant lot. I have to help Pete put down a new home plate.

MRS. ABBOTT: Not this afternoon, darling.

JIMMY (*Stuffing his hands in his pockets*): Shucks! I thought you meant I could go!

MRS. ABBOTT: You know that Pam is counting on your help.

JIMMY: Aw, Mom, I don't want to sit around here with all those square chicks!

MRS. ABBOTT: We settled this at breakfast, son. I don't want to hear any more about it. You'll help Pam conduct her history meeting.

JIMMY (*A step toward his mother*): Mom, without me the Tigers can *never* skunk the Polecats!

MRS. ABBOTT (*Gathering up her book and papers*): I cannot concentrate in this room another moment. (*Rises, starts for stairs*) Now, I rely on your good behavior this afternoon, Jim.

JIMMY (*Crossing to center*): Prison! That's what this house is!

MRS. ABBOTT: You should be proud that Pam wants to use you in connection with her research.

JIMMY: Research? What am I? A guinea pig?

MRS. ABBOTT: You happen to be James Pomfrey Abbott the Sixth . . .

JIMMY: Aw, who cares?

MRS. ABBOTT: You ought to share Pam's pride in the family tree, darling. Never forget that the first man to carry your name stood with Washington at Valley Forge!

JIMMY: I know—but why does Pam want to bend her brains now?

MRS. ABBOTT: Pam wants to make a good impression on Susan White.

JIMMY: Pete's cousin? That teen-age typewriter-tickler? I'll bet Pete'll be glad when those relatives of his get a house of their own and move out!

MRS. ABBOTT: It isn't very often that Pam asks you to do something for her. Isn't that true?

JIMMY: Yeah . . .

MRS. ABBOTT: Well, then—pitch in with vim, son! Remember the legend on the Abbott coat of arms. Excelsior! (*She goes out, her arm raised dramatically.*) *Excelsior!*

JIMMY (*Starts down center, dejectedly*): Coat of arms! Excelsior! (*Punching a davenport pillow*) Pillow-stuffing! (*He throws himself disconsolately on the davenport. There is a knock at the French doors.*) Come in . . . (PETE *darts in, followed by* SUSAN. JIMMY *does not look up.*)

PETE (*Rushing to* JIMMY): Hey, Jim! Why the siesta? Come on! We have to get over to the lot!

JIMMY (*Not stirring*): No dice, Pete. I'm sunk!

PETE: Whaddya mean? This is our big day! (SUSAN *stands near the French doors, watching the boys, a smile on her face.*)

JIMMY: I can't go.

PETE (*Aghast*): You *what?*

JIMMY: I'm benched! I'm liquidated!

PETE: Jim! This is a calamity!

JIMMY: Worse'n that—it's *murder!*

PETE (*Wringing his hands*): But if you don't pitch for us today, we're *cooked!*

JIMMY: I'm a dead pigeon, Pete. Parental sentence has been passed. You'll have to pitch for the Tigers.

PETE: Me! I'm a good catcher, Jim—but I can't pitch against the Polecats! You know who they're puttin' on the mound? Stinky Williams!

JIMMY (*Suddenly sits up, impressed*): Stinky Williams!

PETE: Only the best little side-winder in town!

JIMMY (*Sees* SUSAN *for the first time*): Hey who's the frail?

PETE: Never mind her! Get your glove and come on!

JIMMY: Honest, Pete, I can't. Pam's got some shindig here this afternoon, and Mom says I have to stay and help.

PETE (*Crushed, throwing himself into a chair*): Of all the luck! (*Sighs*) Well, there goes the game! (*Jerks a thumb at* SUSAN) Oh, this is my cousin, Susan White. Sue, he's Jimmy Abbott.

SUE (*Pleasantly*): I'm glad to meet you, Jim.

JIMMY (*Studying* SUE): So you're the mental giant? (*Rises*) I'll tell my sister you're here. (*He starts for the dining room.*)

SUE (*A step after him*): Please don't. Not just yet. I'm here a little early, but Pete offered to bring me over, and I thought he might help me break the ice. I'm rather shy about meeting strangers.

JIMMY: Well, you ought to go back and get an armful of the magazine with your essay in it. You can sell autographed copies to Pam and her friends.

SUE (*Shakes her head, smiling*): Oh, dear! That essay! Ever since it was published, I've been on exhibition. I hoped Maple Valley would be different.

JIMMY: You'll find out!

SUE: I'm sorry to hear the bad news about the game, Jim.

JIMMY: So am I . . .

SUE: I wanted to see that game.

JIMMY: Are you kiddin'?

PETE: She means it, Jim. Sue's a real fan!

SUE: Pete's told me so much about the Tigers. I hear you've got a great pitching arm, Jim. (*Crosses to him*) May I? (*Feels* JIMMY's arm, turns to PETE) You're right, Pete. *Solid!*

PETE: Out where Sue comes from, the girls have a softball team.

JIMMY: Honest?

SUE: I was captain of my outfit. I hated to leave that gang of mine—but Dad got a job with the Maple Valley newspaper, and here we are!

PETE: Sue used to pitch for her team.

JIMMY (*Impressed*): You did? (SUE *nods, smiling*.)

PETE: Show him, Sue!

SUE: Well . . . (*She takes a stance, winds up, and tosses an imaginary ball across the room.*)

JIMMY (*Whistles*): Not bad!

SUE: We have to pitch underhand, you know—softball.

JIMMY: Sure, I know.

SUE: Sometime I'd like to really wind up and let go! (*She assumes a professional ball-player's pitching position, and after an enormous wind-up, she hurls an imaginary ball.*)

JIMMY: Hey! You're all right!

SUE: Dad taught me.

JIMMY: I sure wish you'd get the dames around here interested in baseball. Maybe they'd get off their culture kick and act more human.

SUE: Culture kick?

JIMMY: Yeah. Like my sister Pam. That's why we're sunk this afternoon. She's got this screwy History Club comin' here to meet you, and I have to be Exhibit A!

SUE: I don't understand.

JIMMY: It's all because I happen to be James the Sixth!

PETE: I don't dig you.

JIMMY: I'm the sixth guy in my family with the same name. It's supposed to be important. (*To* SUE) Pam wants to parade me for her bookworms—make a big impression on you. (*Takes a sheet of paper from his pocket*) I even have to read an *essay!*

SUE: Is that the essay, Jim?

JIMMY: Yeah.

SUE: May I see it?

JIMMY (*Hands* SUE *the paper*): Sure—keep it if you want to. (*An idea*) Go ahead, keep it! (*To* PETE) I'll tell Pam I lost it, then maybe I won't have to perform!

SUE (*Looks at paper*): Well—this is very interesting . . .

JIMMY: Just a lot of bilge about my ancestors.

SUE: I ran across a lot of this material when I was doing *my* essay.

JIMMY: What do I care about all those guys? I just want to be *me!* (*Disgusted*) James the First, James the Second, James the Third! Monotonous, isn't it? (SUE *crosses to the French doors, scanning the paper.*)

PETE: I was named for a guy my Dad met in the army. Turned out later Pete wasn't his name at all. Just sort of an *alias*. Mom wanted to change my name, but Dad wouldn't let her. Good thing, too. She wanted to call me *Algernon!*

JIMMY: I'd just as soon be Algernon as to carry a lot of arithmetic on the back of my name! James the Sixth! Phooey!

SUE: Say! This is familiar territory! (*To* JIMMY) Did your sister write this, Jim?

JIMMY: She copied all those facts and dates out of some old book that Mother has.

SUE: Her research is sound—as far as it goes . . .

JIMMY: It goes far enough!

SUE: The Abbott family *did* make a lot of history, Jim. But they weren't quite as dull as this makes out.

JIMMY: Dull enough to spoil our game.

SUE: Listen, fellows. Maybe I can help you out. I'd like to see that game myself. How much time do we have?

JIMMY (*Looking at the mantel clock*): The Polecats will be on the diamond in one hour flat!

SUE: Well, boys, I've got an idea. I don't know if it'll work, but I'm willing to try. O.K.?

PETE: Susie, if you can save the day, I'll never forget it!

JIMMY: Me neither! What's the scoop? (PAM *enters.*)

PAM: I thought I heard voices in here. Hello, Pete.

PETE: Hi, Pam. This is my cousin, Susan White. Sue, meet Pamela Abbott.

PAM (*Goes to* SUE, *flustered, but pleased*): Why, Miss White! This is *such* an honor! (*Offers her hand*)

SUE (*Shakes hands with* PAM): Hello, Pam. I'm sorry to be here early.

PAM: I'm so *glad* you're here! We can get acquainted before the girls arrive. Jim—go get into your costume . . .

JIMMY: Pam, I'm not going to *dress up* for this clam bake!

PAM (*To* SUE, *covering* JIMMY'S *declaration with shaky laughter*): Excuse me. (*To* JIMMY) Now, darling, you know we rented that costume especially for the occasion.

JIMMY: Then you wasted your money!

PAM (*To* SUE): Jim is going to appear as one of the *early* Abbotts, Miss White.

SUE: Please call me Sue.

PAM: We've had so *many* distinguished ancestors, you know. It was a problem deciding which one Jim would represent.

JIMMY: I represent *me!* Jimmy Six—The Demon Pitcher! (*He winds up, hurls an imaginary pitch.*)

PAM (*Trilling to* SUE): Isn't he *amusing?* (*To* JIMMY *she offers an icy glare. Then she speaks to* SUE) We managed to rent a Revolutionary War costume for Jim. (*To* JIM) It's on your bed, dear. Go and put it on. And be careful of the powdered wig.

JIMMY (*A cry of pain*): False hair! *Shoot* me! *Hang* me! *Hog-tie* me! But I'm not going to wear a wig!

PAM: Pete will go up with you and help you get ready, won't you, Pete?

PETE: Well . . .

PAM: You can practice reading your speech to Pete. Remember, Jimmy—good round tones, and *project!*

SUE: Oh, here's your speech, Jim. (*Giving the paper to* JIMMY. *To* PAM) I was just looking it over. I hope you don't mind, Pam.

PAM: Of course not! I'm flattered! A historian like *you,* Miss White . . .

SUE (*Correcting her with a smile*): Sue . . .

PAM: Thank you. Any suggestions you care to make will be very welcome.

SUE: Well . . .

PAM: I have a better idea! Jim, read your speech for Miss White!

JIM (*In anguish*): Oh, *no!*

SUE (*With a wink for* JIMMY *that* PAM *does not see*): Go ahead, Jim. I'd like to hear it.

JIMMY (*Unfolding the paper*): Well, all right . . .

PAM: That's a good boy. (JIMMY *slouches, one hand in his pocket, clearing his throat.* SUE *and* PETE *sit.* PAM *stands nervously near the French doors.* JIMMY *moves self-conciously to center.*)

JIMMY: Where do I start?

PAM (*Sweetly, through her teeth*): At the *beginning,* dear boy.

JIMMY: I don't know what this first word is.

PAM: "Genealogical."

JIMMY: Jeanie-a-*which?*

PAM: "Genealogical Recollections of My Forebears."

JIMMY: Four bears! What is this—a *zoo?*

PAM: Forebears are *ancestors,* Jim.

JIMMY: Oh, sure. Well—that's the title. What Pam said. (*Clears throat, reads*) "My name is James Pomfrey Abbott the Sixth . . ." (*Looks up*) Heck! Everybody *knows* that!

PAM: Go on, please.

JIMMY (*Reads*): "I share this name with a long line of American heroes. James Pomfrey Abbott the First was a friend of Paul Revere. Revere made the famous Abbott silver service . . ." (*Looks up*) I thought Paul Revere rode a horse!

PAM: He was also a prominent silversmith.

JIMMY: I guess that horse must have been a hobby!

PAM: At this point, I thought we might make use of a prop.

JIMMY: I could use one right now. (*Leans on a chair*)

PAM: I plan to have Jim display the teapot from our Revere silver set.

JIMMY: You mean that old plugged teapot that leaks every time we use it?

PAM: Really, Jim! Please continue reading—*if* you don't mind!

JIMMY: I mind—but what can I do? (*He shrugs, reads*) "The first James Abbott fought at Bunker Hill. With Washington, he shared that terrible winter at Valley Forge."

SUE: I remember reading about him when I was gathering material for my essay.

PAM: Honestly, Sue? That's *thrilling!*

SUE: He was a fascinating person.

PAM: *All* the Abbotts were!

SUE: Do you remember the time Washington threw the silver dollar across the Rappahannock River?

PAM: Oh, yes!

SUE: Well, did you know that your ancestor—James the First—was with Washington at the time?

PAM: That wasn't in Mother's book.

SUE: I read about it in an old diary.

PAM: Tell us about it, Sue.

SUE: After Washington threw the dollar, James Abbott took out a shilling, and he tossed that shilling right across the Rappahannock!

PETE: Some pitch!

SUE: Then Abbott turned to Washington and said, "Let's see you beat *that,* George!"

JIMMY: What'd George do?

SUE: The diary didn't say.

PAM: That—that's a very interesting historical sidelight. However . . .

JIMMY: I'll work it in! Thanks, Sue!

PAM: Shall we read on?

JIMMY: O.K. (*Reads*) "James Pomfrey Abbott the Second is known as the Boy Hero of the War of 1812."

SUE: He was a drummer boy!

PAM (*Pleased*): That's right!

JIMMY (*Reads*): "When the British burned our capital city, young James stood firm in the face of the foe, and bravely beating his little drum, he summoned our troops to a gallant charge."

SUE: Thanks to Dolly Madison.

PAM: I beg your pardon, Sue?

SUE: There's an account of that in a Dolly Madison biography I read. You recall that Dolly Madison had to flee the burning city?

PAM: That's a well-known fact.

SUE: Well, on the road, Dolly passed a little drummer boy sitting on a rock. He was crying his eyes out because he had lost his drumsticks. Dolly rose to the situation. She dug into a basket of food she had in her carriage and produced two *chicken* drumsticks, which she gave to the boy. "Now, then," Dolly told him. "Stop whining and beat a loud retreat!"

PAM: *Retreat!*

SUE: Dolly knew the only way to save the troops was by a strategic retreat! So little Jim Abbott dried his tears and pounded the very dickens out of that drum of his!

PETE: Pounded the very *chickens,* you mean!

JIMMY: Hey! That's a better yarn than this one! I'm gonna tell that story.

PAM: Well—it's very *colorful*—but are the facts correct?

SUE: I have the book among my things, Pam. It's by a noted author, and I think it sheds new light on Dolly Madison.

JIMMY: Not to mention Jimmy the Second!

PETE: Let's hear more!

PAM: I'm afraid this may be boring our guest, Jim. (*To* SUE) You can hear the rest when the girls get here.

SUE: Oh, I'm *enjoying* this, Pam! May we hear more?

PAM: Well . . .

JIMMY (*Reads eagerly*): "James Abbott the Third was a famous Indian fighter."

SUE: Indeed he was! And such a brave man! He was scalped in a raid at Point Regret—but he lived to tell the tale! Of course, he didn't have a hair on his head. In later years he was known as Baldy Abbott! (PAM *swallows hard.*)

JIMMY: Old Baldy, huh?

PAM: I don't believe it!

PETE: Keep goin', Jim!

JIMMY (*Reads*): "James P. Abbott the Fourth, sometimes called the Empire Builder . . ."

SUE: If I may say so, Pam, it might be better to skip this one.

PAM: Why? He built a railroad clear to the Pacific Coast.

SUE: There was some question about the manner in which he financed that railroad, Pam.

PAM: That's not true!

SUE: I refer you to the Congressional Record, Volume Number . . .

PAM: Never mind!

JIMMY (*Reads*): "James Abbott the Fifth . . ."

PAM (*Grabs the paper from* JIMMY): I'll take that!

SUE: James Abbott the Fifth was a journeyman printer who later founded one of America's biggest newspapers.

PAM: At least you've got *that* right!

SUE: He is enshrined at Cooperstown, New York, in the gallery of baseball immortals.

JIMMY (*Delighted*): Honest?

SUE: Jim Abbott hit the first home run in baseball history.

JIMMY: *That's* where I get my talent!

SUE: He founded the Millersville Giants, one of the first ball clubs in the East.

JIMMY: Just like me with the Tigers!

SUE (*To* PAM): I think it's a great idea to have Jim tell us about your ancestors, Pam. I know your friends will *love* it!

PAM: Like *fun* they will! Do you think I'll let Jim stand up there and *disgrace* the family name?

SUE: It's fascinating, Pam.

PAM: Susan White, I think you're mean! My whole day is *ruined!*

SUE: I don't see why.

PAM: Just because you happen to be so smart!

SUE: The truth is always good to hear, Pam. We're all human. When we learn that the men and women who made our history were also human beings, it makes us appreciate all the more what they did for us.

PAM (*Miserably*): I'll never be able to hold up my head again!

SUE: Of course you will.

PAM: Jim'll spread this all over town!

JIMMY (*Gleefully*): Yes, ma'am!

PAM: I'll be so *mortified!*

PETE: What for?

PAM: Those dreadful ancestors of mine! (*Recites their crimes*) "See if you can beat that, George!" Chicken drumsticks! *Baldy* Abbott! Swindler! Home run king! (*Wailing*). Oh, it sounds like the Rogues' Gallery!

SUE: Quite the contrary. All those Abbott men had their place in our history, Pam. They were great Americans.

PAM: Not that Empire Builder—that *swindler!*

SUE: I said there was some *question* about his finances, Pam. He cleared himself eventually. In those days most empire builders were men of action and expediency. If they hadn't been, our country couldn't have expanded so rapidly. Abbott the Fourth made fine contributions to our national growth.

PAM: It didn't sound that way to me.

SUE: Pam, I've got an idea. I'd like to do a series of articles about the Abbotts!

PAM: And get us ridden out of town on a rail? No thanks!

SUE: The Historians' Magazine has asked me to contribute some articles, and I've been wondering what to write about. The Abbotts are the answer! From James the First to Jimmy Six.

JIMMY (*Astonished*): You wouldn't put *me* in an article?

SUE: You'd be the final one, Jim. A contemporary study. The Abbotts carry on! A glowing example of history's continuity! And, Sue—I'd like to do a treatment of the Abbott women, too. You, for instance . . .

PAM: Me?

SUE: In fact, I'd like to build the article around you. (*Takes* PAM's *arm*) My first new friend in Maple Valley—the person to whom I owe this wonderful adventure!

PAM: An article about me! Imagine what the girls would say!

SUE: I'd like to start making notes right away. (*Gets pencil and paper from desk*) I want to get to know you both. Your daily lives. Your interests . . .

JIMMY: Baseball!

SUE: Do you think I could watch you play?

JIMMY: Right now if you say so! The Tigers are playin' the Elm Street Polecats this afternoon!

SUE: Is it a major contest?

PETE: Biggest event of the summer!

SUE: Pam—I must see that game!

PAM: But my friends! They're coming here to meet you!

SUE: Couldn't we all go to the game together?

PETE: We'll save you some seats!

JIMMY: In the shade!

PAM: But my plans! I worked so hard on the refreshments!

SUE: Couldn't we come back here after the game and have a victory party? That'd be fun, Pam!

PAM: What if the Tigers *lose?*

PETE: Not a chance!

SUE: I've felt that pitching arm of Jim's, Pam. *I* don't think the Tigers will lose!

JIMMY: She's a baseball expert, too, Pam!

PAM (*With growing suspicion*): Oh, is she? I'm beginning to understand . . .

SUE: (*Smiles at* PAM): You're right, Pam. I did start popping those footnotes to the Abbotts just to help the boys out of a jam—but I overplayed my game. I backed myself right into a corner. Now I won't rest till I do those articles about your family! (*Takes* PAM's *arm*) May we go to the game, Pam? Please?

PAM: Well, if you think it's that important . . .

SUE: *Everything* about the Abbotts is important!

PETE: Golly! Look at the time, Jim! Come on! (*Runs to French doors*)

JIMMY (*Following* PETE): See you at the game, gals! (*Turns at the door*) Thanks, Sue! Thanks a million!

PETE: Step on it!

JIMMY: And Pam—if you want me to—I'll wear that costume at your party. I'll even put on the wig!

PAM (*Beams at* JIMMY): Forget it! Just go out and win that game! We can't have Sue writing about an Abbott *defeat!* Jim—you've got the family honor in the palm of your hand!

JIMMY: Nope! I've got it right here! (*Flexes his pitching arm*)

SUE: Good luck, boys!

PAM: Bless you. Bless you, Jimmy Six!

JIMMY: Thanks, Pam. As we say in the family tree—*Excelsior!* (JIMMY *and* PETE *run out.* MRS. ABBOTT *starts downstairs.*)

PAM: I've got a feeling this may be a great day for the Abbotts!

SUE: It's not such a bad day for Susie White! (MRS. ABBOTT *enters the room, sees* SUE, *comes forward.*)

MRS. ABBOTT: How do you do? I'm Cynthia Abbott. (*Offers her hand*)

PAM: Mother, this is Susan White. This is my mother, Sue.

SUE (*Shaking hands with* MRS. ABBOTT): It's so nice to meet you, Mrs. Abbott.

MRS. ABBOTT (*Warmly*): I can't begin to tell you how enchanted I am to meet *you!* I was certainly impressed by your essay. Frankly, Miss White, I think it shows signs of potential literary greatness.

SUE: Thank you.

PAM: Wait till you *hear* about that potential, Mother!

MRS. ABBOTT: You write so picturesquely—but with such style.

SUE: Thank you, Mrs. Abbott.

MRS. ABBOTT: Since you're interested in history, I must tell you a few things about *our* family . . .

SUE (*Getting pencil and paper ready*): May I make notes, Mrs. Abbott?

MRS. ABBOTT: You won't have to, my dear. I'll lend you my Abbott Genealogy.

SUE: I'm sure I'll enjoy it. But, Mrs. Abbott, *your* side of the family must contain fine material, too.

MRS. ABBOTT (*Pleased*): The Pryors?

SUE: Didn't I read somewhere that Comfort Pryor was the first woman to sail around the Horn in a clipper ship?

MRS. ABBOTT (*Beaming*): My dear Miss White, we must have a good, long talk! Do sit down! (*They sit.* SUE, *with pencil poised, winks at* PAM. *The curtain starts down.*)

MRS. ABBOTT: Now, let's start at the beginning. It was this way: Comfort Pryor's grandmother came from England in Sixteen Hundred and . . .

THE END

Production Notes

Jimmy Six

Characters: 2 male; 3 female.

Playing Time: 25 minutes.

Costumes: Modern dress. Pamela and Sue wear dressy afternoon clothes; Jimmy and Pete wear everyday clothes suitable for playing baseball.

Properties: Wedge of apple pie and sheet of paper for Jimmy.

Setting: The Abbott living room. On one side there is a door leading to the rest of the house; on the other there are French doors, if possible, leading to the outside. The room contains a desk with a book and pencils and paper on it, a bookcase, a davenport, and a few chairs. There is a clock on the mantel over a fireplace.

Lighting: No special effects.

Runaway

By Anne Coulter Martens

Characters

MRS. ADLER, *of Ridge Manor*
GLORIA, *the maid*
JILL
MARTY
JEAN
MARY
GINNY } *teen-agers*
PAT
SUE
SALLY
MISS CONWAY, *their chaperon*
MISS WILLIS, *a photographer*
MISS ROWAN, *an agent*
ANNOUNCER (*off-stage voice*)

TIME: *A Saturday afternoon*
SETTING: *The lobby of Ridge Manor, a small hotel for women.*
AT RISE: *Lively dance music is blaring from the radio*

and GLORIA *is dancing by herself. The telephone rings, but she is unaware of it.* MRS. ADLER *hurries in.*

MRS. ADLER (*Loudly*): Gloria, the telephone! (*Goes behind desk and picks up receiver*) Ridge Manor . . . Who? (*Covering phone*) Gloria, the radio! Gloria! (*On phone*) Excuse me a moment.

GLORIA: You hate music? (*Goes to radio and turns it down*)

MRS. ADLER (*On phone*): Yes, Miss Conway came a little while ago. Hold on a minute, please. (MISS CONWAY, *a friendly and efficient young woman, comes in.*)

MISS CONWAY: Have any of my girls arrived yet?

MRS. ADLER: Not yet. (*On phone*) Here she is now. (*To* MISS CONWAY) Phone call for you, Miss Conway. A photographer from the Ridgeway *Times.*

MISS CONWAY: She wants a picture of my spelling champions. (*Takes phone*) Hello, Miss Willis . . . What time can you come? . . . Oh, good . . . I'm on my way now to meet some of the girls at the bus station . . .

MRS. ADLER: It's just down at the corner. You can see it from here.

MISS CONWAY (*On phone*): Some of them are getting rides and some are coming by train or bus . . . I don't know exactly how many can make it. . . . This is the County spelling match, you know, and each girl is a winner in her own high school. . . . Girls only, yes, because this is sponsored by the Women's Aurora Club, to raise the level of spelling achievement. . . . Oh, I'm sure they're all just terribly excited! . . . Fine, Miss Willis, the match isn't until three o'clock, so we'll see you in a little while . . . 'Bye. (*Hangs up*)

GLORIA: I wouldn't even try to win a spelling contest.

MISS CONWAY: No? If any of the girls come while I'm gone, will you tell them I won't be long? (*Takes an envelope from her handbag*) Here are some name tags already filled out, and some extras. (*Spills name cards from envelope onto desk*)

GLORIA: I'd much rather be a famous dancing star in the movies. (*Eagerly*) Miss Conway, did you know there's a movie company on location just outside of town?

MISS CONWAY: I heard something about it, yes.

MRS. ADLER: That new starlet, Sherry Meredith, is getting a build-up.

MISS CONWAY: I don't seem to remember her.

GLORIA: I saw an article about her in a movie magazine. In her first picture she had midnight black hair. But I think she's blonde in this new one. Or is she a red-head? She looks different in every movie magazine.

MISS CONWAY (*Not interested*): Really? You won't forget about the name tags?

GLORIA: Don't I wish someone would give *me* a build-up! Gorgeous Gloria with the dancing feet! (*Dances around*)

MRS. ADLER: Dance yourself upstairs and make sure all those rooms are ready. We want these spelling champions well taken care of.

GLORIA (*To* MISS CONWAY): Does the winner get a whole lot of money?

MISS CONWAY: A hundred dollars here at the County level. The State champion will get a college scholarship. (*Glances at her watch*) I'll have to dash. (*Goes to door.* MARTY, *a pretty girl in her teens, comes in carrying a suitcase.*)

MARTY: Hello. I'm Marty Hammond from Evansville.

MISS CONWAY: Glad you could come, dear. I'm Miss Conway. I'm in a hurry right now . . . I wonder if you would get your name tag from the desk.

MARTY: I'll do that.

MISS CONWAY (*Turning at door*): Marty, suppose I appoint you temporary chairman till I get back?

MARTY: That's fine with me, Miss Conway. (MISS CONWAY *hurries out.* MARTY *sits on the sofa.* JEAN, *a serious-minded, aloof girl, comes in carrying a suitcase.*)

MRS. ADLER: I'd better check the rooms. (*To* GLORIA) You can show these two up when they're ready. (*Goes out*)

MARTY (*In a friendly tone*): Hello. I'm Marty Hammond from Evansville.

JEAN (*Distantly*): Jean Kinney from Daytonsburg. (*Sits in chair*)

GLORIA: Want to hear some good jive? (*Turns radio volume up to lively music and comes from behind desk.*) Real groovy, what?

JEAN: Not my type of music.

GLORIA (*To* MARTY): Is she a— (*Makes a square in the air*)

MARTY (*Laughing*): Does it matter?

GLORIA (*To* JEAN): What's the longest word you can spell?

JEAN: The longest words are very seldom the hardest.

GLORIA: No kidding! (*The radio music is interrupted by the* ANNOUNCER.)

ANNOUNCER (*Off-stage*): We interrupt this music program to bring you a news bulletin. Police have been alerted to help in the search for young movie starlet, Sherry Meredith, who disappeared from a movie location just outside this city . . .

GLORIA: Oh, my gosh, we were just talking about her! (*Goes to radio*)

ANNOUNCER: Miss Meredith is said to have been under considerable tension lately, and may be suffering from nervous exhaustion . . .

MARTY (*Going to radio*): I hope nothing's happened to her.

ANNOUNCER: It's known that she took with her a suitcase, which she was using in a scene in the picture, and authorities think she is probably heading for the bus terminal or the railroad station . . .

GLORIA: She might be in this very neighborhood!

ANNOUNCER: Her mother, who has collapsed from worry and is under a doctor's care, pleads for her to return. When last seen on the studio lot, Miss Meredith was wearing a bright red jacket, but she may have other clothes with her. Police request that people in those areas contact headquarters or the movie studio if they see a girl with a suitcase who acts in an unusual way. And now, back to our program of jumping jive. (*The music comes on again.*)

GLORIA (*Turning it down a bit*): She may go right past our door to the bus terminal!

MARTY: I've never seen any of her movies. Would you recognize her?

GLORIA: Of course. (*Considering*) Well, I think maybe I would. They wear so much make-up and all, it's hard to tell.

JEAN (*To* GLORIA): Will you show me up to my room? I'd like to unpack my bag and get out my spelling list to study.

MARTY: You're going to study *now?*

JEAN: Certainly, because I intend to win that contest.

MARTY (*Smiling*): I had in mind maybe *I'd* win it.

JEAN: Really? (*Looks at* GLORIA)

GLORIA: Why, Sherry Meredith may even come in here to avoid the cops. (*Struck by a sudden thought*) Oh, my gosh, maybe one of *you*—!

MARTY (*Laughing*): I thought you said you'd recognize her.

GLORIA: Well, I'm not exactly *sure*. (*Turns to board with room keys and hands each girl a key.*) Here are your keys.

MRS. ADLER (*Calling from off-stage*): Gloria!

GLORIA (*Opening door*): What do you want?

MRS. ADLER (*Off-stage*): Towels! Bring the key to the linen closet!

GLORIA: Coming! (*To girls*) Always bugging me about something! Go ahead and I'll be right with you. (MARTY *and* JEAN *go out, taking their suitcases.* GLORIA *gets a key from the board and starts after them.* JILL, *a quiet, sweet-faced girl, comes in carrying a rather distinctive suitcase. She is more dressed up than the other two, wearing a suit and heels. She looks back over her shoulder, then stands near the door.*)

GLORIA: Hi! Are you one of the spelling contest girls? Miss Conway will be back pretty soon. (*The telephone rings as she is about to go out.*)

MRS. ADLER (*Calling*): Gloria, what's keeping you?

GLORIA: Drat! Answer that phone for me, will you, please? And get your name card from the desk. (*Hurries out.* JILL *sets down her suitcase and goes to answer the phone.*)

JILL (*On phone*): Hello . . . Miss Conway isn't here right now . . . Will you repeat that, please? . . . You can't come to the spelling contest . . . Your name? . . . Verna Allen, from Maddenfield . . . Yes . . . No, I'm not one of the contest girls, but . . . Yes, it's too bad you can't be here, Verna . . . Good-bye. (*Hangs up. Goes back to door, looks out, then closes door quickly, rather agitated. Picks up her suitcase and puts it behind sofa, out of sight. As* JILL *is doing this, the* AN-NOUNCER'S *voice is heard again on the radio. She stiffens, listening, then goes to radio.*)

ANNOUNCER: Here's the latest bulletin on the runaway girl. Attention is now centered on the bus terminal, where she was spotted just a few minutes ago, but eluded a police officer before he could reach her. A careful watch is being kept on the entire area, and police expect momentarily— (*When the* ANNOUNCER'S *voice starts,* MARTY *and* JEAN *come in and stand near the door.* JILL *turns off the radio.*)

MARTY: Why did you shut it off?

JILL (*Startled*): No reason. I just did. (*Stands at desk and nervously plays with some name cards*)

MARTY (*To* JEAN): It was about that girl.

JEAN: I couldn't care less. (*She has a notebook, pencil and spelling list, and goes to a chair, where she proceeds to study.*)

JILL: What girl?

MARTY: She disappeared, and the police are after her. Has Miss Conway come back?

JILL: No.

MARTY: She put me in charge for now. Did you get your name tag? (*Goes to desk, looks through some name tags*) Here's mine. Marty Hammond. Evansville.

JEAN: See mine?

MARTY (*Finding it*): Here you are. Jean Kinney, Daytonsburg. (*Gives it to* JEAN, *then turns to* JILL.) Do you have yours? (*Nervously,* JILL *drops a few cards to the floor.*)

JILL: Oh, I'm sorry. (*Stoops to pick them up, but* MARTY *gets them first.*)

MARTY: Which one is yours? (*Reads cards*) Pat Smith, Verna Allen, Sally McCoy—

JILL: Oh, I meant to tell you. Verna Allen—there was a phone call—

MARTY: Anything important? (*Without waiting for an answer*) I'm glad to know you, Verna. Where are you from? (*Looks at card*) Maddenfield. (*Hands card to* JILL) Better pin it on. (*Pins on her own tag.*)

JILL: But *I'm* not—

MARTY: Going to lose it? Maybe not, but it's easier to get acquainted if we wear them. (*Takes card from* JILL) Let me do it for you. (*Pins it on* JILL)

JILL (*Slowly*): Maybe it *is* a good idea. (*Brightening*) A very good idea.

MARTY (*Looking at it again*): Maddenfield. Maybe you know my cousin? Dodie Barrett.

JILL: No, I—I haven't lived there very long.

MARTY: Nice high school, isn't it?

JILL: Oh, very. (MISS CONWAY *comes in with* MARY, GINNY, *and* PAT, *teen-age girls who carry suitcases. At the same time* MRS. ADLER *comes in up center.*)

MISS CONWAY: Here you are, girls, Ridge Manor. And this is Mrs. Adler. Mary, Ginny and Pat. (*Greetings are exchanged.*) I'm sure you'll get acquainted in no time.

MARY (*Looking around*): Nice.

GINNY: No boys? (*Giggles a little*)

PAT: We're supposed to concentrate on spelling.

MRS. ADLER (*Going behind desk*): Would you like to register now?

MISS CONWAY: Line up, girls. (MARY, GINNY *and* PAT *get in line to register.* JEAN *gets up and stands in line.*

MARTY *passes out name tags.* JILL *stands a little apart.*)
Come on, dear. (*Looks at* JILL's *name tag*) So you're
Verna. How's everything in Maddenfield?

JILL: Just fine.

MISS CONWAY: A nice little town, I've driven through it
often. Have they finished the new bridge yet?

JILL: Not quite. (*Gets in line*)

MARTY (*Getting in line behind her*): You and I are to
share the same room. Our names are posted on the door
upstairs.

JILL: Oh? (*Each girl registers as she reaches the desk.*)

MISS CONWAY (*To* MRS. ADLER): There was a little excitement at the bus terminal. The police are looking
for a girl who disappeared.

MRS. ADLER: Gloria was chattering something about it.
(SUE *and* SALLY *come in, carrying suitcases.*)

MISS CONWAY: Hello, girls. Over here, please. (*They cross
over and stand in line.* GLORIA *comes in.*)

MARTY: Hi. What pretty suitcases you both have!

SUE: Thank you.

GLORIA: Did you know there's a cop across the street?

SUE: We saw him. Is anything wrong?

MISS CONWAY: Not in here. Your name, dear?

SUE: Sue Mason. (MARTY *gives them some name tags.*)

MARTY: Look for your name tag, and if you don't find it,
fill one out.

SALLY: I'm Sally McCoy. I was so afraid I wouldn't get
here in time for the spelling contest. My dad had a flat
tire on the turnpike, of all places! (SUE *fills out a tag
and pins it on her jacket.*)

MISS CONWAY: The match is at three, so we'll leave for
the auditorium before too long. Afterward we have a
very nice weekend planned for all of you.

GINNY: My boy friend Joe gave me a rabbit's foot for luck. (*Shows it, giggling a little.*)

SUE: I sure hope I win.

MARTY: You'll have to beat Jean first. And me.

JILL: And me!

SALLY, PAT *and* GINNY (*At same time*): And me! (*They all laugh.*)

GLORIA: Why do you think that cop's still hanging around here?

MRS. ADLER: Forget it, Gloria. (*Gets keys from board*) Ready, girls?

MISS CONWAY: You may want to freshen up, and then unpack a few things. (MARY, GINNY, PAT, SUE, SALLY, *and* JILL *follow her.*) The Aurora Club hopes this will be one of the very best weekends you've ever had—no matter who wins the contest. (MRS. ADLER, MISS CONWAY *and the* GIRLS *go out.* GLORIA *gets busy behind the desk.* MARTY *goes to* JEAN.)

MARTY: Jean, I have a funny feeling.

JEAN: Butterflies in your stomach? (*Half to herself, spells the word "benefit."*)

MARTY: It's about that girl, Verna Allen. (JEAN *spells "peninsula" half to herself.*) She says she's from Maddenfield.

JEAN (*Impatiently*): So?

MARTY: But she told Miss Conway that the new bridge isn't finished yet, and it is! (JEAN *spells "veterinary."*) It's been finished for a month. I rode across it last Sunday!

JEAN: So?

MARTY: So maybe she isn't from Maddenfield at all. Maybe her name isn't Verna Allen!

JEAN: Now, really.

MARTY: Maybe *she's* the runaway starlet, Sherry Meredith.

GLORIA: Oh, my gosh! (*Impressed*) She *does* look sort of like those pictures in the movie magazine.

MARTY: I think she ducked out of the bus terminal and came in here to get away from that policeman!

JEAN: You're way out. (*Studies her list, then spells "recommend"*)

MARTY: Jean, aren't you even interested? Everybody's trying to find Sherry.

JEAN: So?

MARTY: You heard what the radio said—her mother's just sick with worry.

JEAN (*Calmly*): I have the spelling contest to think about.

GLORIA: Shall I go out and tell that cop? (*Starts out*) Or should I call the movie studio and tell them she's here?

MARTY: Wait. We want to make sure we have the right girl, or everybody'll laugh at us. Jean . . . (JEAN *spells "corruptible."*) Please help me find out for sure.

JEAN: How?

MARTY: We can question her, and try her on some spelling words to see if she's really a champ.

GLORIA: The more I think about it, the more I'm *sure* she's Sherry! (SUE *comes in.*)

MARTY: Sue, we think Verna Allen is the runaway movie starlet, Sherry Meredith.

SUE: Oh, my glory, what makes you think so?

MARTY: Lots of things.

SUE: But didn't someone say Sherry was wearing a red jacket?

MARTY: Maybe she changed to something else. I'll bet that red jacket's in her suitcase right now!

SUE: And where's her suitcase?

MARTY: Probably upstairs in my room, because we're roommates.

SUE: Want me to go up and search, when she comes out of the room?

MARTY (*Excitedly*): Take my key. (*Gives her key to* SUE) Open her suitcase if you can.

SUE: If you're wrong, I sure hope she doesn't catch me at it! (*Goes toward door as* JILL *enters*)

MARTY (*With a warning cough*): I'll be glad to lend you my cologne, Sue. Go right up to my room.

SUE: Thanks so much. (*Goes out.* JEAN *spells "judgment."*)

MARTY (*To* JILL): That's not such a hard one, is it, Verna?

JILL: Oh, no.

MARTY: The one I keep forgetting is mileage. (*Spells it "m-i-l-a-g-e"*) Is that right?

JILL (*Nodding*): Right. (*Sits on sofa, ill at ease.* MARTY *gives a little gasp and changes it to a cough.*)

MARTY (*Whispers*): Jean, did you hear that?

JEAN (*Impatiently*): Will you leave me out of this? If I win the County contest and then go on to win the State finals, I'll get a college scholarship.

MARTY: I know all that.

JEAN: Maybe *you* can go to college without a scholarship, but *I* can't. (*Studies again*)

MARTY (*Shortly*): Sorry I bothered you. (*To* JILL) Let's you and I practice, shall we? Here's a word for you. "Synonym."

JILL (*Uneasily*): I didn't study that one.

MARTY: How about *siege?* S-e-i-g-e. Right?

JILL: Yes. (*As* JILL *looks toward left,* MARTY *shakes her head to* GLORIA, *indicating that it is incorrect.*)

MARTY: Are there two "l's" or one in tranquil?

JILL: Why—two. (MARTY *shakes her head to* GLORIA. GLORIA *points to* JILL *and then to the telephone.* MARTY *shakes her head "no."*)

MARTY: Too bad you don't know my cousin Dodie in Maddenfield. She's a real cute girl. (*After a pause*) What street do you live on?

JILL: Elm Street.

MARTY: That's the street the library's on, isn't it?

JILL: Yes. (MARTY *shakes her head to* GLORIA *that this is not true.*)

MARTY: I went to a football game once in Maddenfield. Right after they built the new stadium. It sure is a huge stadium, isn't it?

JILL: Oh, yes. Really big. (MARTY *shakes her head to* GLORIA.)

GLORIA: I think it's time to make my phone call.

MARTY (*Looking at her watch*): It certainly is! I'll watch the desk, if you want to make it upstairs. (GLORIA *goes out, as* SUE *comes in.*)

SUE: I couldn't find—the cologne.

MARTY: That's funny. (MISS WILLIS, *a trim young woman with a camera slung over her shoulder, comes in.*)

MISS WILLIS: Good afternoon. Are you spelling contest girls?

MARTY: We are.

MISS WILLIS: I'm from the Ridgeway *Times.* (MISS CONWAY *comes in, followed by* MARY, GINNY, SALLY *and* PAT.)

MISS CONWAY: Hello, Miss Willis. My girls are ready if you are. (*Glances at her watch*) Time's getting short.

MISS WILLIS (*Adjusting her camera*): Some of you on the

sofa, some behind it, and a couple of girls sitting on the floor.

Miss Conway: All right, girls. (*They group themselves as suggested, except for* Jill, *who holds back, and* Sue, *who stands near watching her.*)

Marty: Come on, Verna.

Jill: Excuse me. I—I have a headache. (*Starts for door*)

Miss Conway: But you must have your picture taken!

Jill: Never mind. I'll just lie down for awhile. (*Goes out*)

Sue: I'll get her an aspirin. (*Goes out*)

Miss Conway: I guess Verna has the contest jitters.

Miss Willis: Too bad. Now, let's have your names, girls. (*Writes as each girl gives name and town*)

Miss Conway (*Uncertainly*): Maybe I should go after Verna.

Miss Willis: Later. I want you in the picture, too. (Miss Conway *joins the girls at sofa.*) All ready? (*Aims camera*) Say cheese! (*Takes a flash picture*) Thank you, that's it. (*Briskly*) Good luck to all of you, and I'll take a picture of the winner tomorrow. (*Goes to door*) 'Bye, now. (*Goes out as they call goodbye.*)

Miss Conway: You girls are free to amuse yourselves for about fifteen minutes. Stay together, and don't go far away.

Ginny: I'm going down the street to the five-and-dime to buy a card for Joe. (*Giggles*)

Pat: Let's all buy cards. (Pat, Mary, Ginny *and* Sally *exit.*)

Marty: Miss Conway, I have something to tell you.

Miss Conway: Later, dear. (*Goes to door*) I want to see about Verna.

Marty: This is about Verna. Remember that radio report we heard? I'm almost sure—

MISS CONWAY: Tell me when I come down. (*Goes out as* GLORIA *comes in.*)

GLORIA: I called the movie studio!

MARTY: What did they say?

GLORIA: They're sending someone for Sherry right away. Her agent, I think.

MARTY: Poor Sherry! I feel sort of guilty about telling on her. She seems so nice and sweet, just like an ordinary girl.

GLORIA: But she's jittery as can be.

MARTY: Yes, I noticed that. *Why* do you think she ran away, worrying her mother and everybody else?

GLORIA: Maybe she flipped her lid. (*Dances a few steps.*)

MARTY: Oh, no, I'm sure not. (*Thoughtfully*) But she must have had a reason.

GLORIA (*Dancing behind sofa, pausing*): Who left a suitcase back here? (*Picks it up*)

MARTY: It must be Verna's—I mean, Sherry's! She plans to get out of here just as soon as she can. (JEAN, *sitting left, spells a word now and then, or writes on her pad.*)

GLORIA (*Setting suitcase in front of sofa*): Let's open it and see if the red jacket's in it.

MARTY: No wonder Sue didn't find it upstairs.

GLORIA: Come on, open it.

MARTY: I have a better idea. If Verna really *is* Sherry Meredith, she'll come back in here for the suitcase. Let's put it back where we found it. (*Puts suitcase behind sofa*)

GLORIA: And then what?

MARTY: We'll hide and wait. The girl who comes for that suitcase is Sherry Meredith! (*Goes behind desk*) Come on, Jean.

JEAN: Why me?

MARTY: Hurry! She may come back any minute.

JEAN (*Going behind desk*): Oh, all right.

MARTY: And stop worrying so much about the contest. The world won't come to an end if you don't win. (*Stoops down behind desk*) Down, both of you. (JEAN *and* GLORIA *stoop down.*)

GLORIA: I feel like maybe I'm going to sneeze!

MARTY: You'd just better not! (*After a pause*) Do you hear someone coming?

GLORIA: I *am* going to sneeze!

MARTY (*In a loud whisper*): Don't you dare! (JILL *comes in. She looks around, making sure the room is deserted, then gets the suitcase from behind the sofa.* GLORIA *sneezes.* JILL *stands very still, startled.* MARTY, JEAN *and* GLORIA *get up from behind desk.*)

GLORIA: I couldn't help it!

MARTY: Going some place? (*Goes towards* JILL)

JILL (*Upset*): My head still aches.

MARTY (*Opening door to street, looking out*): Funny, that policeman is still across the street.

JILL (*Quickly*): Maybe if I sit down awhile, I'll feel better. (*Sits on sofa*)

MARTY: You don't really have a headache. And your name's not Verna Allen.

JILL (*Surprised*): How did you—(*Breaks off*) It is!

MARTY: You're not good at spelling. And you've never been to Maddenfield.

JILL: What makes you think that?

MARTY: Because the library *isn't* on Elm Street. And the high school doesn't have a new stadium.

JILL (*Lifelessly*): Oh.

MARTY: I wondered about you when I first heard the radio report. You were afraid to have your picture taken, and you're afraid of that policeman.

JILL: Leave me alone!

MARTY: I don't know why you ran away, but why don't you make up your mind to go back?

GLORIA: It doesn't make sense to run *away* from a movie studio!

JEAN: *Are* you Sherry Meredith?

JILL (*Startled*): What? (*Jumps up, suitcase in hand*) I'm Jill Denning!

MARTY: Please, Sherry, don't deny it.

JILL: I'm not Sherry! And I don't know anything about her. I thought that radio broadcast was about *me*. I thought my dad found the note I left and sent the police to find me.

GLORIA: She's such a good actress, it sounds almost like she's telling the truth.

JILL: It *is* the truth. And I *want* to be an actress. I had the lead in our school play, and everybody said I should go to Hollywood. But my dad wouldn't listen; he said I'm too young. That's why I ran away!

MARTY: Don't make up stories. Your mother is frantic with worry.

JILL: I don't even have a mother!

MARTY: There's one way to find out. Sherry was wearing a red jacket, and we think it's in her suitcase. Open your bag and let's see if it's there.

JILL (*Angry now*): You have no right to doubt my word!

MARTY: Then open your suitcase. (*Reaches for it*)

JILL (*Pulling away*): No! (*Holds tight to suitcase as MARTY pulls it. Suddenly it flies open and the contents spill out. Among them is a bright red jacket.*)

GLORIA (*Pouncing*): Here it is! (*Holds up the jacket. At the same time,* MISS CONWAY *and* SUE *come in.*)

SUE: So you *are* Sherry Meredith.

MISS CONWAY: What is this? (JILL *looks from one to the other, then stares at the jacket.*)

MARTY: She's the movie starlet who ran away.

SUE: The jacket! (*Takes it from* GLORIA *and puts it back in the suitcase, picking up some of the spilled things.*)

JILL: You're all wrong! I don't know how that jacket got in my suitcase. (*Suddenly, as she sees* SUE *putting back the things*) Those aren't my clothes. It isn't my suitcase at all!

GLORIA: Then whose is it?

JILL: A girl sat next to me in the bus station—I must have picked up her suitcase by mistake!

MARTY: What did she look like?

JILL: I didn't notice. Oh, please believe me!

MISS CONWAY (*Gently*): Try not to be so upset, Sherry, dear. (*Notices that* SUE *is going right with suitcase*) Sue, where are you taking the suitcase?

SUE: I'll put it in a safe place while you call the movie studio.

GLORIA: I've already called them.

MISS CONWAY (*Reaches for the suitcase*): Better let me take charge of it.

SUE (*Moving out of her reach*): Just leave it to me.

MARTY (*Suddenly aware, to* SUE): *You* had a suitcase just like that when you came in!

SUE (*Casually*): Rather like this, yes.

MARTY (*Blocking the door before* SUE *can reach it*): You were the girl she sat next to in the bus station! You followed her here to get your own suitcase back!

SUE: Don't be silly.

MARTY: No wonder you wanted to go upstairs to find it. You're Sherry Meredith!

SUE: No! (*But as they all look at her, she breaks down.*) All right, I am! (*Sits on sofa and covers her face with her hands*) Why didn't you let me go?

MISS CONWAY: We're only thinking of what's best for you.

SHERRY (*Sue*): How do you know what's best? (MISS ROWAN, *an attractive young woman, comes in and pauses as* SHERRY *speaks.*) *You* haven't been pushed and driven, and made over into somebody who isn't you at all!

MISS ROWAN (*Going to her*): Did we do that to you, Sherry?

SHERRY (*Surprised*): Miss Rowan!

MISS ROWAN (*To the others*): I'm her agent, and thanks for calling me. (*To* SHERRY) Sherry, dear . . . (SHERRY *jumps up and backs away.*) Why did you run away from us?

SHERRY (*Her voice rising*): "Sherry, dear, get your hair set." "Sherry, dear, watch your manicure." "Sherry, dear, you don't *really* want a cheeseburger for lunch —how about a delicious cottage cheese salad?"

MISS ROWAN: Please darling—

SHERRY: "The photographers are waiting. Smile, Sherry!" "Hurry, Sherry, it's time for the interview." "Wear the green dress, Sherry." "Take your dancing lesson." "Take your voice lesson." "Watch your weight." "Count the calories." "Smile, Sherry." "Hurry, Sherry. Hurry, hurry!" (*She is near hysteria.*)

MISS ROWAN (*Gently*): It's all right, dear. (*Puts her arm around* SHERRY) It's all right now. We've been pushing you too hard. I didn't realize.

SHERRY (*After a pause, in a calmer tone*): All of a sudden I just couldn't take it any more. I had to find a place where I could be quiet, and alone, and *me*.

MISS ROWAN: I'm really sorry. If you decide you don't want to be in the movies after all—

SHERRY: Oh, but I do! Honestly, I do. Just—not so fast. Not so much of everything all at once.

MISS ROWAN: Then that's the way it will be. Are you ready to go home now? (MISS CONWAY *gives her the suitcase.*)

SHERRY (*After a pause*): Yes. Yes, I'm ready. (*Turns a dazzling smile on the others*) Please forgive me for all this.

MISS CONWAY: There's really nothing to forgive. We wish you the very best.

SHERRY: Thank you. (MISS ROWAN *and* SHERRY *go out.* MARY, PAT, GINNY *and* SALLY *come in and stand near the door.*)

MARTY: Jill, I feel like a perfect fool.

JILL (*Contritely*): I'm the foolish one. But know something? I think I'm glad this happened. Because after listening to Sherry, I know Dad's right. I'm not anywhere near ready for that kind of life.

MISS CONWAY (*Putting an arm around her*): Maybe some day. (MRS. ADLER *comes in and goes behind the desk.*)

MRS. ADLER: Not forgetting the time, are you? Going on three o'clock.

MISS CONWAY: Oh, my goodness! Everybody ready? (*Leads the way to door.*) Come on, spelling champs! (MARY, PAT, GINNY *and* SALLY *go out after* JILL *and* MISS CONWAY.)

MARTY (*Ruefully*): Me and my imagination! How wrong can you get?

JEAN: I was wrong, too, getting so worked up about winning. Marty . . .

MARTY: Yes?

JEAN: If *I* don't win that match, I hope you do!

MARTY (*Laughing a little*): Why, thank you, Jean. (*Names a word as they go to the door.* JEAN *spells it rapidly and names a word for* MARTY *to spell.* MARTY *spells it. They keep this up with friendly laughter as they go out the door.*)

MRS. ADLER (*Calling after them*): May the best girl win! (*Curtain*)

THE END

Production Notes

Runaway

Characters: 14 female.

Playing Time: 25 minutes.

Costumes: Modern dress. Gloria may wear a uniform. The girls wear attractive outfits, some dressy, some sport. Jill wears a suit and heels. Sue wears a white jacket, dark skirt and heels.

Properties: A suitcase for each contestant, an envelope with name tags, a pencil, keys on a board, a spelling list, and a red jacket.

Setting: The lobby of Ridge Manor. A registration desk is near the corner up right with a telephone and registry book on it, and a chair behind it. A board with room keys hangs on the wall. A small radio is on the desk. There is a sofa left of center. Two easy chairs with a table between them are down right, and another easy chair is down left. Other chairs are near the walls. Flowers, lamps, pictures, etc., may add to the attractiveness of the room. A door in the upstage wall leads to the other rooms, and a door at left leads outside.

Lighting: No special effects.

The Straw Boy

By Paul T. Nolan

Characters

THE STRAW BOY (ARTHUR)
GERALD MAKER
MR. WONDER
ADAM ⎫
ROAM ⎪
TONY ⎪
DAN ⎬ the Eight Circles
EVE ⎪
JULIE ⎪
CLEO ⎪
BEA ⎭

SCENE 1

TIME: *The present; early afternoon.*

SETTING: *The workshop of* GERALD MAKER. *Parts of old cars litter the floor. Motors litter the worktables. On one table is a telephone.*

AT RISE: GERALD *sits on a stool in stage center. In front of him, bent over like a rag doll, is the* STRAW BOY.

GERALD (*Fixing a broomstick under the coat of the* STRAW BOY *and straightening it up*): There, that ought to do it. Now you've got a little backbone. (*The* STRAW BOY *now stands erect. There are big blobs of clay on his nose and cheeks, and wisps of straw stick out from under his cap.*) Yes, sir, you look enough like a teen-ager to give my father grey hair. If you just had a guitar, I could get you on TV. (*Reaches up and removes a little of the clay from his face*) But maybe I've put just a little too much clay in making your face.

MR. WONDER (*Off*): Gerald, you down there?

GERALD: Yes, I'm here. Come on down. I want to show you something. (MR. WONDER *enters.*)

MR. WONDER: What have you done now? Made an atom bomb?

GERALD: Better than that, Mr. Wonder. (*Points to the* STRAW BOY.) Behold, I'm Frankenstein. My monster.

MR. WONDER (*Examining the* STRAW BOY): Well, he certainly looks like Boris Karloff.

GERALD: I thought he was quite a swinger, in a macabre way.

MR. WONDER: Well, maybe. What are you going to do with him?

GERALD: I don't know yet. I thought I might play a joke on the Eight Circles.

MR. WONDER: The Eight Circles?

GERALD: Yeah, you remember, I told you about those kids at school.

MR. WONDER (*Smiling*): Oh, yes. The four couples at school who don't want anyone to think they're squares.

GERALD: Yeah, they're the ones. They really think they're cool cats. They have a club, and only "real cats" are allowed to join. So far, they haven't admitted anyone. They say all the kids in school are squares.

MR. WONDER: So?

GERALD: I thought if I could get Mr. Straw Boy here into the club, that would really be something.

MR. WONDER (*Laughing*): They're not that silly, are they?

GERALD: I don't know. He's dressed right.

MR. WONDER: Yes, but . . .

GERALD: And he's got the right amount of brains—and the right kind—(*He pulls a few strands of straw from under the hat*) straw.

MR. WONDER: Yes, but . . .

GERALD: If I could just teach him to say "Cool, Man" and "Gone, Man," he'd have it made. That's all they say.

MR. WONDER: You may have something there.

GERALD: Oh, I can put a loud-speaker inside his chest and then run a wire to . . . Only one trouble.

MR. WONDER: What's that?

GERALD (*Reaches inside back of* STRAW BOY *and removes the broomstick*): When I take this out, Straw Boy folds. (STRAW BOY *bends over until his head hangs at his knees.*)

MR. WONDER: Put the stick back. He looks horrible.

GERALD (*Fixing* STRAW BOY *back in place*): You know, Mr. Wonder, you could help me . . .

MR. WONDER: No, sir, Gerald. Every time I do some of my magic, it backfires. Remember when I made that cat talk?

GERALD: How did we know that the cat we picked had seen Miss Perkins kissing the biology teacher?

MR. WONDER: We should have known that it was a mistake to allow any cat to talk. Cats have no discretion.

GERALD: Miss Perkins thought that we had hired a ventriloquist. I thought she was going to flunk the whole class.

MR. WONDER: That's the trouble with black magic. It always backfires.

GERALD: Yeah, but that was different. What could go wrong if you would make Straw Boy alive for one night? I would just take him to the dance the Eight Circles have every Friday night. And anything that happens to them, they have coming. Who could get hurt?

MR. WONDER (*Laughs*): You could, for one—when they find out that you have passed off a dummy on them as one of their own kind.

GERALD: I'll take that chance. And besides, if anything happens, I have it coming.

MR. WONDER: All right. You probably have something there. If this shocks them out of their silliness, my black magic will have done something good. And if they knock you down, I guess you need that, too. I'll do it.

GERALD: Good. Wait a minute. Let me call them to be sure that I can bring the Straw Boy to their dance tonight. (*He starts for phone.*)

MR. WONDER: You'd better get another name for your creation. If you keep calling him Straw Boy, you'll give the joke away.

GERALD: I'll call him Edgar. That's the principal's first name.

MR. WONDER: Careful there, Gerald. When you start to make fun of people, you're just asking for trouble.

GERALD (*Reaching for phone*): Oh, he'll never know. (*Into phone*) Hello, Sadie. Give me the Sugar Bowl, will you. (*To* MR. WONDER) This will be wonderful.

(*Into phone*) Hello, Gus, any of the Circles around? Yeah, you know—Roam, or Adam, or Tony, or Dan? No? Any of the girls there? No, I don't want to talk to Sadie Elkins. Is Eve there? Julie? Cleo? Is Bea there?

MR. WONDER: What names! Adam and Eve? Roam and Julie?

GERALD (*To* MR. WONDER): Yeah, that's really funny. Wait a minute. I think Bea's there. (*To phone*) Hello, Bea. This is Gerald. Yeah, Gerald McBoing-Boing. (*With sarcasm*) You know who I am—Gerald Maker. Look, a friend of mine just got in town. A real cool cat. He'd like to meet your crowd. Sure, *naturally!* May I bring him? He's a personal friend of The Four Howls. No, I'm not kidding. All right, I'll have him there at eight tonight. But you'd better tell that gang of yours to be on their good behavior. This guy is real gone. O.K., so long. (*Hangs up*) She fell for it. Now, let's get to work. (*He goes back over to* STRAW BOY.) What do we have to do?

MR. WONDER: First you have to promise that you won't tell anyone that I had anything to do with this.

GERALD: Why, sure.

MR. WONDER: Then, you have to let me go with you tonight.

GERALD: I don't know about that.

MR. WONDER: You can tell them I was real gone forty years ago. One of the original hotcha boys of the Roaring Twenties.

GERALD: Well, all right.

MR. WONDER: Then, we ought to fix Straw Boy here up a little bit. You have too much clay on his nose. (*He removes excess clay from nose.*) And the cheeks. (*Removes excess clay from the cheeks*) And these eyebrows look crazy, but I guess we'll leave them. And we ought to get this extra straw off his head. (*Starts picking straw off*) When I give the magic words, Straw Boy will come alive. What time is it?

GERALD (*Looks at his wristwatch*): Exactly four.

MR. WONDER: Then, he'll be a real boy until exactly midnight. This charm only lasts eight hours.

GERALD: O.K. O.K. Let's go.

MR. WONDER: And another thing. He'll be alive, but he won't know anything. He won't be able to say anything or do anything.

GERALD: That's all right. I can teach him everything he needs to know in four hours. He can learn, can't he?

MR. WONDER: He'll remember everything you can tell him and act any way you want him to.

GERALD: Come on, then; let's go.

MR. WONDER: All right, if you are sure you want to go through with it.

GERALD: I'm sure.

MR. WONDER: Very well, then. (*In solemn voice*) Powers of atoms and Ford V-8's and stockcar races and Friday-night dates, I summon you. (*The lights go out*) Hear me, Magic Powers. Make Straw Boy into Edgar. Let him be whatever Gerald wants for eight hours. Hear me, Powers. (*The lights flash on, and* STRAW BOY *turns his head.*)

GERALD: You did it! You did it! He moved! He's alive!

MR. WONDER: Now, he's your responsibility. And, Gerald, don't do anything you'll regret.

GERALD: He's really alive. (*To* STRAW BOY) Gone, man, gone!

STRAW BOY: Gone, man, gone.

GERALD: He spoke! He spoke!

MR. WONDER: Remember, Gerald, don't do anything you'll regret. (*Exit* MR. WONDER.)

GERALD (*To* STRAW BOY): I'm going to teach you to talk and walk, simper and giggle, to strut and wiggle with the best of them. Gone, man, gone. You'll be a real cool cat.

STRAW BOY: A real cool cat.

CURTAIN

* * * * *

SCENE 2

TIME: *Ten minutes before midnight, the same day.*

SETTING: *The club room of the Eight Circles. The room is empty except for a jukebox, upstage right.*

AT RISE: *The jukebox is playing "You Ain't Nothin' but a Hound Dog." Downstage right,* STRAW BOY *is standing, combing his hair and preening before his audience,* EVE, JULIE, CLEO, *and* BEA, *who sigh with each stroke of the comb. Downstage left,* MR. WONDER *and* GERALD *stand talking. Upstage center,* ADAM, ROAM, TONY, *and* DAN *are standing glaring at the* STRAW BOY *and the* GIRLS.

GERALD (*As music goes off*): Boy, these girls have gone crazy for Straw Boy. I mean Edgar.

MR. WONDER: The boys don't seem to share the enthusiasm.

GERALD: No, they don't. (*Laughs*) Look at them.

MR. WONDER: I don't suppose it's very nice—even for cats—to have your girl simper over some other boy.

GERALD: They had it coming. Besides, it will only be for another ten minutes. It's almost midnight.

MR. WONDER: I hope this doesn't cause any permanent break between the couples.

GERALD: Why not? It would probably do them good.

MR. WONDER: They seem to be suited for each other. Adam and Eve. Roam and Julie. Tony and Cleo. Dan and Bea. I suppose the names are short for Romeo and Juliet, Antony and Cleopatra, Dante and Beatrice.

GERALD: Those aren't their real names.

MR. WONDER: They're not?

GERALD: No. Roam's real name is Dennis. And Julie's real name is Minnie. I suggested that Dennis and the Menace sounded just as good, but they didn't like it.

MR. WONDER: I can see their point. (*Pause*) Have you decided what you're going to do at midnight?

GERALD: I'm just going to tell the truth. That's what I'll do. Then, I'll take Straw Boy apart, and I won't mention it again, if they don't. But we both will know. I guess they are willing to give up being the Eight Circles in the future.

MR. WONDER: I hope it works out all right.

GERALD (*Looking at wristwatch*): We have just five minutes till midnight. I'll tell them now. (*Goes to middle of floor and talks in a loud voice*) Circles, may I have your attention? Straw—I mean Edgar—and I have to leave now.

JULIE (*Grabbing* STRAW BOY's *arm*): No.

CLEO (*Grabbing same arm*): No.

EVE (*Grabbing other arm*): I'll just die if you do.

BEA (*Grabbing same arm*): I'll just die, too.

ROAM: Good.

ADAM (*To* EVE): You're dead now—as far as I'm concerned.

STRAW BOY: I don't want to go. I dig these crazy chicks.

GERALD: But, Edgar, we have to go.

STRAW BOY (*Pathetically*): Have to go?

GERALD: It's almost midnight. Your eight hours are just about up.

STRAW BOY (*Going to* MR. WONDER): Couldn't I stay just another hour?

MR. WONDER: I'm sorry, Edgar. Eight hours is always the limit.

STRAW BOY: But what happens to me now?

MR. WONDER: You'll have to go back to what you were.

STRAW BOY: I don't want to go back to what I was.

MR. WONDER: There's nothing I can do.

STRAW BOY: I don't want to go back. I like being what I am. I want to stay here.

EVE: We want you to stay here. You don't have to go, Edgar.

ADAM: I don't want you here, but nobody—not these creeps—can make you go. If you belong any place in this town, it's with the Circles. You're one of our kind.

EVE: Why, thank you, Adam. That was very nice. I thought you didn't like Edgar.

ADAM: I don't like him, but we Circles have to stick together.

GERALD: You don't understand. Edgar can't stay.

ROAM: Why not? You think you own him?

JULIE: Yeah, what's his staying have to do with you? You can leave, Gerald McBoing-Boing. You're a square.

GERALD: But he's not like you. He looks like you, and he talks like you. But he's really not like you.

TONY: He's like me. I can tell that.

CLEO: And we like him. He can stay if he wants to. What do you think he is—a prisoner?

GERALD: You don't understand. Edgar isn't a boy.

DAN: What is he, a girl?

BEA: He just couldn't be.

GERALD: He's not a boy or a girl. He's a . . .

STRAW BOY: Don't say it! Don't say it! I don't want them to know. I'll leave. (*He runs off through the door left.*)

ADAM (*Runs after him*): Don't go, Edgar.

EVE: We want you to stay. We don't care what you are.

ROAM: You're one of our kind. (*Exit* EIGHT CIRCLES *following* STRAW BOY.)

GERALD (*To* MR. WONDER): What am I going to do?

MR. WONDER: I warned you about black magic. It always backfires.

GERALD: How did I know he was going to act like that?

MR. WONDER: How about the Circles? Do you think they are so much worse than other kids now?

GERALD: No, they were real fine about the way they stuck up for him. Adam, Roam, Tony, Dan—not a one of them liked him.

MR. WONDER: At least, they didn't like their girls hanging around him all night.

GERALD: But they all defended him.

MR. WONDER: He was one of their own, and they are loyal to him.

GERALD: What am I going to say to them?

MR. WONDER: What *were* you going to tell them?

GERALD: I was . . . going to tell them . . . that they were so silly that even a boy made of straw was more sensible.

MR. WONDER: And now?

GERALD: Now, that doesn't seem right any more. You know . . . I like Straw Boy. I feel . . . sorry for him.

He never hurt anyone. He just wanted to stay and play. There's nothing wrong in that, is there? Is there anything you can do? Mr. Wonder, please?

MR. WONDER: There's nothing anyone can do. As soon as the clock strikes twelve, he'll be just a pile of old clothes and straw.

GERALD: With a broomstick for a backbone. (*Clock strikes twelve.*) That's it. Midnight. Straw Boy's dead.

MR. WONDER: No, he's not dead, for he was never alive! But something in us is dead. Maybe there is a good lesson for us in this—if we ever find it. Things haven't gone the way you planned them, have they, Gerald?

GERALD: It doesn't seem quite fair that we get the lesson and Straw Boy just gets . . . poor Straw Boy. (*Enter* EIGHT CIRCLES, *each carrying some object from the* STRAW BOY'S *costume.* ROAM *has the broomstick.*)

ROAM: As soon as the clock struck, he fell in a heap.

JULIE: And when we got there, this was all there was.

DAN: Straw, some old clothes, and a broomstick.

GERALD: That was his backbone.

ADAM: What?

GERALD: I made Edgar out of straw, and rags, and old clothes. I used the broomstick for a backbone.

EVE: Edgar was just made of straw?

GERALD: A straw boy.

TONY: But why? Why did you do a thing like that?

GERALD: I just wanted . . . I thought I could . . . I don't know. I guess I was mad because you all thought you were so good. I wanted to show you that you were no better than something made out of straw—a scarecrow.

CLEO: If I were as good as Edgar, I . . .

TONY: If we're as good as Edgar, I'm satisfied.

ADAM: He was a good fellow.

EVE: You shouldn't have done it, Gerald.

ROAM: You shouldn't have done it.

GERALD: It was only a joke. Can't you take a joke?

JULIE: We can take it. But what about Edgar?

ROAM: You shouldn't have done it to Edgar.

GERALD (*To* MR. WONDER): What am I going to do, Mr. Wonder? I feel rotten.

MR. WONDER: You should. Now all of you, listen. Edgar was just so much straw. He didn't say anything. He didn't do anything. He didn't feel anything.

EVE: He did, too. I saw a tear on his cheek.

MR. WONDER: No, you didn't. You just thought you did. Straw Boy was just what you thought. And it's a fine thing that you thought that he was human—that you thought he could cry—that you thought he had feelings. You know, in some ways, we are all straw men until somebody looks at us—and thinks that we are human, and thinks that we have feelings, and sees a tear on our cheeks. Keep your souvenirs—your hunk of straw, the old cap, the broomstick. Look at them every once in awhile. And any time you're tempted to treat somebody as though he is straw—as you Circles have treated your classmates like Gerald McBoing-Boing here (*He smiles*)—or as Gerald has treated you tonight, remember Edgar, the Straw Boy. Straw Boy will stay alive as long as your sympathy stays alive.

TONY: But why can't you bring him back alive—really alive—with magic? You did it once.

MR. WONDER: There are two kinds of magic: black magic that makes things seem what they are not and white magic that makes things seem what they should be. Edgar was created out of black magic—spite and anger.

And when you have black magic, it always has a kick-back. But your sympathy for Edgar—even when you knew he was nothing but straw—is white magic. It will bring good. Wait and see. (*There is a knock on the door. A voice calls.*)

ARTHUR: May I come in?

CLEO: It's that jerk, Arthur.

TONY: Every time we have a dance, he comes by and asks if he can come in.

ADAM: Let's chase him home.

MR. WONDER: What about some white magic?

EVE: What? Oh, some white magic?

TONY: Oh, I get what you mean.

ROAM: Let's try it. What do you say, Circles?

JULIE: It's all right with me.

ALL: O.K. Let's let him come in.

ADAM: O.K., Arthur, come on in. (ARTHUR *enters. He looks exactly like* STRAW BOY.)

ARTHUR (*Gesturing with his hand*): Hi, Cats.

CLEO: It's him. Edgar.

GERALD: Straw Boy!

ARTHUR: Hey, what's the matter with you? I'm Arthur. I'm not any Edgar or Straw Boy. I'm just plain old Arthur. You remember me. You chase me home every Friday night.

EVE: He *looks* just like him.

TONY: And he talks just like him.

JULIE: Has he always looked this way?

ROAM: And talked this way?

ARTHUR: Hey, what's going on?

GERALD (*To* MR. WONDER): How about it, Mr. Wonder? Is this Arthur or Edgar? Is this some of your magic? Have you brought Straw Boy back?

MR. WONDER (*Smiling*): It's not my magic. If it's magic, it's yours.

JULIE: And, is this for real? Arthur and Straw Boy are really one?

MR. WONDER: I think so.

CLEO (*Grabbing* ARTHUR's *hand*): Then what are we waiting for? Turn on the music. Arthur and I are going to dance.

TONY: O.K. But hereafter, Arthur has to get a girl of his own.

JULIE: I know a girl we can bring for him. And she has the right name too—Guinevere.

MR. WONDER (*Turning aside and shaking his head*): Arthur and Guinevere. The Round Table. What won't they think of next? (*The music starts. All start dancing, as the curtain falls.*)

THE END

Production Notes

The Straw Boy

Characters: 7 male; 4 female. (Mr. Wonder may be played as Madame Wonder, if desired.)

Playing Time: 20 minutes.

Costumes: Modern dress. Straw Boy wears dungarees, a sweat shirt, a black motorcyclist's jacket, and cap. There are big blobs of clay on his nose and cheeks, and wisps of straw stick out from under his cap, in Scene 1.

Properties: Some motor parts, straw, a broomstick, a jukebox or record player, telephone.

Setting: Scene 1 is in Gerald Maker's workshop. There are a couple of workbenches and motor parts strewn about the room. There is a high stool for Gerald, and a telephone on one of the benches. Scene 2 is in the clubhouse of the Eight Circles. There is a jukebox or record player upstage right. There may be a few chairs at the sides.

Lighting: No special effects necessary, but lights may go out when Mr. Wonder is saying the spell to make Straw Boy into a real boy.